AUTOMATION

IMPLICATIONS FOR THE FUTURE

AUTOMATION

IMPLICATIONS
FOR THE FUTURE

■ ■ ■ ■ ■ ■ ■ ■ ■ ■ ■ ■ ■ ■

EDITED BY

MORRIS PHILIPSON

VINTAGE BOOKS

A DIVISION OF RANDOM HOUSE

New York

CONTENTS

■ ■ *Part One* ■ ■

THE
GENERAL
VIEW

■ 1 ■

The Challenge of
"Industrial Revolution II"*

by Arthur J. Goldberg

SECRETARY OF LABOR

President Kennedy has charged a group consisting of seven of American management's foremost officials, seven top-flight labor leaders, five eminent private citizens, Secretary of Commerce Hodges and me with the task of recommending to him policies that may be followed by labor, management or the public for dealing with such major economic questions as foreign competition and "the benefits and problems created by automation." We have gone to work against a background of sharply contrasting economic features. Employment in February had a monthly record of 64,700,000. At the same time, unemployment had risen to 5,705,000—the largest number of persons without jobs since the summer of 1941.

* Reprinted from *The New York Times* Magazine, April 2, 1961, by permission of the Author and *The New York Times*.

I have spoken with hundreds of jobless persons in Chicago, Gary, South Bend, Detroit, Pittsburgh and in the iron range country of Minnesota. In those places, the economic trend breaks down into its living components—men and women with names and faces, families and problems, pasts and futures. Some were machine tenders, some were carpenters or painters, some were coal miners, some were assembly-line operatives, and so down a long list of occupations. All shared a single feeling: what would they do?

For many of them, recovery would mean jobs. They would go back and try to pick up where they left off. For others, however, their jobs had become lasting casualties of the change surging through economic life, especially industrial enterprises.

This change, defined loosely by the generic term "automation," is becoming so pronounced that some economists have labeled it "a second Industrial Revolution."

Automation is the most recent phase in the centuries-long search for ways to replace human with mechanical or other forms of energy. In the Industrial Revolution of the nineteenth century, power-driven machinery freed man's hands from some forms of labor for the first time in history. The process has continued. In early developments like Oliver Evans' flour mill, with its conveyors and chutes, James Watt's automatic controls for his steam engine and Charles Babbage's calculator were the seeds for today's mammoth automatic processes that refine oil, make artillery shells, bake cakes, process chemicals, generate electric power, cast engine blocks, dig coal, produce atomic materials and perform thousands of other jobs.

Since the war, a new element has spurred automation: the growing knowledge of information handling, as in electronic systems and computers. The advent of the electronic brain controlling the mechanical muscle has made possible fully automatic factories and offices—but it has also raised the specter of severe dislocation in the American work force.

The issue being joined in our economy today—one that is present in some form in every major industrial negotiation—is simply stated: how can the necessity for continued increases in productivity, based upon labor-saving techniques, be met without causing individual hardship and widespread unemployment?

It is a familiar issue to Western economies. In Samuel Gompers' autobiography, for example, appears a moving reminiscence from London of the eighteen fifties:

> One of my most vivid early recollections is the great trouble that came to the silk weavers when machinery was invented to replace their skill and take their jobs. No thought was given to these men whose trade was gone. Misery and suspense filled the neighborhood with a depressing air of dread. The narrow street echoed with the tramp of men walking the street in groups with no work to do. . . .

Such severe dislocations, with their burden of great human suffering, are historical phenomena.

Today the effect of technological change has been tempered by an economy generally characterized by broad job opportunities, by an expansion of jobs in service and trade fields, by Government programs like unemployment insurance and by privately negotiated devices such as Supplemental Unemployment Benefits, payable in some cases to a worker even while he is training for a different industry.

Also, major technical changes in the past have occurred over a period of many years. If they had been telescoped into five years, the effects upon both the economy and the social equilibrium would have been far more severe.

Now, however, the pace of automation is quickening under many pressures. Perhaps the most important of these is the obsolescence of the American industrial plant. A competent estimate has been made that it would cost ninety-five billion dollars to replace our plant and equipment now obsolete.

At the same time, we see in Western Europe a whole new industrial structure—modern plants and automated equipment—risen from the rubble of war. The goods from those plants are giving us stiff competition in markets that at one time were almost exclusively ours.

The combination of these factors—obsolescence here and growing competition abroad—gives real drive to the desire to improve and modernize.

To this is added the momentum provided by the consistent desire for higher standards. A highly developed technology underlies the American success in providing better goods and services for a steadily expanding population. We continue to expect that of it.

We are already witnessing the effects of automation. Between 1947 and 1960, for example, productivity (output per man hour) in the total private economy increased at an annual average rate of nearly 3.5 per cent—as against the long-term increase of 2.4 per cent. Even with agricultural productivity taken out of this figure—and agriculture has, of course, been the most greatly affected of all industries by technological change—the average postwar gain has been about 2.7 per cent, compared with the long-term nonagricultural rise of 2.1 per cent.

With this acceleration have come employment declines in several industries. During the postwar period, for example, productivity in bituminous coal mining rose an astonishing 96 per cent while employment was falling 262,700. Railroad productivity rose 65 per cent in the same period while employment fell 540,000.

There is no way to measure the exact amount of unemployment due strictly to technological change. We do know that manufacturing employment lost 900,000 jobs in 1960 while total employment was making records in every one of the first ten months. How many of those jobs are permanent losses we do not know, but the indications are that the technological attrition in industrial employment is becoming high. Thus, each of the four postwar recoveries from recession has shown a higher unemployment rate than the previous one. Also, one of the distressing aspects of much of current unemployment is its long-term nature; 647,000 of the unemployed in January had been looking for work for twenty-seven weeks or longer.

The shadow of technological unemployment has fallen across mill towns, mining towns, textile towns and manufacturing towns across the nation. This past winter, men in West Virginia gathered around open fires on street corners listening for rumors of jobs. The coming of spring brings hope, but each spring in many industries finds fewer men at work.

Yet the long-term legacy of industrial progress has been a good one. To define the problem is also to state the promise, and to envision the progress is to define the problem.

Automation, for example, upgrades the entire labor force by requiring higher educational and occupational attainments. It sets a bright new premium on skill and intelligence. But are we equipped to handle the educational and training needs inherent in such change?

Automation frees human hands from labor, lifts the burden of production from the backs of men. But are we, as a people, prepared to turn the leisure time we gain to constructive use, to recreation in its true meaning, the "re-creation" of our lives?

The broad goal of realizing the promise and solving the problems is acknowledged by all Americans. The question of means may often become divisive.

Labor and management have, in the past two or three years, developed a realistic technique of referral—that is, they refer the problems raised by automation *away* from, rather than *toward*, the bargaining table. The device most frequently used is that of the special committee, sometimes including public members, which operates outside the bargaining arena, away from its pressures and deadlines and crosscurrents. Such committees are now at work in a number of industries—steel, meat packing and construction, for example.

There is also the government-created Presidential Railroad Commission, with labor, management and public members, studying the complex problems of work rules and practices in that industry.

Can this technique of study and recommendation work?

While it is an example of good will, and good sense, it is also an indication of a failure in the past to anticipate the impact of automation. These are substantially ex post facto bodies, some brought into being after strikes, some rushed together when the urgency for them became clear. I feel that they can find solutions. At the same time, studies made by the Department of Labor make it clear that if labor and management, in particular industries, plan in advance for technological change, measure out the effect of such change before it takes place, then its impact upon employment is greatly lessened, often nullified, while its benefit to the industry is enlarged.

One of the nation's largest manufacturers of radios, phonographs and television sets, for example, switched to automatic assembly a few years ago. Union officials were consulted in advance and changes and procedures were established for retaining some workers, reassigning others, upgrading still others.

Not a single job was lost. Pay for some of the new automated jobs increased by 5 to 15 per cent. Incentive pay systems were established in other, older jobs whose character had been transformed. The transition was orderly and effective.

A large life-insurance company had a similar experience. One of its divisions handled 850,000 policy transactions a month, used 125 punch-card machines and employed about 198 people. The company decided to install a computer, which it estimated would reduce expenses by more than $200,000 a year, cut the number of punch-card machines to 21 and reduce employment to 85 people.

After the decision, the company planned most carefully for the personnel adjustments. Affected employes were consulted well in advance. Each was interviewed at length concerning his preference in other operations of the company, and all who wished were successfully placed in new jobs.

The same story was repeated in a large bakery, an oil refinery and other companies we studied.

All of these studies highlighted several important factors that were present to make automation a human, as well as a mechanical, success. They were:

(1) An adequate lead time between the decision to automate and the actual change-over.

(2) Thorough consultation between labor and management concerning employe displacement and job changes.

(3) Open and honest reporting to the people directly affected.

(4) Perhaps most important of all, the timing of the change to coincide with a period of employment or market expansion.

The experience of successful companies indicates that automation in a context of expanding national employment and economic growth presents few problems that adequate and open planning cannot solve. At the same time, automation in a context of declining opportunity and slow economic growth can have a serious effect upon the work force.

When national employment opportunity is reduced by declining business, for example, the worker faced with technological unemployment has limited alternatives, not only in his own locality, but elsewhere as well. Laggard economic growth also may impair the ability of a company to provide alternate employment within its own structure.

One of the most important lessons learned thus far is that the need for training and retraining the work force exists across the board in American life. No employer or employe is exempt from the need, and each ignores it at his own cost.

It is evident, also, that no master plan can be drawn for lifting the skills of a work force as varied and diverse as ours. The situation in each community, and within each industry, requires its own devices and tools. What each does have in common is the need for maximum cooperation among important segments of the community—education, business and labor, to name three.

Recent developments in Hazleton, Pennsylvania, and Phoenix, Arizona, are cases in point:

Hazleton has been in a difficult unemployment situation because of the decline of the anthracite coal industry. In 1958, a corporation agreed to take over an abandoned railroad roundhouse that had been purchased by the Hazleton Industrial Development Corporation and converted to modern industrial use. Last spring, the company found itself desperately short of skilled machinists; only two of forty applicants met the strict technical standards the work required. The company began to consider moving.

At that juncture, the Development Corporation, the Chamber of Commerce, representatives of the State Employment Service and the United States Department of Labor's Bureau of Apprenticeship and Training met together. The result was a community-wide training program for machinists. Classes were given in the Hazleton Vocational School, and pupils included not only workers from the company but unemployed workers from the area as well.

The State of Pennsylvania provided additional funds for equipment and facilities needed by the public school. A six-man labor-and-management committee was formed to conduct the program. The Chamber of Commerce initiated a survey of the skills of the work force in the Hazleton area, and as a result two classes in supervisory development were started on the Hazleton campus of the Pennsylvania State University on January 23 of this year. Courses in engineering, drafting and shop mathematics have been recently added.

That is the Hazleton story—one of wide community cooperation to fill the need to update and retrain workers. It occurred against a background of substantial unemployment as a result of the coal decline. In Phoenix, the economic context is different—but the need and response were the same.

Following a skills survey of the area a few years ago, farsighted Phoenix employers and labor organizations joined with civic and school groups to start training programs that would insure them the skilled manpower the future seemed to require. These educational programs are now in operation, supported by men from all segments of the community whose self-interest is also their city's interest, and, in the broad picture, their nation's as well.

Many other communities have launched cooperative attacks on the skills problem. However, they will succeed, aided by some Federal programs, only if the national economy is providing jobs and business opportunity.

The issue before the President's Advisory Committee on Labor-Management Policy, then, has been not merely one of means or methods of communication, but of much broader scale considerations, aimed at creating an economic life within which automation can function freely and without harm.

The study of automation, a boon to some and a bogeyman to others, brings one eventually to an essential element in American life: the public responsibility that resides within private decision in a free economy. It points up for the businessman the fact that the conduct of his business influences not only the lives and welfare of his employes, but the national welfare. It reminds labor leaders that constructive and creative planning must replace opposition based on short-term considerations. And it brings home to the public the realization that the cost of freedom in economic life is responsibility.

Enlightened businessmen, farsighted labor leaders and a responsible public can, together, make automation a general blessing. The policies and programs that will be emerging from industrial and national committees should be carefully watched by all Americans. They could well be the blueprint for a better world.

■ 2 ■

*Congressional Testimony**

by John Diebold

PRESIDENT, THE DIEBOLD GROUP OF MANAGEMENT
CONSULTING COMPANIES

Mr. Chairman and members of the subcommittee, it is
most appropriate at this time to consider the role of automation and technological change in our economy. The
committee is to be commended for once more turning its
attention to this subject—a subject which has assumed increasing importance as a domestic issue and powerful force
in the entire world.

The original hearings of this committee marked the first
national recognition of the important role of automation
and technological change in our society. The proceedings
of those hearings have been widely read and liberally
quoted from. Those hearings provided one of the first

* Reprinted from Testimony Submitted to the Sub-Committee
on Automation and Energy Resources, 86th Congress, Second
Session. Reprinted by permission of the Author and The Joint
Economic Committee.

comprehensive publications containing the views of many persons representing different sectors of the economy, all concerned with automation.

The present compilation of testimony is perhaps of even greater import in view of the present economic and world political situation. I welcome this opportunity to bring my original testimony up to date.

INTRODUCTION

Many of the promises, and certainly some of the problems of automation, have become realities in American life. The uses of automation that we predicted in 1955 have, for the most part, come to pass. No longer must we speak of the "advent of the automatic factory." Automation has "arrived." During these few years, since the hearings in 1955, automation itself has become an industry. The increases in manufacture of automatic equipment for machine and process control in the factory have been complemented by the phenomenal growth of the electronic data-processing equipment industries servicing both factory and office. The whole new field of computer technology has passed from its infancy stages to one of high complexity and sophistication. It was only several years ago, when I first testified before this committee, that the first computers became available for office use. Yet, today, electronic data-processing equipment is a common tool of industry.

Both office and factory automation have been most instrumental in increasing our productivity and national output. In fact, their importance in the economy has made it necessary to transcend our present thinking of these techniques as simply "tools" of production. Automation, and the concepts that it embodies, has become a *national resource*—a source of strength to the nation and a stimulus for technological change.

It is questionable whether we have used this resource as effectively as we should or could, although our achievements seem spectacular. The uses to which we put our energies and the results derived can no longer be compared only with our own historical performance. The world has changed too fast for that. We have seen very graphically in the last few years the results of efforts in the technological area. We have watched our chief competitor, the Soviet Union, make remarkable gains both militarily and economically. If we do not make the fullest use of the techniques we have developed, you may be sure that the Soviets will do just that.

Neither technical nor economic reasons have prevented us from making optimal use of automation. Perhaps the most important single fact surrounding automation has been that fear it has engendered—*fear* of the human consequences of automation. Much of it has been irrational, some of it reasonable. The fact remains that we must improve the environment for achieving technological changes. But we must also recognize that in order to reap the benefits of technological innovation, we must be prepared for innovation in the social environment. We must be willing to consider new solutions to human problems we cannot solve with old methods.

We are in a critical economic war. The United States Government should do all it can to stimulate private enterprise to produce cheaply and efficiently, and increase business' reinvestment rate. This calls for a positive national policy toward productivity and technological change.

At the same time, government, business and the community must work together to minimize—and hopefully eliminate—the human hardships that may appear locally due to rapidly changing economic conditions.

The fact remains that we still do not know enough about the effects of automation, or indeed technological change, to deal intelligently with it. This lack of facts stimulates the fear. In the five years that have elapsed since the initial hearings on automation and technological change, no concerted effort has been made on a national basis to overcome our ignorance. Certainly the efforts of this committee will do much to help meet this need.

Chairman Patman in his recent letter inviting me to submit testimony before this subcommittee asked for my views on:

The progress which automation has made since the earlier hearings in 1955.

The growth of the automation industry.

The extent and type of employee displacement.

And the problems of retraining and reallocation of workers.

Representative Patman specifically asked where I felt that events had reinforced my earlier views and where my views had changed in light of current trends. I will address myself initially to these questions. I believe it would then be helpful to discuss in more detail various aspects of automation of interest to this subcommittee—to attempt to bring automation up to date. My discussion will include the following sections: Automation Today, more on the concept of automation; Applications and Uses for Automation; The Automation Industry; and Economic and Social Aspects of Automation. The statement will conclude with my views on the need for a national policy to deal with automation and technological change.

CHANGES IN VIEWS

In 1955, I stated before this subcommittee that I did not feel that automation requires any special legislation. I still think the legislation should not be directed specifically at automation—as much as it is necessary for government recognition of the total problem of coping with technological change.

The hearings, which this subcommittee inaugurated in 1955, stressed the potential impact of automation and technological change on the United States. During the intervening years, this potential has partially been realized. The introduction of automation technology has resulted in changes within industry and government. It is not difficult to determine the importance that industry places in automation; the growing amount of industrial capital expenditures for automatic equipment speaks for itself. Unions have recognized automation and have made an issue of it at the collective bargaining tables. The Federal Government, in its various agencies, is continually installing substantial amounts of electronic data-processing equipment to obtain greater efficiencies (and, indeed, recent Congressional committee hearings were devoted to measuring the effects of electronic data processing in government). Individual state governments have held conferences to consider the economic and social consequences of automation for their states—the governors of both Massachusetts and New York convened such conferences recently. Automation has become a national issue.

In these last few years other issues have become crystallized in the public's eye: our rate of national economic growth, the political and economic competition with the Soviet Union, the growth of the free world as a source of competition and as a market and the problems of bringing underdeveloped countries into the twentieth century economically, technologically and socially. All these issues seem to me to be interdependent with each other and with the issue of automation and technological change. We cannot sustain a high national growth rate, we cannot compete effectively in the world markets, we cannot adequately aid foreign countries, unless we make the fullest use of our productive capabilities. We have not accomplished this in recent years. I believe we will have continued difficulties in overcoming our domestic and international problems unless we tackle this issue—how to employ automation and technological change most effectively.

To my mind, there is a clear need for *national policy* aimed at making the most effective use of technological change. It is not a question of dealing with automation alone. Automation is part of a complex pattern of continuing technological sophistication within our economy. In fact, it is most difficult to isolate the effects of the uses of automation techniques from other change. The Bureau of Labor Statistics, for example, correctly recognized this difficulty when they recently announced the sizable productivity increases in 1959 over 1958. They pointed out that this increase could not be attributed to one factor alone but to "the combined effect of a number of interrelated influences, such as skills of workers, managerial skill, changes in technology, capital investment per worker, utilization of capacity, layout and flow of material, and labor-management relations."

The problem, it would seem, is much broader than simply attempting to control automation through special legislation. We cannot "legislate" automation into existence, just as we cannot legislate its disappearance. Automation is a philosophy of technology—a set of concepts. In itself, it makes available to us only the knowledge of how to better satisfy our material and intellectual desires. Automation does not "cause" anything. To attribute any inherent evils to automation or technological change is like aiming at the shadow instead of the object.

For years we have allowed the turn of phrases, such as "Automation causes . . . ," to direct erroneously our approach to the subject. These phrases are really shortcut ways of saying, "When we *apply* a set of automation techniques, these sets of results occur." Our own actions or inactions actually *cause* the results.

It has been frequently said that "technological change causes unemployment"; but if a person literally believes what he has said, it is like saying "atomic energy causes war." Atomic energy does not cause war and technological change does not cause unemployment.

We know, for example, that the economy is going through a period when the unemployment rate is much higher than the national average for the unskilled, uneducated worker. This state is expected to continue for a long time to come. Is automation or technological change keeping the unskilled unemployed? Or rather is there a more basic problem of the failure to eliminate substandard education and training?

My personal belief is that the prevailing fear of automation and technological change is totally misdirected. If there must be concern over change, it should be directed toward our own actions in coping with change. We have not even devoted sufficient efforts to examining the "change" phenomenon—and this is necessary before we can act properly.

Ironically enough, the nation presently finds itself in a state in which it is not making the fullest uses of the available labor man-power and productive capacity; this at a time when there is an international economic necessity to do the opposite. The national productivity and output has

increased only rather sluggishly in recent years. My original views on the rate of speed at which automation would
be introduced were that it would "take a long time to effect." I believe that the problems of application are even
greater than were anticipated at the time of the initial
hearings. Much of the difficulty has not been technological
so much as it has been the human problems encountered:
the introducing of new concepts within business organizations not readily adaptable to change, consciousness on the
part of management and labor to minimize decreasing employment opportunities within the company and such.
These kinds of problems have not been solved to a sufficient degree to increase substantially the rate at which automation will be introduced into industry.

In connection with the above problem is the one of
education and re-education. This problem seems more impressive to me now than during the original hearings. The
question of what are the changing skill requirements of
industry still goes unanswered. On a national scale, we still
have not given this question sufficient study, though it has
already become a problem among large localized groups
of unskilled workers.

Greater understanding of the extent of the problem is
needed. A recent study by the State of New York dis-
sected the problem of its future man-power needs and
showed what the educational requirements would most
likely be in the near future. The Bureau of Labor Statistics
through its fine case studies has shed further light on this
problem area. I would think that more research is needed
on a national scale to determine our needs in this area.

Because of some of the difficulties that have developed
in the introduction of automation, some of the benefits that
I anticipated earlier may not come to pass so readily. I do
not expect that excessive leisure will be of concern to us
in the near future. The problem of increasing our national
output would seem to me to take precedence over this. In
the same view, I would not expect any drastic reduction
in the average work-week figures. In some industries, I
would expect that my earlier estimate of decreases in
the work-week to the low thirties may come to pass.
(Some industries have already achieved this level.) How-

ever, the greater reductions in work-week will probably
continue to occur in those industries with high work-week
levels, agriculture and services.

VIEWS THAT HAVE BEEN REINFORCED

I began my original testimony by emphasizing the need
"to derive some factual information about automation and
its impact upon the economy." This need is more urgent
than it was before. While I don't feel that automation has
been introduced at as high a rate as has been technically
possible, its introduction and its impact have far out-
stripped what little we have learned about it. My original
recommendations included an outline of a factual study of
automation. I have submitted a more complete guide to
such a study, once again, in the following section in this
statement. Studies are still vitally necessary. Academic
groups and governmental agencies have effected fine studies in this area, but they have been limited by serious lack
of funds to carry this work further. This would seem to be
a proper area for supportable research by all levels of government—federal, state and local. Private foundations
could also do more to support study in this field. A solid,
comprehensive body of facts on the economic and social
effects of automation is still nonexistent!

Though we are far from making the best uses of automation, I am most encouraged by the greater recognition
that it has received as a new set of concepts rather than as
an extension of mechanization. I previously referred to automation as "a basic change in production philosophy . . .
a means of organizing or controlling production processes
to achieve optimum use of all production resources—mechanical, material and human."

While industry is far from being organized along these
lines, more people are beginning to understand the concepts behind it. We learn of more imaginative uses for automation technology every day.

Many of the feasible applications for automatic controls
that I talked about in 1955 are already operational facts.
Especially in the process industries, optimal control is now
closely approachable. "It makes it possible to do things
that you could not do before, in addition to doing the

things we have been doing more efficiently." This still seems to me to be the greatest contribution automation can make to our economy.

The new levels of achievement and doing present tasks more efficiently have not been limited to large business organizations. Small business can make extensive use of automation techniques both in the factory and the office. Manufacturers have given attention to the design of electronic data-processing systems specifically for the use of small business. We have also experienced in recent years the widespread application of the service bureau concept. These bureaus have been designed to care for the needs of smaller organizations without their own computers (I have discussed the service bureaus in more detail in the section on applications, also, data on the extent of usage of small electronic data-processing systems is found in the section, "The Automation Industry"). In the factory, the availability of flexible machine tools with numerical control may serve to increase the competitive power of smaller business. My initial opinion that numerical controls would be slow in coming seems to have been borne out. Only recently this technique has started to catch hold in industry, but its rate of acceptance will increase rapidly for years to come (I have included growth estimates of the numerical tool controls industry in the section on industry).

The total automation industry has grown to major proportions within the economy. As I recall, the growth potential of the automation industry seemed doubtful to some witnesses on account of what was considered the high investment needed to obtain automation equipment. However, versatile systems, special designs, lower cost per operation and the service bureaus have succeeded in making automation available to practically all sectors of the business community. According to my firm's estimates there were more than ten thousand computer systems installed by July, 1960; this includes 6,717 card calculators (see Exhibit I). When the initial hearings were held, the electronic computer systems in operation could be numbered in the dozens. Of this July, 1960, total, about 2800 were small computer systems. We have estimated that more than 4500 systems are on order. My firm's long-run projections for this industry put electronic data-processing equipment annual sales well into the billion-dollar category.

Other sectors of the automation equipment industry, machine and process controls, are expected to grow at comparable rates.

As the installation of these equipments is accomplished, I think we will begin to notice "where automation is introducing changes in our concepts, our ways of thinking about management. The organizational structure of business [will] start to shift." This opinion, that I stated in 1955, I still hold today. My feelings now are that the restructuring trend will continue in business organizations. "This makes for many changes in the requirements of what people are doing in firms. It again calls attention to education, and to areas where it is necessary to understand precisely what is happening."

The issue of education has taken on major proportions with respect to business needs: greater need for the professional college-trained scientist, engineer and technician, less need for the unskilled. New applied sciences have developed in the last few years which have centered about the concepts of automation; these sciences have synthesized the worlds of mathematics, electronics and business. As business grows more sophisticated in its applications of automation, the demand for management personnel trained in these sciences will grow. Now is the time when these people should be trained. I feel quite strongly that this task—of training management personnel who can make the fullest use of automation concepts and techniques—is not being carried out. With all the profusion of data-processing courses and surveys of automation attached to business school curriculums, we have few examples of institutions of higher learning in business which fully integrate the concepts of automation into the entire course of study. One of the bottlenecks, then, in making the fullest use of automation may very well be the lack of adequately trained management man power.

No doubt the most prominent aspect of automation is how industry's use of this technology affects employment

levels. I pointed out earlier that automation is part of the
continuing process of technological change. As part of this
change, it has contributed to the "dynamic movements
from one industry to another" within the civilian labor
force. The long trend of a decreasing percentage of the
labor force engaged in manufacturing will most certainly
continue. In the last decade, the manufacturing sector has
not only shown percentage decreases, but has decreased
in terms of absolute number of employees. Following both
the recessions of 1954 and 1958, the manufacturing employment highs have failed to reach prerecession levels.
The heavy capital equipment expenditures to further automate and mechanize facilities certainly contributed in
some part of this trend.

Most of the manufacturing employment decreases were
taken in the production work force. This was accompanied
by higher employment levels for nonproductive workers,
those in the managerial and clerical work force.

Recent estimates for this latter sector show it to be per-
ennially behind production workers in raising its productivity and in absolute productivity as well. In the years to
come, I would expect productivity in this sector to rise at
a faster rate than it has previously; this should result, to a
great extent, from the increased (and more skillful) use
of automatic data-processing equipment.

The major employment opportunities can be expected
in the services and nonmanufacturing, nonagricultural industries. I would expect that in some sectors of the latter
category—transportation, public utilities, finance and insurance—further increases in productivity may affect employment opportunities somewhat.

I would like to re-emphasize here my earlier comment
that if we are to cope adequately with any human problems arising out of dislocation of industry, minimized employment levels in certain industries, new skills and education requirements, we must direct attention to the basic
reasons why these problems exist. If industries relocate
to new areas, there is a basic problem of stimulating economic growth in the vacated area. If certain industries reduce their employment roles, facilities and man power
must be made available to help the displaced develop

new skills and obtain different employment. Technological change cannot be encouraged, any temporary problems that may develop in its path cannot be solved, by dealing symptomatically with the change itself.

BRINGING
AUTOMATION UP TO DATE

AUTOMATION TODAY

Throughout the testimony submitted before this sub-committee, you will come across definitions of automation. Though views will differ, depending on the background of the witness, I think that the concept of automation as a *new* way of analyzing and organizing work will be more heavily stressed than at the original hearings.

As I pointed out earlier, I still feel that the concept of the system is most crucial in describing automation. It is the main contribution that automation will make to business organization. If automation means anything at all, it means something more than a mere extension of mechanization. I believe that it marks a break with past trends, a qualitative departure from the more conventional advance of technology that began with jagged pieces of flint and progressed up to the steam engine. It implies a basic change in our attitude toward the manner of performing work. Perhaps because we see things more easily than ideas, this meaning of automation as a way of thinking has been obscured by a fascination with the machines of automation. As a result, when we hear the word automation we tend to think of electronic computers, massive transfer machines, numerical tool controls or perhaps the instrument panel of an oil refinery—machines that new concepts have made possible. Automation, however, is much more than machines, and it is important to understand this if the full social and economic implications are to be understood.

Unquestionably, industrial progress began hundreds of years ago. Great strides were made in the Industrial Revolution of the eighteenth century. This was the period of mechanization. Mechanization provided power-driven tools, eliminating many manual tasks and freeing labor from much of the physical work required in production. But no matter how small a portion of brute strength was involved in running a machine, a human worker was always needed to operate and control it. Production processes, therefore, were necessarily designed around the human worker as operator. His reaction time, his powers of perception and concentration and discrimination, his height, his power to withstand heat and cold, his two arms and ten fingers and his ability to coordinate them dictated what could and what could not be done.

Now, through systematic application of the principle called feedback, machines can be built which control their own operations, so that production processes do not have to be designed to take into account the human limitations of a human worker. To me, this is one of the distinctive facts about automation. It is no longer necessary to think in terms of individual machines, or even in terms of groups of machines; instead, for the first time, it is practical to look at an entire production or information-handling process as an integrated system and not as a series of individual steps. It is through the new technology of automation that we are now beginning to possess the ability and the tools to build such systems.

In the past our limited knowledge of the nature of feedback and control made their application dependent upon the ingenuity of individual inventors who used these principles for the sporadic construction of individual machines or segments of overall systems. Even if we had been inspired by the idea of integrated systems, as some men have certainly been at different times in history, we did not in the past possess the technical knowledge to turn this idea into reality. Today, because of advances in the theory and technology of control, communication and information, we do possess that knowledge and, equally important, we are beginning to apply it in many fields of endeavor.

Automation is more than a series of new machines and more basic than any particular hardware. It is a way of thinking as much as it is a way of doing. It is a new way of organizing and analyzing production, a concern with the production processes as a system, and a consideration of each element as part of the system. It is something of a conceptual break-through, as revolutionary in its way as Henry Ford's concept of the assembly line. Indeed, it may in the end have an even more widespread effect on business and industry, since its technology rests on a firm theoretical foundation rather than on a specific method of organization or particular kind of machine. Automation is, therefore, adaptable to many different kinds of operations—office work as well as factory work—in small concerns as well as large.

I think that a good part of the confusion which has resulted in attempts to describe automation has come about from defining the word in terms of the nature of its applications. Many of the definitions offered in the past have not conflicted with one another so much as they have neglected one another. That is, they have defined only one segment of what can properly be considered automation (this is the difficulty one encounters when a definition is attempted in terms of "hardware," or machinery, instead of concept).

Although we are in a position to draw some valid conclusions from an adequate study of today's manifestation of automation, we must remember that automation has not really got off the ground. The concept of automation is what is important. Future machines and hardware will undoubtedly be different from anything that we can presently envisage, but I feel that for a long time to come they will simply be extensions and realizations of the concept of automation.

APPLICATIONS AND USES OF AUTOMATION

As it has developed in the United States, automation takes many forms and can be classified in several ways.

One such classification is as follows:

Computers: Automatic handling of information by use of electronic systems.

"Detroit" Automation: Integration of machines; linking together, by means of automatic transfer devices of the machines of production.

Process Control Systems: Computer and integrated control systems for operation of process (oil, chemical, atomic) plants.

Numerical Control: The use of tape and other automatic control devices to direct operation of machines and machine systems.

The mechanization of what we already do today is the part of automation that has received the most attention. The automated engine lines in automobile plants and massive transfer machines are familiar examples of automation. These machines and the jobs they do are important, for they contribute to increases in productivity. But they represent the least significant way in which automation increases productivity.

Eight or ten years ago, I was inclined toward this definition of automation, but with more practical firsthand experience, I soon changed my mind. The more I have been engaged in the actual application of automation to industry and government, the more convinced I am that the fundamental importance of automation is not so much the connecting of machines as it is the ability to create automatic information and control systems. The machines change from year to year, but automation is important as a combination of theoretical understanding, information handling and of the practical application of this theory to build self-correcting systems.

The truly great gains from automation come when it extends the range of man's capability by permitting him to undertake new tasks and reach hitherto unattainable ob-

jectives. It is in this area that man's productivity is multiplied, not a few times, but by many orders of magnitude.
And it is here that the greatest difficulties are encountered
in determining automation's economic consequences.

For example, the principles of long-range weather forecasting are well understood, but the digesting of the mass
of data necessary to produce accurate long-range forecasts has until now been beyond the reach of man or machine. Just recently, a computer was designed capable of
doing more than 100 billion arithmetical computations a
day. A giant like this will soon be able to provide accurate
long-range forecasts, with repercussions that are breath-
taking to contemplate for agriculture, construction, transportation and other industries.

Our experience has shown that the motivations for automating have been very diverse. Apart from the fact that
many considered it a band wagon on which they should
climb, the overriding factors dictating a decision to automate usually were, and still are, (1) to cut production
costs, (2) to reduce labor requirements, (3) to do existing
things faster, (4) to do things not possible before, (5) to
increase productivity, and (6) to aid in decision making
by providing fuller and faster information.

Probably the most common, and the worst, reason for
embarking on an automation program is to save labor costs.
Office management in particular has been bedeviled for
years by rising clerical costs and the difficulty of hiring
enough clerks to get the work done. Mindful of claims to
the effect that one man can be taken off the pay roll for
each five thousand dollars invested in automatic equipment, management has looked on automation as the
answer to a nightmare.

At first glance, this looks like a good enough reason. Ordinarily, an automatic machine does reduce labor costs,
though seldom as much as management had hoped. Here
is a simplified example of the economics of the situation
which shows why.

COMPUTER ECONOMICS

A computer system with tape, tape printer and
peripheral equipment may rent for about $20,000 a

month. In addition, the cost of going from the old to the new system can easily reach $275,000. It may cost more if the old system is particularly antiquated. The new system, therefore, has to relieve enough clerks to pay for the equipment and to yield a return on the investment. For a 3-year pay-out on the investment, annual savings above machine costs must be $92,000. To produce this savings from personnel alone, these costs would have to be reduced $332,000 a year. At $5,000 a year per clerk, this means a net reduction of 66 clerks for the investment to be barely justifiable. And this net reduction has to absorb the extra personnel costs for programmers and machine operators.

The main trouble with this approach is not that savings usually fail to match expectations.

When labor saving is the main goal, it automatically demotes to second place what should be the primary aim of any company installing automation equipment—to exploit fully the potentialities of these machines for doing things that cannot be done well, or cannot be done at all, without them. But even so, automation can cut costs in other less obvious directions.

A Department of Labor study of an insurance company, which installed a computer in the classification sections of one of its divisions, reveals where some of these savings lie. The computer reduced personnel in this particular area from 198 to 85 workers and freed more than 15,000 square feet of floor space for other uses. It reduced the number of punched card machines from 125 to 21, and the yearly rental for these machines from $235,000 to $19,000. Monthly punch-card requirements have been cut by nearly 2.5 million. Altogether, the computer is expected to cut the classification section's budgets in half.

Indeed, management has often introduced automation largely to reduce labor costs and then finds that it has done the right thing for the wrong reason. One chemical company figured that for every dollar saved by reducing the man-hour content for each unit of product, it saved at least three dollars because it could produce a better product more efficiently and with less waste.

"DETROIT" AUTOMATION IN PRACTICE

Among the first examples of the Detroit type of automation are the two Brooks Park engine plants of the Ford Motor Company near Cleveland, which since 1951 have been turning out six-cylinder engine blocks from rough castings. The castings, which are first produced in an automated foundry, are fed into a broaching machine, which then "just goes 'whoosh' and it is done," as one startled observer described the process. Altogether, 42 automatic machines, linked together by transfer devices that automatically move the blocks through the complete process, perform 530 precision cutting operations and borings. A rough casting goes through the line and emerges as a finished engine block in just 14.6 minutes, as against nine hours in a conventional plant.

From the start to finish along the 1,545-foot line, no operator touches a part. "I don't do nothing but press these two buttons," the operator of the broaching machine on an automated Ford Line at Dearborn remarked. "Sometimes I use my thumbs [to push the buttons], sometimes I use my wrists and sometimes I lay my whole arm across. The only time I sweat on the job any more is when the sun is 100 and something outside."

All too often today the economies expected of automation do not bear fruit in actual practice. The expected savings from high cost installations may turn into unrealized hopes.

The following, by now famous, case story clearly illustrates that automation can be a two-way street, if the moves are not properly planned.

Late in 1952, a well-known Midwestern automative supplier began planning a new and highly automated plant that was to prove almost disastrous.

This new facility was an industrial automation scheme designed for the production of body frames for the 1955 model of a popular low-priced automobile. The heart of the plant was a 39-station riveting and welding transfer line for assembling the frames. Anticipated rate of production was 200 frames an hour, which represented 40 per cent of the customer's total requirements.

A new plant in northern Illinois, specially designed to house the machinery, was scheduled to go into production in the summer of 1954—allowing a leadtime of eighteen months between preliminary design and full operation. Although the machinery was installed on time, a continuing series of mechanical defects prevented the line from working properly. For example, the lack of complete drawings and proper references from the equipment vendor resulted in misalignment by one-fourth of an inch of a thirty-foot station, which, in turn, prevented transfer through the station. Similarly, a number of transfer clamps had to be redesigned because original plans proved inadequate.

Mechanical problems continued to hold up production throughout the summer of 1954. By autumn, the body frame manufacturer was forced to install manual machines in order to meet delivery commitments for the beginning of the 1955 model year. This meant hiring 2,500 workers rather than the originally planned 1,000. Because of local labor shortages, unskilled workers were hired. Although the plant was located in an area which had a history of labor trouble, little weight had been given to this fact when an automated facility had been planned. As things turned out, the company was faced with severe jurisdictional disputes and slowdowns.

The company succeeded in meeting production schedules with the manual equipment while debugging progressed on the automatic line. The line ran at reduced speed during the spring and summer of 1955, but in the fall the machinery began to have frequent breakdowns. Pressure for production prevented, for a time, the shutdown needed for correcting the engineering defects, but the line was finally shut down and rebuilt, with redesigned parts substituted for the ones which were faulty. This work took more than a year to complete. In the spring of 1957, the line was finally started up again. It ran almost perfectly for four months, turning out superior frames at better than the originally planned rate of production.

The 1957 production year then ended. The 1958 model of the automobile was redesigned on a new frame, which was all welded. The original investment in the automatic line was about $4 million.

The estimated cost of retooling for the 1958 frame was about $2 million. In the meantime, because of the frame manufacturer's poor delivery performance, the automobile manufacturer cut his order by about 40 per cent. The economic justification for the automatic line was destroyed. As a result, the 1958 frames were produced on a semiautomatic line in one of the supplier's original plants. The estimated loss on operation of the automated plant was almost $10 million.

Why should all this have happened? The series of difficulties this manufacturer experienced—unanticipated mechanical trouble, labor trouble, insufficient time for debugging the new equipment, severe pressure for production—might at first glance be put down to nothing more than a run of plain bad luck.

But it was not bad luck. Every one of the difficulties that made automation a fiasco for this company can be traced to inadequate planning and insufficient leadtime. In short, the company grossly underestimated the magnitude of the change it was undertaking.

PROCESS CONTROL

When the material being processed is not a rigid, solid object but something that flows by its very nature—a liquid, a gas, electric energy, a solid in crushed or powdered form—continuous flow is a good deal easier to achieve. Thus it is not surprising that automation began earlier and has gone much further in the processing industries than in manufacturing, although these industries are still a long way from full automation.

In chemical manufacture and oil refining—the industries that have gone the furthest in automating—entire systems of control instruments regulate the production processes, making it virtually automatic from raw material to finished product, and sometimes to finished by-product as well. A modern oil refinery, oil men estimate, is 80 to 90 per cent automatic. In Esso's refinery at Fawley, England, six men on any one shift operate distillation units processing 5.5 million gallons of crude oil a day. In another plant in Iran, one operator in a central control room regulates 50,000 barrels a day, the total output of four wells single-handed. "A man may work for months on a pipe line, or in a refinery, or even in the production fields and never see or touch oil," an official of the Oil Workers Union has said.

Here are a few more examples that further illustrate the advantages of more automated process control:

The chief instrument engineer of a chemical company stated: Our most significant improvements in purity, increases in throughput for existing equipment, and increases in product uniformity have been brought about by the addition of either analytical instruments or by rearranging the existing instruments into tighter control loops, or by the combination of both. When we have studied the economics after installation, it has not been unusual for us to find savings to the company of anywhere from $50,000 to $150,000 per year by adding instrumentation that costs from $10,000 to $15,000.

Installation of automatic product gauge controls in a plastic film extrusion operation yields savings on materials of $33,000 per year. The cost of the controls was $24,500.

The installation of computer to control a catalytic polymerization unit in a refinery, in conjunction with chromatograph stream analyzers, other new sensing elements and pneumatic to electric and electric to pneumatic transducers yielded an increase in yield from 86 per cent of theoretical maximum to 93 per cent plus an annual savings in cost of catalytic material of $75,000. Total annual savings are approximately $350,000. The total cost of the control installation was $300,000.

The installation of new instrumentation system in a pulp plant resulted in increasing the yield of one cord of wood from .57 tons to .8 tons of pulp.

NUMERICAL CONTROL

Numerical control automation, which has just recently begun to be applied on a widespread basis, is especially applicable to small shops with short runs of greatly varying products—typical job shops. There are roughly seven hundred and fifty of these tape-fed machines in existence today. As I mentioned in earlier testimony, the bulk of United States hard-goods production is in lots of less than 25 identical units. But today's plant automation is largely of the Detroit type—large transfer machinery, suitable for only a small portion of our national production. The solution of this problem is on hand in the numerically controlled machine tool. The development of smaller versions of this equipment will be of principal importance to the factory in the future. Such machines will be capable of producing a short run of one product and then, with a change of tape, producing a few more units of an entirely different product, all from the same tool.

Individual companies adopt automatic control because they expect to benefit from its use by doing existing things better through cutting labor costs, increasing the yield from a facility, reducing in-process inventory, facilitating change in product characteristics or for other reasons. However, the greatest gains in productivity from automation will come from being able to do altogether new tasks and achieve previously unattainable goals. Manufacturers have stated that, using a new numerical controlled machine tool, the total cycle times in the fabrication of an assortment of different parts are reduced from one-half to slightly more than one-tenth the cycle time using under numerical control than comparable tools under manual or tracer control.

Just recently a large manufacturer announced that it already had put into operation seventy-five "program-controlled machines" in the last few years. The company was specifically interested in applying automation to its job shop operations.

The next decade will see the spread of this kind of system in the plant, as the last decade has seen the spread of the computer in the office.

For several years now, my firm has conducted comprehensive surveys of users of automative data-processing equipment to find out what have been their experience. We have generally found that proper uses of the hardware through careful planning has opened possibilities of greater control and analysis than ever existed before.

In a survey we took three years ago of two hundred and eighty users of computer systems, the areas of greatest satisfaction occurred where the inherent speed of the equipment led to satisfaction. There seemed to be less feeling of success applying the computer where more complex management problems arose (improvement in employee morale, for example) and where there was greater need for management science (long-range decisions) techniques. These problems rather than the equipment have been the major stumbling blocks to successful automation —these, rather than any technical problems that may have developed. Technical developments, new machines and all the results of competition and new ranges of equipment are all of no avail unless they are properly applied. For a long time, it has been this area of application that cast a shadow over the data-processing field. The lag between technical achievement and actual application was, say two years ago, so significant as to be almost dangerous. The lag still exists, but at least there have been worth-while developments in the application of computers. Information instead of paper work is becoming the *raison d'etre* of more and more machine systems, and the imaginative developments in 1959 have been quite interesting.

A textile manufacturer in New York uses a computer almost entirely for information on inventory, sales analysis and material available for sale. Not only has this been found to be profitable, but the company is developing new applications and further information requirements that will require a larger system in the next two years. A major oil manufacturer is developing a complete program for marketing accounting that will not only reduce costs, but will provide marketing managers with up-to-date information on sales and sales tendencies all over the country. A drug and consumer goods manufacturer is using a computer to keep constant track of area sales in relation to a national index of purchasing power for a given area. As soon as discrepancies are detected between actual sales and sales that should be expected, corrective action is taken and the results can be measured on a week by week basis.

Another producer of consumer goods has been able to

use a computer system to determine the effect of money spent for advertising and promotion, and to test the probable effect of expenditures on different types of advertising. The result has been a significant change in his advertising and promotion policy.

A chemical company is developing a program for patent searches and classification that will save large amounts of the time of skilled research workers, while the computer is also being used to provide the company's customers with optimum mixes of fertilizer for specific conditions. A utility company will use one of the new generation of computers to overcome the problem of providing customers with up-to-date, accurate answers to inquiries, in addition to performing the basic data-processing work. The Boeing plant in Wichita, Kansas, is using direct connections from the factory floor to the data-processing center in order to gather production data as part of an integrated system of production control.

There are many other examples, but it is enough to say that, although they remain the exception rather than the rule, many companies have made significant progress toward utilizing some of the real potential that computers offer.

The present uses for electronic data processing can be summarized under three headings: (1) business data processing, (2) analysis for management, and (3) scientific and engineering applications. This is similar to the breakdown we use for our computer surveys.

One of the areas of discussion prominently raised at the previous hearings was the application of electronic data-processing techniques to small business. Though most small businesses are far from knowing the fruits of automation, many have already tasted it—and many more will do so in the near future. This has come about due to two developments: one, the addition to computer manufacturers' product lines of small-scale computer systems specifically designed for the capacity needs and pocketbooks of smaller businesses; second, the expansion in number of service bureaus and data-processing centers. The latter only rents its customers time on computer systems. The service bureaus mostly offer complete services in addition to renting machine time to customers; these services include programming, systems design and consultation.

The service bureau has significantly opened up automatic data processing to small firms. Though they could not justify equipment of their own, use of the service bureaus has been proven economical for such continuing applications as pay roll, sales analysis, inventory control and particularly beneficial for special problems in the operations research category involving linear programming methods.

One of the largest computer center networks, the Service Bureau Corporation, a subsidiary of IBM, has reported that the backbone of its business is from small firms, most of whose gross sales are under five million dollars annually. Their customers include insurance agencies, schools, hospitals, union locals, small manufacturers, medical clinics, dairies, banks, mortgage companies, independent telephone companies and other smaller utilities.

The impact of the service bureau concept on business should be even greater within the next few years. All the leading computer manufacturers have opened large numbers of such centers, and are continually opening more of them. These companies include IBM, Remington Rand, RCA, Minneapolis-Honeywell, General Electric and Burroughs.

In addition to manufacturer-run service bureaus, independent service organizations are cropping up all over the country. The independent service bureaus do not have the built-in contacts and customers that manufacturers' service bureaus have. They must offer results at rates reasonable to the customer, and, at the same time, must operate a profitable business.

Entirely independent service bureaus are in most cases offering punched-card tabulating services. They will usually have punched-card calculators or small computers for jobs which require more complicated analyses. In order to provide a low-cost service, these companies will specialize in one application, design a standard program which can handle simple variations of that application and will sell this to small firms at an economic rate. The large volume obtained through many customers makes this possible.

An example of this type of operation is located in New York City. This company has standard punched-card equipment and a small punched-card calculator. They have designed a pay-roll application on this equipment which can be used for several of the companies which they service. One of these companies has a one-thousand-man pay roll, a fairly large operation. It is a construction firm which found it very difficult to prepare accurate pay-roll records under their working conditions. This service relieved their accounting office of a big problem and also prepares the pay-roll checks and records at a lower cost.

This company has recently installed a computer which will increase its capacity considerably. The company expects to be processing pay rolls for companies employing as few as twenty-five and as many as one thousand employees. The significant factor in the economics of such an operation is that a standard pay roll is designed and the equipment is set up to process a series of pay rolls in one run. Only the imprinter changes so that the check and journal headings will show the proper company name. This provides the means for very small companies to take advantage of savings available through large volume processing.

It seems that the small independent service bureaus will be specializing in particular areas, such as pay rolls, or insurance calculations, for assisting large companies during peak periods, or survey results analysis or general accounting functions. Through standardized systems, they will be able to provide low-cost service to the small companies and not only increase their own business but also provide benefits to their customers. The customers, in so many cases, cannot afford their own equipment and even cannot afford specialized treatment, including systems design and programming on a large computer, at a service bureau.

The service bureau concept has gone beyond specific applications to small business. Large service bureaus operate high speed computers for use of the larger corporations to solve highly complex problems. Cooperative service bureaus have also been formed. While many companies are solving their data-processing problems through the use of outside service bureaus, a number of companies have found it more feasible to buy a computer on a cooperative basis with other companies. In most cases, the companies who have banded together have done so because their competitors were able to buy computers of their own. In order to compete, the smaller companies had to have the use of computers and had to have them close enough geographically to perform their daily requirement.

One of the earliest groups of this type is SPAN, a group of fire and casualty insurance companies in Hartford, Connecticut. These companies installed a computer system in early 1958 for processing their paper work.

A similar arrangement was accomplished and is operating in the Midwest, except that the companies involved are seven engineering firms.

A third group which has seen the need for electronic equipment is a group of banks in Texas. This group of banks will buy equipment and establish a joint computer center.

The important economic fact to recognize is that each cooperative group is applying the computer for the same type of application—banking, insurance and engineering. The hardware of the system can, therefore, be designed for the application. The computer operation also has a steady flow of customers. These factors make for a more economical operation than service bureaus who are soliciting different kinds of business.

All these factors—the service bureau, the data center, the cooperative bureau, the new small-scale computer systems—would seem to indicate that what can be called small business will have an economic opportunity to make use of automative techniques. It may be further concluded that it will be an economic necessity for them to do so.

WHO USES AUTOMATION

Despite the burgeoning use of automative techniques, both in the factory and the office, woefully little quantitative data are available as to usage by industrial and commercial sectors of the economy. The extent of penetration of automation equipment within any industry group is still not clearly ascertained.

As a firm, we assemble this kind of data. We are pres-

ently in the process of updating past computer surveys.
From a qualitative standpoint, the bulk of computer installations can be accounted for among the following industries: aircraft manufacturers, transportation, insurance
companies, computer component manufacturers, financial
firms, public utilities, other manufacturing, military and
research, science and engineering.

More data is available for the controls and instrumentation industry. I will show in the following section, The
Growth of the Automation Industry, that this industry can
be expected to grow at a fast rate.

During the next decade, the developments in automation should have a growing impact on American industry.
Research now being conducted by electronic equipment
manufacturers should yield these results. I think it is only
fitting to conclude this section with a short discussion of
the kind of developments we can expect in these next ten
years.

The most immediate progress will be made in the area
of communication equipment. Large corporations, which
took the lead in initiating the use of large-scale computing
equipment for data processing, will give more management attention to integrating accounting, purchasing, inventory control and shop scheduling through centralized
processing.

Until now, automatic data processing has been largely
confined to batch processing. This means collecting data
during the day, usually in the form of punched cards.
These cards are then sorted and processed against a se-
quential file in a daily processing run. However, several
improvements in the punched-card system soon to be introduced should speed up the operation and reduce the
input preparation costs.

FASTER FACT GATHERING

Equipment will be available this year for card-to-card
transmission of data over regular long-distance telephone
wires. Relatively inexpensive sending machines installed,
for example, in a company's branch plants and sales offices
will be used to send information at the rate of forty cards a
minute (and for the price of a phone call) over the tele-

phone lines to headquarters where a receiving machine will produce the data on another card.

An extension of this system, the card-to-card information station, also will be available. It would work like this:

A production worker drops his time card into a "remote station" computer located on the production floor and, using a keyboard, inserts such variable data as employee number and quantity produced. This information is then transmitted over cables to a central information station which punches a transaction card. The transaction cards transmitted from this and all other remote stations are accumulated and subsequently converted to magnetic tape and fed into the computer.

Improvements in magnetic tape transmission, however, will eventually do away with the extra operation of converting punched cards to tape. By 1961, tape-to-tape transmission utilizing long-distance telephone lines will be available. Even higher-speed tape-to-tape transmission will be possible with the use of coaxial cable. This advance is expected about 1964.

Before the decade is out, it will be possible to feed information from remote stations in plants and offices directly into a central computer, which will maintain an up-to-the-minute file and will immediately feed back answers to requests for any data contained in the file.

In-plant information stations, which will be introduced in 1961, will permit direct continuous transmission of punched-card data from the remote station into the central computer. The computer will be able to maintain an up-to-the-minute file. It will also produce daily summary reports of operations.

By 1963, continued advances will make possible the in-plant inquiry and control station, which could automate the whole scheduling process. A medium-sized computer will do the basic file maintenance of incoming data, but it will be attached to a bigger computer which will draw its information from the file, coordinate such complex processes as scheduling and relay any changes back to the remote stations.

Service industries, such as banks, will use inquiry stations, for example, to check customer accounts and to re-

cord transactions. Airlines will be able to make and confirm
reservations quickly, and, at the same time, record billing
information. Department stores will check credit and account balances automatically.

AUTOMATING THE PLANT

The truly automatic factory is still far from a reality
today, but during the next decade, improvements on existing equipment and systems will bring it closer to realization.

With existing tape-controlled machine tools, extensive
calculations are required to prepare the instructions for
the coded magnetic tapes. Today these calculations are
performed on a computer using specially prepared programs for each specific part. By 1963, a common input
language for computers will simplify this job.

A few companies, both here and abroad, are already
using tape-controlled transfer equipment to link together
several of these automatic machine tools into an assembly
line. Further development of this equipment can be expected in the next ten years.

To be efficient, automatic tools today can perform only
one specific function. But automatically controlled tools
which can perform a number of different jobs, such as cutting and stamping, will be in use by 1962. The next step
after the development of these general purpose machine
tools will be the development of general-purpose assembly
machines.

VERSATILE NEW "BRAINS"

Behind all of these advances are a number of major improvements in the computer itself.

General-purpose computers, installed this year, will be
able to handle equally well such business functions as inventory and scheduling, and such engineering functions as
the design and development of new equipment.

New compact computers, which will be available by
1964, will be smaller, faster and more flexible. They will
be able to do more jobs simultaneously and will make a
bigger file of information easily accessible.

Wider usage of magnetic ink character recognitions systems will take place during the decade. Many banks are already using magnetic ink account numbers, which can be "read" electronically, on their checks. Character translation by scanning is another development in this area. In this process, a photoelectric eye scans the numerals and records them.

By 1966, it will be possible to instruct a computer verbally by means of audio translation. In another four years, a mechanical stenographer attached to the computer will give back the recorded data on a sheet of paper. To get the most out of its investment in this revolutionary equipment, management will give more attention to finding broader uses for these new tools of industry.

GROWTH IN THE AUTOMATION INDUSTRY

In the last five years, the growth in the use of automation techniques has certainly been great. But it is my guess that this billion-dollar automation equipment industry of today is still in its infancy. I don't think this statement is optimistic. On the contrary, it is quite realistic. In the late 1940's I remember hearing of a statement that "fewer than a dozen electronic computers will be able to satisfy the entire computational requirements of this country." There is no need belaboring this prediction.

I said earlier that I felt that there were real problems in application, that automation would be slow in coming. But slow is a relative word. Automation will be slow in being applied as compared with its *potential* applicability. In absolute terms of dollar value of equipment delivered, diversity of machines introduced and number of units installed, the growth rate of the automation industry will generally outstrip that of the entire economy for a while to come.

Several factors can account for this growth: continuous interest on the part of businessmen in methods which may lead to cost reductions and better management control, technological development within the automation field and more competition in the industry itself.

One department in my organization is specifically concerned with analyzing the automation equipment market.

We are always in the process of updating our estimates and projections. It is significant that projections of the future market usually must be revised upward as we receive more data on present market conditions!

This section will mainly include some of my firm's data on the industry's historical growth and some projections for future growth.

PROCESS CONTROLS AND INSTRUMENTS

This industry should grow threefold by 1970. My firm's estimates of the potential market for automatic controls and instrumentation indicates that we may expect expenditures for this type of equipment to approach and even exceed three billion dollars a year by 1970.

The process industries, such as chemicals and food processing, have been the major users of controls and instrumentation. Companies dealing with products manufactured in continuous flow systems have been quickest to adopt the use of this equipment. We can expect spectacular growth in process industries during this next decade. Chemical production is estimated to rise more than 125 per cent by 1970, for example. Not only will process control equipment production grow because of growth in its market; new technological developments yielding new uses will expand this market to an even greater extent. Of the total expenditures in 1970 for controls and instrumentation, that equipment going to the process industries may account for about two thirds of this total, or about two billion dollars. The growth rate in these industries' expenditures will be greater than 10 per cent per year during these next ten years. Most certainly, it will outstrip our national growth rate rather dramatically.

NUMERICAL CONTROL EQUIPMENT

Numerical controls have shown the greatest growth rate of any sector of the automation equipment field largely because it is the newest of commercially acceptable automation techniques—and there are relatively few actual units installed. Numerical control is only six years in existence, but its acceptance by industry seems complete.

In the last few years, annual sales of this equipment have been doubling the previous year's sales record. We can expect this high rate of growth to continue for years to come. In the next three years, my firm's estimates show this industry growing by 500 per cent to within the one-hundred-million-dollar range.

Already, more than forty companies have developed numerical control equipment and are promoting its sale. The technique has demonstrated distinct advantages over conventional machine tools that outweigh its initial high cost: large potential reductions in production costs, greater accuracy and more speed—to name just a few.

Undoubtedly, the large capital outlays needed to install numerical controlled machines will keep many small businesses from employing them at this time. Many may simply be reluctant to lay out money for new tools when it would seem that the ones they have are perfectly good. Eventually, competition may drive the smaller businesses to use of this technique. Making these automated tools economically feasible for them will require that the machines have great flexibility—which they are technically capable of—and good service on the part of the manufacturers. I think the latter will certainly occur. The analogy may be made here to the role of the manufacturers of computers who have done a great deal in bringing the technical know-how to the equipment users.

The impact of numerical controls on the economy has yet to be strongly felt. This aspect of automation has not received the wide public attention given to computers and transfer equipment; but this phase of the industry alone may well have a most significant impact within certain manufacturing industries. When you consider that about 70 to 80 per cent of the metal-working industry deals with production runs of twenty-five units or less and that these operations have been the last to yield to cost reduction efforts, numerical controls are bound to have a major effect on this manufacturing industry. One prognosticator says that "within five years, 50 per cent of the new machine tool facilities will be represented by numerically controlled tools." No doubt this subcommittee will hear other estimates of future numerical control usage from witnesses identified with that industry. Suffice to say that growth in the application of numerical controls even to 25 per cent of new machine tool facilities will have national economic consequences.

ELECTRONIC DATA PROCESSING

I think that it can be safely said of electronic data-processing that it is the most extensively used technique developed within the concept of automation; there seems to be little doubt that the influence in our economy will grow even greater. The intelligent use of electronic computing machinery and its peripheral equipment hold out promises of productivity which we do not, at present, even know how to measure—the productivity found in accomplishing things we never thought of doing or simply could not do before. There is still a long way to go, however, in extending the use of this equipment within industries to accomplish day-to-day business functions—pay-roll processing, inventory control, production control and other such applications.

The number of companies that have computer systems is still a minute fraction of total American industry. Total installations, as of July, 1960, were almost eleven thousand. This is more than a 34 per cent increase over last year's total. These figures only denote computer systems delivered; hundreds more are on order.

I think I can summarize the basis for this recent progress by considering four factors that have had far-reaching influence in automatic data processing: first, development and introduction of new machines and new technical developments; second, significant developments in automatic data processing for the small and medium-sized company; third, the growth of competition in the computer field; and fourth, the improvement of the use made of computers through better planning and better applications.

Technological improvements in electronic computers have been made in such areas as data storage and retrieval, computing speeds and a host of developments leading to special capabilities of hardware to cope with specific problems. The most recent important development has been the transistorized computer. We are now faced with a new generation of computers with new capabilities. Generally, the new computing machines have the following attributes:

(1) Greater reliability. Machines will make even fewer mistakes (if this is conceivable) and they will be in operating condition in a greater proportion of the time.

(2) Costs of installation will be lower, partly because the machine systems are smaller and partly because of the fewer environment requirements for the installation.

(3) Lower cost per unit of performance. This has several additional implications. The greater speed of processing will permit applications that were impossible before for economic reasons.

(4) Greater flexibility. One machine is now able to serve many more functions than before. For instance, it is, at least from a technical viewpoint, much more reasonable to combine scientific and business applications than it was before.

The development of smaller machines has opened up new areas of business to the computer manufacturers. In terms of absolute increases in number of installations and percentage increases in number of installations and percentage increase, small-scale computer systems have shown the most impressive growth. Many of these systems have gone to the smaller and medium-sized companies. The growth in the use of service bureaus, discussed in the previous section, has also expanded EDP usage considerably.

The third major development has been a healthy increase in competition among the computer manufacturers. This has resulted in a direct increase in number and kinds of systems available. There is also considerable pressure for the computer companies to provide even better service to customers.

Competition in computers has gone through three stages. Several companies have entered and then withdrawn from the field to leave three or four dominant firms manufacturing business data processing equipment. The third stage began in 1958-59 when a whole new group of powerful firms entered the computer field.

The industry presently is still dominated by a few companies. IBM, which has maintained its position as the largest in the industry in terms of sales volume, may find it difficult to hold its share of the market in the face of stiffer competition from the rest of the industry. Estimates of IBM's share of the computer market have declined from approximately 80 per cent levels more recently to about 75 per cent. Other computer manufacturers are predicting that this percentage will fall even further. In terms of dollar volume of the market, this should increase for the next few years. From an installed value of about $75 million worth of equipment in 1955, 1960's installation value should be about $650 million. The industry is capable of doubling this 1960 figure within 5 years. However, projections vary considerably, but even the conservative projections for annual installation values are higher than those presently. Personally, I expect the computer market to achieve its high growth potential.

ECONOMIC AND SOCIAL ASPECTS
OF AUTOMATION

I do not believe that we are presently experiencing the full economic and social influence of automation—that is, of fully utilized automation concepts and techniques. The acceptance of automation techniques by industry has been more gradual than it might have been. Technical or economic feasibility did not hold back the introduction of automation; lack of understanding the new technology, fear, improper planning and other human mistakes are more likely reasons. I think it would not be too great an exaggeration to say that the economic and social environment had a greater limiting impact on automation than the impact of automation on the environment.

An inspection of the aggregate productivity figures would not reveal any abnormally high productive influence in the postwar economy. Even if the recovery year 1959 is included in productivity calculations, total United States private industry still only had an annual rate of increase in output per man hour of about 3 per cent for the entire postwar period 1947-59. The nonagricultural sector of the economy had an annual average of about 2½ per cent for the same period. More recent average productivity growth is even lower. The annual average increase in productivity from 1953-59 in nonagricultural industries is slightly less than 2.3 per cent. In terms of impact on the total economy, it would be difficult to discover where any revolutionary element had been introduced into the works. Of course, substantial productivity gains have been made in a number of individual industries as a result of the introduction of mechanization and automation equipment. In some cases, human hardships have developed; in others this has not been so. But in the aggregate sense, automation has not so greatly affected the economy that it can be isolated from advances in technology that we continuously experience.

I do not want to give the impression that I intend to minimize the economic effects of automation. The subcommittee will, no doubt, be provided with many statistics documenting the dislocations of workers and job eliminations attributed to technological change. However, I want to avoid incorrectly attributing these results to automation. I made the statement earlier that automation is a set of concepts and techniques; it is a body of knowledge making available to the nation more efficient means for producing goods. This technology does not cause anything; how we use it yields the results. In other words, how the economy is operating has an influence on what the results will be.

If normal technological change takes place in a rapidly expanding economy, usually the benefits of change are only noticeable: increased productivity, higher wages, new products, and so on.

When these same changes take place in a slow-moving economy, disruption may occur. The basic problem in this case is not attacking the problem of change. Clearly, the problem here is the slow growth of the economy.

This may seem like a most academic point, but I believe that it is very important to realize when dealing with the difficult problem of integrating technology in our highly complex economy. There have been times in the history of man when technological developments were so potent and their introduction so rapid that normal economic growth could not accommodate the changes without much human suffering. But I would suggest that in our case we may not be suffering from too rapid an introduction of technology so much as we are experiencing a slow rate of economic growth—the recent war average of about 2.5 per cent.

ECONOMIC ASPECTS OF AUTOMATION

Automation has continued to be most strongly utilized in the manufacturing sector of the economy. The transportation, communications, utilities, finance and insurance industries are also making use of these concepts to a growing degree.

In terms of the effects on total industry employment, automation has probably most affected the manufacturing sector; I say probably because whether the use of automation or mechanization has been more responsible for the decreases in employment needs is still a moot question. The Federal Government has also made extensive use of automation techniques; the effects on government employment were investigated recently by the Committee on Post Office and Civil Service of the House of Representatives.

The economic effect on individuals in an industrial situation experiencing the introduction of automation has varied greatly from industry to industry. A lot has depended on what kind of automation technique was being employed, whether it was electronic data processing, Detroit automation, process control or machine tool control. Labor-management relations have also played an important role in affecting the outcome. The versatility of the work force, age levels, education levels, all influence what will happen after automation has been installed.

I have generally found, from my firm's experience, that the installation of automation equipment does not lead to mass layoffs of company personnel. Through the means of retraining, natural attrition, transfers and retirements, dislocation of personnel is minimized. In all cases of successful introduction of automation, management planning for the installation was carefully executed.

Not in all cases could layoffs be avoided. In certain instances, employees were not capable of learning new skills that would be required of them. When transfer possibilities were not available, termination of employment eventually proved necessary. Even here, I found, in several instances, that management maintained the employment level of an operation significantly above what was necessary after the automation equipment was installed. Though it is difficult to generalize that this is standard practice, I have heard others in the field relate this same experience.

Within the last year or two, automation seems to have become a national issue on two counts. First, on the domestic side, it has caused a good deal of fear. To be more precise, I should say that automation has been used to create fear, specifically, fear of unemployment. Second, on the international front, we recognize that we need the production efficiencies that automation allows us if we are to compete effectively in the free world markets; we also need increased productivity if we are to maintain our defense position and yet increase our standard of living. These two positions would seem to contradict each other, but they simultaneously exist.

In some of those industries where it is recognized that displacement of labor has continued and will continue to occur, some action has been taken. The Armour automation fund, set up last year, attempts to study the automation problem, tries to find opportunities for employment for workers displaced by automation and inaugurates retraining programs. This company-financed program is paid for by a levy of one cent per hundred weight of meat shipped, up to a maximum of $500,000 in the fund. The Armour fund has been referred to as having "set a pattern" for other industries. Several other companies are actually setting up study committees in the Armour fashion. Judging by the publicity received by a company when it embarks on such a program, there seem to be relatively few companies attempting this. However, a start has been made.

It is also encouraging that other institutions have begun

to take steps to train both those who are already in the working force and those who will one day join it for the new jobs that automation creates. Several universities, for example, are now offering courses in computer programming, and a number of computer manufacturers are training clerical personnel on the job. A technical high school in Buffalo offers a course in which students build a digital computer and then learn to solve problems with it. At least one union, Local 1 of the International Brotherhood of Electrical Workers in St. Louis, in cooperation with the Federal Office of Apprentice Training and a local vocational school, has set up what it calls a "postgraduate school" for training in new electrical techniques.

Within a short time, four hundred members had signed up for a three-year course and were attending thirty-eight different classes four nights a week.

Two state governments, as I previously mentioned, held conferences to discuss the economic and social implications of automation. Both in New York and Massachusetts, the problems of coping with the effects of technological change and automation were aired. At these conferences, at others and in private discussions, I have usually found recurring arguments in both the optimistic and pessimistic camps of automation.

I noted these arguments in my study of automation written under the sponsorship of the National Planning Association.

Here is a summary of some of the arguments most generally used by those who consider automation a blessing rather than a menace.

Automation is nothing new, so there is no reason for concern. Technological changes have occurred throughout history without dire results, and automation is just another technological change. There is no more need to legislate against automation than there was need to slow down the introduction of the assembly line. Technological change is progress and should be welcomed.

Everything will work out in the long run. The natural forces in the economy will make whatever adjustments may be necessary to the introduction of automation. This can be brought about through the movement of displaced workers to other industries, through the expansion of output of industries that automate or through the introduction of new industries into the economy. If the industries that apply automation expand their output, there may be the need for the same number of workers, but they will be producing a great deal more than before. The introduction of new industries, through invention and research, will take up whatever slack may develop in the economy.

Automation is the key to a shorter work week. There is an unmistakable trend toward less work and more leisure. To realize this goal without sacrificing our real standard of living, we must increase productivity. And automation is the means to increase it. The result of automation will not be forced idleness or unemployment but the enjoyment of more leisure.

Unlimited demand for goods and services will prevent unemployment from automation. Since human wants are unlimited, increased productivity and production through automation will find a market in satisfying these wants. Through greater productivity, earnings will increase to such an extent that there will be a tremendous rise in our standard of living. These increased earnings can come about through higher wages or through lower prices or through a combination of the two.

Automation will create a bigger pie, so that everybody's slice will be larger. This is far better than trying to limit the size of the overall pie and then fighting about how the smaller pie is to be distributed.

Automation will come slowly and in limited quantity. It is neither big enough nor fast enough to warrant concern. Its speed is limited by the long-range planning it requires, the shortage of trained personnel, and the huge investment required. At best, it will affect only a small segment of the total economy, and even those who are so affected will have plenty of time to adjust.

Automation is the only means of maintaining our standard of living in the face of a significant labor shortage. The future problem will be unavailability of labor, not unavailability of jobs.

Employment has been increasing. While everybody is shouting about the harmful effects of automation on employment, there has been a steady increase in employment in the past few years during which the impact of automation should have been at its highest. What unemployment there has been can be attributed to cyclical swings similar to those which occurred before the advent of automation.

Automation brings about lower prices.

A more responsible management will not permit automation to have harmful effects on employment.

Development and growth may occasionally mean hardship, but it is a small price to pay for progress. (This is a rare argument, but as an attitude it may be prevalent.)

The growth of the automation industry itself will provide employment for a good number of those put out of work by the products of the automation industry.

Automation is the key to national survival. The only way that the United States will be able to stay ahead of, or keep pace with, Russia is through a strenuous increase in productivity. At the same time, more leisure, more comfort, and more consumption goods are the goals of American economic policy.

Automation will bring economic stability. In an automated plant, labor costs will be so low and capital costs so high that it will pay to continue production and lower prices rather than to cut production and lay people off. And even if production is cut, the cut in employment will not be proportionate, because most of the work will be indirect labor that does not vary with volume of production. Furthermore, automation programs must be long-term in nature, and their completion will not depend on short-term changes in sales.

This means that investment expenditures will be more stable. In these ways, cyclical fluctuations will be reduced.

Some of these arguments or points of view are sound. Some are false. Others are a mixture of fact and fancy. The dilemma is increased because there are contradictions and disputes even among those who agree that automation is a blessing and should not worry anyone. The most significant characteristic of all these approaches is that they are weak arguments for the point of view they espouse. The strongest arguments are those that are founded on world politics rather than on economics.

The reason for the weakness of these arguments as they now stand is that there are no facts to back them up. There are no facts on which to base an evaluation of their worth, and there are no structures of theory within which the facts can be developed, sorted and evaluated. The only strength that these viewpoints have is the fact that the counter arguments are also weak and unfounded.

The more common arguments for concern over automation are indicated below. The wide diversity of appeals that they have and the difficulty of evaluating theory—can be seen even from this limited presentation.

The boom has helped up to now. The advent of automation—which is still in its infancy—has been accompanied by the greatest period of boom that America has ever experienced. A backlog of wartime demand and huge government expenditures have created the boom. This cyclical upswing has masked the effects of automation on unemployment because the temporary factors of a boom have enabled the economy to absorb those technologically displaced.

Automation is an accelerating phenomenon. As yet we have not seen its real effects. There have only been instances of complete automation, and some factories that can be considered partly automated. But the real impact will come in the future, when the gestation period is over, and the technical difficulties have been overcome. At that time, there will be a sudden surge forward, at an accelerating rate, and the resulting unemployment will wreak havoc with the economy.

There will be no purchasing power. As automation replaces workers and permits the manufacture of products without labor, these workers will be unemployed. As a result, they will not be receiving the wages that permit them to buy the products of American industry. The result will be the piling up of stocks in warehouses and the biggest depression that we have ever had.

And, like every depression, it will spread to those areas of the economy that are not directly affected—the nonautomated areas.

The growth of job opportunities cannot grow as fast as necessary.

Markets will become saturated. There is really no sense in pretending that automation will permit the same number of workers to turn out more products, because there will be no desire for these additional products. After everybody in America has two cars, he will not want a third. The truth is that there will be fewer workers turning out the same amount of products, because there is a certain point beyond which additional units will not be absorbed. In addition to the sufferings of those workers who are actually displaced, the drying up of their purchasing power will create a national depression that will eventually have repercussions on those who were not displaced by technology.

In comparing the pessimistic point of view with the optimistic, two things become clear—and without any need to pass judgments on the validity of either point of view. In the first place, the pessimistic side—or those favoring control and mitigation—is much the more powerful. It is on the offensive, it has much more active advocates, and it can appeal to the emotions much more effectively. Second, the pessimistic

side has a definite program which it can champion.
The higher minimum wage, the guaranteed annual
wage, the four-day week, the granting of specific
guarantees, and eventually the control of investments
in automation—these are all specific points that can
be put forth as a constructive program to avoid the
dire consequences that are predicted. The opponents
of these viewpoints have nothing concrete to offer,
and they are constantly on the defensive.

The issues are most closely drawn by organized
labor, as they have a direct stake in employment
movements. The attached chart is a summary of some
of these key issues, and how labor wants these issues
resolved.

SOCIAL ASPECTS OF AUTOMATION

Automation's social consequences are broader than its
economic effects. Results in the social sphere also depend
on the speed and degree of automation. Although automation can influence nearly every phase of our life—from
what we do to how we are governed—there is as great a
lack of factual information as there is for the economic
questions. Even the immediate effects of automation at
the work place are hard to ascertain. There are only a
few thorough studies of this subject. The few that exist
are not sufficient to come to any generalized conclusions.

AUTOMATION: HOW LABOR SEES THE ISSUES AND THE ACTION TO BE TAKEN

MAJOR ISSUES	ACTION TO BE TAKEN
Industrial	*by Industry*
Decreasing job opportu-nities in manufacturing, min-ing and transportation in-dustries.	Through collective bar-gaining establish provisions for:
Workers are being "dis-located," they need more job security.	Shorter work week. Stronger seniority rights.
Change in wage structure and job evaluation systems.	Severance payments and other supplemen-tary benefits.

Labor not sharing in the gains of productivity from automation.

Industry's labor needs are changing fast, workers must be retrained.

New systems of compensation, eliminating incentive-type wage payment plans.

Higher wages.

Earlier retirement.

Retraining programs.

Special funds to cope with automation problems.

Advance notice of employment changes.

National

The slow rate of economic growth: The GNP should be growing at a 5 per cent annual rate as opposed to the recent 2½ per cent growth trend.

Rate of increase in real earnings per worker is too low, not as high as early postwar growth rate.

Increased number of economically distressed communities.

High sustaining unemployment levels, the possibility of automation leading to a "wholesale unemployment and depression."

by Government

Stimulate economic growth through increased Federal spending, foster "job-creating, job-inducing programs."

Promote a Federal Training and Retraining Program.

Government legislation inducing lower work-week levels.

Greater aid to economically distressed communities.

State governments should increase unemployment benefit.

Change Social Security regulations to provide retirement benefits at earlier age.

The individual studies come to different conclusions, depending on the kind of automation that was introduced (factory automation or electronic data processing), where it was introduced and the conditions under which the

change to automation took place—to name a few. There
have been cases reported, for example, where the introduction of automation in a process plant led to higher
morale among the workers, a more highly developed social
unit in the plant and an upgrading in skills. But these reactions have not been true in all cases studied—or even in
a majority of the ones that I have seen. A study of an automated assembly-line operation reported "increased feelings of tension" among the workers, nor is this an isolated
case. Recent studies of automatic data-processing installations report a high level of routine work—as high or higher
than before the introduction of the automatic equipment.
In other establishments, routine work decreased in a comparable situation.

From my own experience, I find that one generalization holds true for the entrance of electronic data
processing into an operating unit: there is an increase in
the percentage of skilled personnel for the given operation
unit after EDP is installed. At the very least, we can see
the newer skills are needed—programmers, systems analysts, systems engineers. Certain valid generalizations can
be made about the need for retraining programs and
especially for education.

On all levels of working and living we will need more
education. Beyond retraining those who already have jobs
to prepare them for more highly skilled work, we must
face the larger problem of how we are to increase our resources of engineers, scientists and trained technicians. At
present, a good part of our most talented raw material
goes to waste every year. About half of the high school
students in the upper 25 per cent of their classes do not
attend college at all, and another 13 per cent drop out before the finish. All told, almost two-thirds of those best
fitted to exercise scientific and technical leadership are
not being trained to their highest capacity.

This problem will grow more acute in the years ahead,
and not only because the need for trained men will grow.
We are still drawing heavily on the knowledge and the
trained personnel developed under the pressure of military needs. But we cannot go on living off our hump
indefinitely. We will have to develop ways of making

higher training available to those best suited to make good use of it.

On the high school level, where technicians are trained and where the decision for or against science as a career is often made, the situation is equally acute. High school programs must be reassessed and so must the supply and quality of high school teachers.

As Dr. Allen V. Astin, director of the National Bureau of Standards, has pointed out, "with the great shortage we now have of scientists and engineers, it is difficult to get anyone with any competence to do the teaching in the high schools at the present time."

But the question of education goes far beyond better training for work in specialized fields. Many of the new jobs that automation will create (supervising the intricate workings of delicate machines, for instance) will require an increasing ability to think and to judge, increased understanding of mathematical and logical methods, in short, increased education in the largest sense of the term. Management will need these abilities on a higher level. And all of us, if our increased leisure is to mean something more than just another day when we can sleep late, will need to develop some of these qualities. In view of these needs, one of the great mistakes we could make would be to concentrate all our attention on the specialized problems of educating scientists and technicians.

More than that, the fact that the new machines are capable of providing us with more information than we have ever had raises questions of the highest importance. Just as they can provide answers to scientific questions that could never be answered before, so machines can provide answers to questions outside the field of science that could never be answered before because no one person or group of people could comprehend all the facts. Man could become a cog in the machine, accepting, in Norbert Wiener's words, "the superior dexterity of the machine-made decisions without too much inquiry as to the motives and principles behind them." It is here that our ability to think, to judge and to understand will stand us in best stead. For machines are only machines. It is up to men to decide how to use them.

FOREIGN ASPECTS OF AUTOMATION

In the practical application of automation concepts and techniques to industry, the United States leads the world at the present time. In terms of growth rate in application and absolute number of automated installations, we are ahead of any country in the free world. I have not included the communist bloc nations because there is no substantial data to estimate their progress accurately.

Qualitatively, we know that they are moving ahead at a fast rate. To the extent that they are employing automation, it is interesting to consider Premier Khrushchev's report to the Twenty-first Congress of the Communist Party of the Soviet Union. He gave some indication of the widespread applications intended for mechanization and automation under the Soviet Seven-Year Plan for Economic Development (1959-65).

Mr. Khrushchev reported that "integrated mechanization and the *automation* of production processes constitute the chief and decisive means for ensuring further technical progress in the economy and, on this basis, a new rise in labour productivity, the lowering of cost prices, and the improvement of the quality of products." This theme is further amplified in Mr. Khrushchev's statement of the "target figures" with regard to level of *automation* to be obtained. Of particular note was the indication of plans for the "establishment of more than 50 experimental model enterprises where the latest patterns of integrated automation will be put into effect."

In a final section, in a discussion of specific provision of the "plan" as it pertains to educational development, it was stated that "the greatest increase in the number of engineers graduated [during the years of the 'plan'] will be in the specialties of chemical technology, *automation*, computing engineering, radio electronics and other branches of new technique." Stress will also be placed upon scientific development and, "in particular the successes of computing mathematics [which] are directly connected with the development of *automation*."

I would suggest that it would be sheer folly to take these words lightly, in view of the Soviet Union's accom-

plishments in the field of engineering education and the
science of mathematics. Recent reports point to a gap between theory and application in the field of automation in
the Soviet Union. I would not expect this state to last very
long (if, indeed, it is an accurate picture of present
achievement levels).

It would also be a mistake to take a complacent attitude
toward European business. Though we outautomate Europe by sheer volume alone, the level of sophistication in
automatic techniques is high, especially in factory automation.

My company continually surveys the Western European
electronic data-processing market. We have found the European attitude to be more cautious of EDP hardware
than is true in the United States. The cost factor of automatic equipment is given heavier emphasis. However, we
have found that the average European computer user can
be expected to make better use of the hardware's capabilities than his American counterpart once it is installed.
He has been predisposed by his educational background
to more easily accept the theoretical capabilities of the
electronic hardware.

Western Europe has a total of over two thousand computer installations, or about 20 per cent of total United
States installations. However, over 90 of this total are
small computer system installations. What is most significant is that France and Germany, between themselves,
have almost 70 per cent of total European installations.
Orders for computer systems number in the hundreds for
all Western Europe.

Between the Russians on one hand and Western Europe
on the other, we literally have our hands full. It seems to
me that we are in a most tragic plight as a nation when we
must worry about the ill effects of introducing automation
—even at a slow rate!

GUIDE TO A STUDY OF AUTOMATION
IN THE UNITED STATES ECONOMY

In my final recommendation before this subcommittee
in my initial testimony, I suggested that a study of auto-

mation be undertaken on a comprehensive basis. This
study is still needed. Other witnesses will no doubt make
this same suggestion to this subcommittee; I have seen testimony of people who have made this recommendation at
other Congressional hearings.

Some excellent studies concerned with automation have
been accomplished. Certainly, the Bureau of Labor Statistics of the United States Department of Labor is to
be congratulated on its Studies of Automatic Technology
series. The bureau's recent studies on the introduction of
office automation were most welcome. People in the academic world have also produced some significant work in
this field. Quite frankly, I still feel that the problem of
gathering adequate data has not been surmounted.

The following discussion and guide is taken from a planning pamphlet that I prepared last year for the National
Planning Association:

Automation is only one of the many complex inter-
locking factors that shape the economy. While it may
not be practicable or possible to study all of the factors that make up the economy, we can make an in-
dustry-by-industry study of what automation has
meant so far, and thus foresee with some certainty
what it is likely to mean in the future. We do know
that the potential impact of automation is such that
we cannot disregard planning for it. We need complete enough information to plan for the kind of action automation will require from industry, labor
and government. It is for the purpose of obtaining this
type of information that I here propose an initial
study of the economic consequences of automation.

In making a study of automation, we must also give
emphatic attention to the education problem in all its
aspects—a problem that is corollary to the economic
one. I feel very strongly that the educational problem
is the most challenging one we shall have to face as
the age of automation advances. We must first determine what the economic direction is likely to be,
and then meet it with reasonable human foresight.
We must ascertain in some detail the nature of the

industrial, managerial, labor and social problems experienced by the industries that have already begun to automate, if we are to determine just how we are to train people to meet them.

It seems to me that, at this point, the most useful way of collecting, organizing, and analyzing the information necessary to such a study as this is a detailed case-by-case approach to a number of specific industries that are representative of the several types of applications of automation practiced today. It would be valuable also to study a few typical industries where there is some especially interesting aspect to the way automation has been applied or has affected them. The following list should provide a good starting point:

THE AUTOMOTIVE INDUSTRY

This industry has solved some immense problems in automating some of its processes and illustrates well the kind of automation that has come to be called Detroit automation. A study of the industry should develop useful information on how workers and working conditions are affected in factories which have learned how to handle long runs with specially designed automatic machinery.

PAPER MANUFACTURING

This is a processing industry which is just beginning to use feedback control systems. The effects of automation on labor here are likely to be slight, since there will probably not be much reduction in working force, but there are other interesting aspects to be studied. A change in the productivity of the capital equipment is one of these. In addition, the technical problems in this industry give a good deal of insight into the fundamental technical problems that must be overcome before automation can become complete in the processing industries. For example, present methods of measuring or testing paper consistency involve actually tearing the paper and letting water seep through it. If this area of the industry is to be effectively automated, this method, which is now an art, must be turned into a science.

FOOD PROCESSING

This is one of the traditional automatic machinery areas and would be an interesting study from the standpoint of determining whether there are really any differences between the social and economic effects of introducing the older style of automatic machinery and the newer developments.

AIRFRAME MANUFACTURE

Since production runs are very short and engineering changes are frequent, the airframe industry has many of the problems of job shop manufacturers, even though it is dominated by a few large companies. In a sense, it could be said that the airframe industry is pioneering in job shop automation. Appropriate case studies, therefore, could shed considerable light on the potential forms and the pace of job shop automation.

The airframe manufacturing industry is again worth studying because it relies heavily on computers for scientific calculation. From my own experience, I suspect that there has been an enormous increase in employment as a result of these techniques and it would be important to see whether the situation in this area is applicable to the wider problem of employment opportunities. In addition, the aircraft industry is starting to use computers on a wide scale for office use. But perhaps an even more valuable study could be made in this field on insurance companies, since this industry is already using computers and is certain to be one of the heaviest users of them in the future.

OIL AND CHEMICAL PROCESSING

These industries are highly instrumented and have introduced a certain amount of centralized control. They would provide a valuable study of the relationship between manufacturing areas and the office in an industry where there is almost no labor directly involved in the manufacturing process. As more is learned about the use of computers, considerable change is bound to occur in this industry through automation, and it is an area which should be explored. It is also an industry where we can measure the effects of automation over a considerable period of time. A case study could record what happened in the original shift from batch to continuous processing twenty-odd years ago.

ELECTRONIC ASSEMBLY

This industry is interesting because the problem of considerable and continuous variation of the product is involved. The methods that are being used to attack this problem, and their effects on an industry that even today relies on an enormous amount of woman power for production, would illuminate the problem of other industries faced with this kind of situation.

OFFICE AUTOMATION

In this area, several kinds of studies might profitably be made. For example, it would be worth-while to compare the approaches used by Sylvania, which has a large number of branches and a single computer center for all of them, and by Allstate Insurance or Prudential, which also have a large number of branches and are introducing computers into each of them.

It is also important to find out what will happen when medium-sized business introduces computers into the office. There are a few cases where this has already been done, and I think one or two case studies of such businesses would be very worth-while.

NONBUSINESS USES OF COMPUTERS

One of the most far-reaching influences of automation may well be the use of computers for cultural and purely scientific applications. Their use in such tasks as tracing satellites and codifying the Bible has received much publicity. Their possible capacities for extending the frontiers of present knowledge may have a significant influence on education and on the direction of future research.

It would also be of value to make similar case studies of industries that have not yet automated to any significant degree. These studies could be less thorough, but their objective would be to determine the factors that limit automation. Clearer definition of these barriers would enable us to determine whether automation in these areas is merely a question of time or whether the present obstacles are permanent ones. Some industries that would be appropriate for study in this area are construction, transportation, small job shops and companies producing custom goods.

STUDY PROCEDURE

As for the procedure to be followed in conducting these case studies, I would suggest the following steps for each industry:

(1) A general introductory survey of the particular industry should be made so that the study team can get a general idea of the kind of developments that have been taking place.

(2) On the basis of this introductory survey, one or two specific companies should be selected for more intensive study. These companies should be typical of the industry in the sense that they are doing things which other companies could and probably will do—that is, they should not be uniquely large, in a particularly dominating position or financially capable of doing things other companies in the industry could not afford. However, they should also be companies that either have done or are doing a good deal in the automation field, and, in this respect, they may not be typical of their industry.

(3) Before a detailed approach is made on the case study of the company, the study team should obtain general and background information on the history and development of the company.

(4) The study team should conduct a pilot study which would include: interviews with key people; discussion with both the personnel department and the union about actual personnel shifts; discussion with manufacturing and planning departments about existing and planned changes; meeting with the controller's department about changes in data processing; and estimate of the relationship of this company to the industry at large.

(5) From study and analysis of the pilot study results, it should be possible to develop a plan for a more detailed

study, including check lists and a carefully devised plan of action.

(6) Based on the data that have been obtained, further observation and interviews should be undertaken. During this time, the study team should primarily observe what is happening. Individual workers, as well as members of management, should be interviewed and their observations studied in detail. All related files and interoffice memos should be examined and, during the course of the study, all pertinent interoffice data should be available to the study team. The team should plan to spend a substantial amount of time on the company's premises, since the more revealing findings may come from a study of a process in the course of development, even though a good deal may have been done toward automation. The team should attend meetings and talk freely with people, but it is important that they remain noncommittal and make clear that they do not represent a particular bias, or endorse a particular doctrine.

The preceding paragraphs suggest some of the major aspects that must be considered in a study of automation but, of necessity, other problematic aspects will emerge in the course of the study. The questions that follow are intended to suggest a more specific outline, although by no means an exhaustive one, of questions that must be asked and answered in a study before we can determine the implications of the present and future developments of automation. For purposes of simplification, I have divided these questions into impact areas. Obviously, any such division is arbitrary—for whatever affects industry affects labor, and, in turn, the entire community.

AUTOMATION AND INDUSTRY

A. Extent and Rate of Automation

What industries not highly automated could be so if present technological advances were applied? What has prevented the introduction of automation in these industries?

In automated industries, what degree of the total production capacity of the industry can be described as automated? What percentage of the individual plants that have introduced automation can be described as large, medium or small?

Within an individual company, what percentage of operations are automated? Which operations have been automated? Which have not? Why are the nonautomated operations not automated? Because of cost? Because they are not suitable for automation?

When did the company first begin deliberately to automate? When was the automation equipment installed? Was it installed all at once, or over a period of time? How much did the equipment cost? How did its cost compare with the replacement cost of machines it replaced? What percentage of the automation equipment replaced machines that were obsolete? What percentage of the total spent on equipment in each of the last five years was spent on automation equipment? What is the estimated total cost of automating to date?

Did the product or process have to be redesigned before automation could be introduced? What did this involve? How long did it take? Did the new machines have to be specially designed and built? Were there any special problems in getting them designed and built?

Is the company planning further automation? What current technological or economic development might affect the rate and/or degree of automation? What percentage of operations, and which operations, are expected to be automated within the next five years? Within the next ten years? How much equipment will be replaced because of obsolescence in the next five years? Will it be replaced with automatic or conventional machines?

Has automation permitted the production of new goods or services?

If automation has not been introduced, what are the reasons? Is it because of high costs? The difficulty of integrating automatic machines with conventional machines? The financial risk involved in automating? Because there seems to be no need for it? Because of worker or union hostility?

B. Effects of Automation

On production: Has total production risen for the entire

industry and in given companies within the industry since the introduction of automation equipment? If so, how much of this increase can be directly attributed to automation?

On productivity: To what extent has the introduction of automation increased the productivity of labor? Of capital? To what extent does it force us to re-examine the productivity concept itself? How useful is a measure of output per man hour when machinery is so large a determining factor in output? Can we still talk meaningfully of direct and indirect labor?

On costs: How have production costs been affected? If they are lower, where have the principal savings been effected? Have capital requirements been reduced? What part of the direct labor and capital saving has been offset by the cost of design, production and maintenance of automatic equipment? Has the cost of automation warranted its use?

On purchasing power: If automation has lowered cost, how have the savings been apportioned? Are profits higher? Have wages been raised? Have dividends or reserve funds been increased? Are prices lower? If so, how have markets responded?

C. The Automation Equipment Industry

What is the nature and size of the firms producing automation equipment? What proportion are new firms? How great a part of the total production effort is performed by old firms? Does this represent a major diversification? How rapidly have firms expanded in this field? What is the incidence and nature of mergers?

What portion of the total output is absorbed by military or defense needs? What is the extent and what are the types of government participation in research and product development? What is the effect of patents?

D. How Is Industry Structure Being Affected?

Automation and competition: What happens to competition as a result of high capital requirements? As a result of optimizing productivity? As a result of patents?

Does automation in one firm or group of firms curtail output and employment in other firms?

What is the prevalence of mergers in automated industries as compared with nonautomated industries?

How is small business faring? What is the percentage of new firms in the industry? What is the percentage of business failures? How many of these are small businesses? Have small companies been able to automate? Have they been able to automate to a comparable degree with larger firms?

Automation and centralization: Is there a tendency toward greater geographic centralization or decentralization? Have new plants in the industry been built in the same location as the old ones? If not, are the reasons for moving attributable in whole or in part to automation, or are they attributable to other causes? What are the future plans of companies in this connection?

Automation and company organization: Is there a tendency toward greater administrative centralization or decentralization? How have management responsibilities changed? What new kinds of problems has management had to meet? In recruiting new members of management, have men with new kinds of skills been needed?

Automation and labor: Because the effects of automation vary not only from industry to industry, but also from firm to firm, labor implications must be distilled from case studies analyzing specific instances.

E. Automation and Employment

For both whole industries and individual companies within an industry, how have total labor requirements been affected since the introduction of automation? How have the proportions of production, maintenance, supervisory and clerical workers changed since the introduction of automation?

What change has there been in total employment in the automated segment of a company? What changes has automation made in the proportions of direct and indirect labor in this segment?

How many workers have been displaced by automatic

machines? Were other jobs found for them within the
company? If so, how many were downgraded, how many
were upgraded, and how many moved into jobs similar to
the ones they left? If they had to leave the company, how
many found jobs in the same locality? In the same industry?

F. Automation and Retraining

What is the proportion of skilled and unskilled labor
employed before and after the introduction of automation?
What new job skills have been needed? What job skills
have been made obsolete?

How many workers needed some retraining to handle
a new job? How was this retraining accomplished and
how long did it take? Who paid for it? Was it done on
company time? Did it take place within the plant, or was
it necessary to perform it outside? If so, what institution
handled the retraining? Was it adequate?

What special problems did older workers present? How
were these handled?

Did automation create jobs that could not be filled
from within the company? If so, how many were there,
and how were they filled?

What are the estimated future demands for skilled,
semiskilled and unskilled labor?

G. Automation and Industrial Relations

How has automation affected the general level and
structure of wages? How has it affected the particular
wages of displaced employees who were transferred to
another job within the company? The wages of employees working in the automated segment?

How does automation affect job equity?

What are the worker attitudes toward automation? How
has it affected working conditions in terms of safety, machine pacing, increased responsibility and improved work
area?

How are industrial relations policies and hiring policies
changed? What provisions have been made for displaced
employees in the form of severance pay, early retirement
or other benefits? How has automation affected collective

bargaining? How have union jurisdictions been changed; how has internal union organization changed?

EDUCATION AND AUTOMATION

How has the present supply and quality of engineers and technical personnel affected the degree and rate of automation? Has a shortage of trained personnel discouraged any firms from introducing automation? How has the availability and quality of needed personnel affected the development and production of automation equipment?

Are existing institutions adequate for giving vocational training to adults? Are there enough of them widely enough distributed? Are their programs adequate? Are secondary school programs adequate? Or are the high schools teaching skills that will be outmoded before they can be used?

What role can subprofessional training play in providing those workers who do not have engineering backgrounds with sufficient facility in automation skills to fill needed positions? How, and by whom, can such training best be provided? To what extent does such training depend on the redefinition of job titles and descriptions?

Will engineering and technical skills be the key to the important jobs in an age of automation? Must we train engineers to be managers, or managers to be engineers? Are the skills required of the successful manager in a world of ever more complex technology the same as those required in a world where business success depended upon the artful use of insufficient information? If not, what does this imply for management education?

What kind of training can be provided for individuals who have already completed their formal education? How successful have union programs been? Management or company sponsored courses? University extension programs? Home study courses?

CONCLUSIONS

The United States Government should formulate a national policy that will effectively stimulate automation and other technological change.

I find it totally unreasonable—and dangerous—that as

a nation we permit the waste of a potent national resource, automation. We are faced with a continuous economic and political challenge on the international front that demands sizable outlays for military security, aid to foreign nations and other international programs. At the same time, we continuously try to raise our material standard of living.

To keep increasing our standard of living and, simultaneously, maintain our economic and political position in the world, we must sustain a high economic growth rate. Real increases in our national output will continue to be heavily influenced by our productivity increases—and productivity increase is a basic result of technological change.

I think we must face up to the fact that we have not made any concerted effort to deal with the problems that retard economic growth. The nation cannot long sustain a high rate of technological advance without coping with these problems; we simply cannot wait for evolutionary forces to solve our internal problems.

The national policy that will foster automation and technological change should be aimed mainly at bettering the environment for change. (For purposes of formulating national policy, automation should be considered as part of general technological change. It is difficult to separate automation out of the mainstream of change and somewhat useless to do so.) This policy should be geared to set in motion two programs simultaneously.

A program for identifying the effects of automation and technological change within our society should be initiated. We must learn how to stimulate automation to best advantage and, at the same time, minimize any harmful effects that may accompany it.

Second, mechanisms that can encourage economic and technical growth where such growth has stagnated must be designed. I do not feel that this can be accomplished through the efforts of private enterprise acting alone; the resources of local communities and of the state governments are sometimes not sufficient to overcome stagnancy. Individual action by the Federal Government is also insufficient.

A cooperative effort employing the resources of all these sectors of the economy must be brought to bear on these problems if they are to be solved. The government can do much to encourage business through enlightened tax policy and technical aid; communities and states can do more to provide worker training and retraining facilities and assisting in area redevelopment; business can initiate programs to assist employees in adapting to change situations.

A program of continuing study will provide more knowledge on how best to cope with change. It will supply the data needed to influence the social and economic results of the introduction of automation and other technology.

However, no study will be of value if it is an expedient way to avoid taking action on national issues. The extensive knowledge gathered can, perhaps, be best employed in helping to recognize—in advance—where action should be taken to stimulate technological and economic growth.

I also think it is very important that through national policy we encourage the widespread application of basic science to industry. Most of the significant innovations of the postwar period have come about through military research programs. Private industry has been unable to make the fullest use of these advances. The government can do much to encourage the dissemination of this kind of information to business. Private enterprise can be further stimulated to employ new techniques and equipment through fiscal policy.

The encouragement of innovation in industry must be supported by labor, if we are to achieve its full benefits. Featherbedding in industry has become a valid issue; it is wasteful not only to the individual company in which it occurs but to the entire economy as well. In many instances, labor has shown that it can facilitate change by sponsoring its own retraining programs and by intelligent collective bargaining. The responsibilities of labor in this area will be much greater in the years to come. It remains to be seen whether present labor-management relations, which mainly revolve about periodic collective bargaining sessions, are sufficient to cope with future problems.

These recommendations are far from new. It is vital, however, that they be carried out. I recommend the study of automation at the first congressional hearing, as others have since. Concerted action of government, community and business to make the fullest use of this most important national resource—automation—has been suggested previously, although in vain.

I think it is worth remembering that a national resource, as well as a natural resource, can be lost forever if it is not conserved with intelligence and farsighted planning.

▪ 3 ▪

Cybernation:
The Silent Conquest*

by Donald N. Michael

DIRECTOR OF PLANNING AND PROGRAMS,
PEACE RESEARCH INSTITUTE, WASHINGTON, D. C.

* A Report to the Center for the Study of Democratic Institu-
tions. Copyright © 1962 by The Fund for the Republic, Inc.
Reprinted by permission of the Author and The Fund for the
Republic, Inc., Santa Barbara, California.

■

INTRODUCTION

Both optimists and pessimists often claim that automation is simply the latest stage in the evolution of technological means for removing the burdens of work. The assertion is misleading. There is a very good possibility that automation is so different in degree as to be a profound difference in kind, and that it will pose unique problems for society, challenging our basic values and the ways in which we express and enforce them.[1]

In order to understand what both the differences and the problems are and, even more, will be, we have to know something of the nature and use of automation and computers. There are two important classes of devices. One class, usually referred to when one speaks of "automation," is made up of devices that automatically perform sensing and motor tasks, replacing or improving on human capacities for performing these functions. The second class, usually referred to when one speaks of "computers," is composed of devices that perform, very rapidly, routine or complex logical and decision-making tasks, replacing or improving on human capacities for performing these functions.

Using these machines does not merely involve replacing men by having machines do tasks that men did before. It is, as John Diebold says, a way of "thinking as much as it is a way of doing. . . . It is no longer necessary to think in terms of individual machines, or even in terms of groups of machines; instead, for the first time, it is practical to look at an entire production or information-handling process as an integrated system and not as a series of individual steps." [2] For example, if the building trades were to be automated, it would not mean inventing machines to do the various tasks now done by men; rather, buildings would be redesigned so that they could be built by machines. One might invent an automatic bricklayer, but it is more likely that housing would be designed so that bricks would not be laid. Automation of the electronics industry was not brought about through the invention of automatic means for wiring circuits but through the invention of essentially wireless—i.e., printed—circuits (though today there are automatic circuit wirers as well).

The two classes of devices overlap. At one pole are the automatic producers of material objects and, at the other, the sophisticated analyzers and interpreters of complex data. In the middle zone are the mixed systems, in which computers control complicated processes, such as the operations of an oil refinery, on the basis of interpretations that they make of data automatically fed to them about the environment. Also in this middle zone are those routine, automatic, data-processing activities which provide men with the bases for controlling, or at least understanding, what is happening to a particular environment. Processing of social security data and making straightforward tabulations of census information are examples of these activities.[3]

Cybernated systems perform with a precision and a rapidity unmatched in humans. They also perform in ways that would be impractical or impossible for humans to duplicate. They can be built to detect and correct errors in their own performance and to indicate to men which of their components are producing the error. They can make judgments on the basis of instructions programmed into them. They can remember and search their memories for appropriate data, which either has been programmed into them along with their instructions or has been acquired in the process of manipulating new data. Thus they can learn on the basis of past experience with their environment.

They can receive information in more codes and sensory modes than men can. They are beginning to perceive and to recognize.

As a result of these characteristics, automation is being used to make and roll steel, mine coal, manufacture engine blocks, weave cloth, sort and grade everything from oranges to bank checks. More versatile automatic fabricators are becoming available, too:

U.S. Industries announced . . . that it had developed what was termed the first general-purpose automation machine available to manufacturers as standard "off-the-shelf" hardware. . . . The new machine, called a TransfeRobot, sells for $2,500. . . . The Westclox Company of La Salle, Ill, has been using a TransfeRobot to oil clock assemblies as they pass on a conveyor belt. The machine oils eight precision bearings simultaneously in a second. At the Underwood Corporation typewriter plant in Hartford, the robot picks up, transfers and places a small typewriter component into a close-fitting nest for an automatic machine operation. In an automobile plant, the device feeds partly fabricated parts of a steering assembly to a trimming press and controls the press. The device consists basically of an arm and actuator that can be fitted with many types of fingers and jaws. All are controlled by a self-contained electronic brain.[4]

At the other end of the continuum, computers are being used rather regularly to analyze market portfolios for brokers; compute the best combination of crops and livestock for given farm conditions; design and "fly" under typical and extreme conditions rockets and airplanes before they are built; design, in terms of costs and traffic-flow characteristics, the appropriate angles and grades for complex traffic interchanges; keep up-to-date inventory records and print new stock orders as automatically computed rates of sales and inventory status indicate. Computers have also been programmed to write mediocre TV dramas (by manipulating segments of the plot), write music, translate tolerably if not perfectly from one language to another and simulate some logical brain processes (so that the machine goes about solving puzzles—and making mistakes in the process—in the ways people do). Also, computers are programmed to play elaborate "games" by themselves or in collaboration with human beings. Among other reasons, these games are played to understand and plan more efficiently for the conduct of wars and the procedures for industrial and business aggrandizement. Through such games, involving a vast number of variables, and contingencies within which these variables act and interact, the best or most likely solutions to complex problems are obtained.

The utility and the applicability of computers are being continually enhanced. For example, after a few hours of training, nonspecialists can operate the smaller computers without the aid of programmers simply by plugging in prerecorded instruction tapes that tell the computer how to do specific tasks. Instruction-tape libraries can supply preprogrammed computer directions for everything from finding the cube root of a number to designing a bridge. When the machine is through with one task, its circuits can be easily cleared so that a new set of preprogrammed instructions can be plugged in by its businessman operator.

But the capabilities of computers already extend well beyond even these applications. Much successful work has been done on computers that can program themselves. For example, they are beginning to operate the way man appears to when he is exploring ways of solving a novel problem. That is, they apply and then modify, as appropriate, previous experiences with and methods of solution for what appear to be related problems. Some of the machines show originality and unpredictability. To take one example from a recent paper of Norbert Wiener:

The present level of these learning machines is that they play a fair amateur game at chess but that in checkers they can show a marked superiority to the player who has programmed them after from 10 to 20 playing hours of working and indoctrination. They thus most definitely escape from the completely effective control of the man who has made them. Rigid as the repertory of factors may be which they are in a position to take into consideration, they do unquestionably—and so say those who have played with them—show originality, not merely in their tactics, which may be quite unforeseen, but even in the detailed weighting of their strategy.[5]

Another example of a machine the behavior of which is not completely controllable or predictable is the Perceptron, designed by Dr. Frank Rosenblatt. This machine can learn to recognize what it has seen before and to teach itself generalizations about what it recognizes. It can also learn to discriminate, and thereby to identify shapes similar to those it has seen before. Future versions will hear as well as see. It is not possible to predict the degree and quality of recognition that the machine will display as it is learning. It is designed to learn and discriminate in the same way that it is believed man may learn and discriminate; it has its own pace and style of learning, of refining its discriminations and of making mistakes in the process.

It is no fantasy, then, to be concerned with the implications of the thinking machines. There is every reason to believe that within the next two decades machines will be available outside the laboratory that will do a credible job of original thinking, certainly as good thinking as that expected of most middle-level people who are supposed to "use their minds." There is no basis for knowing where this process will stop, nor, as Wiener has pointed out, is there any comfort in the assertion that, since man built the machine, he will always be smarter or more capable than it is.

It may be seen that the result of a programming technique of [cybernation] is to remove from the mind of the designer and operator an effective understanding of many of the stages by which the machine comes to its conclusions and of what the real tactical intentions of many of its operations may be. This is highly relevant to the problem of our being able to foresee undesired consequences outside the frame of the strategy of the game while the machine is still in action and while intervention on our part may prevent the occurrence of these consequences. Here it is necessary to realize that human action is a feedback action. To avoid a disastrous consequence, it is not enough that some action on our part should be sufficient to change the course of the machine, because it is quite possible that we lack information on which to base consideration of such an action.[6]

The capabilities and potentialities of these devices are unlimited. They contain extraordinary implications for the emancipation and enslavement of mankind.

The opportunities for man's enhancement through the benefits of cybernation are generally more evident and more expected, especially in view of our proclivity to equate technological advances with progress and happiness. In the words of the National Association of Manufacturers:

For the expanding, dynamic economy of America, the sky is indeed the limit. Now more than ever we must have confidence in America's capacity to grow. Guided by electronics, powered by atomic energy, geared to the smooth, effortless workings of automation, the magic carpet of our free economy heads for distant and undreamed horizons. Just going along for the ride will be the biggest thrill on earth![7]

But the somber and complex difficulties produced by cybernation, which already are beginning to plague some aspects of our society and economy, are only beginning to be recognized. Thus, although this paper will describe, first, the advantages of cybernation, which make its ever expanding application so compelling, it will, on the whole, emphasize the less obvious, sometimes acutely uncomfortable aspects of this development with which we must successfully contend if we are to enjoy the benefits of both cybernation and democracy.

THE ADVANTAGES OF
CYBERNATION

In recent years deteriorating sales prospects, rising production costs, increased foreign competition and lower profits have led business management to turn to our national talent for technological invention as the most plausible means of reducing costs and increasing productivity, whether the product is an engine block or tables of sales figures. And the government, faced with the need to process and understand rapidly increasing masses of numerical facts about the state of the nation and the world, is already using 524 computers and is the major customer for more of them.

What are the advantages of cybernated systems that make government and private enterprise turn to them to solve problems?

In the first place, in a competitive society a successfully cybernated organization often has economic advantages over a competitor using people instead of machines. As *U.S. News and World Report* says:

> In one line of business after another, the trend is the same. Companies are spending millions of dollars to mechanize their operations, boost output and cut costs. Says an official of a big electrical com-

pany: "It is no longer a question of whether or not to automate, but rather it is how far to go and how fast to proceed. If you don't, your competition will.[8]

Not only must many organizations automate to compete, but the same principle probably holds for competing nations. We are by no means the only semicybernated society. Europe and Russia are well under way, and their machines and products compete with ours here and in the world market. The USSR is making an all-out effort to cybernate as much of its planning-economic-industrial operation as it can.

In the second place, reducing the number of personnel in an organization reduces the magnitude of management's human relations tasks, whether these be coping with overlong coffee breaks, union negotiations, human errors or indifference.

In the third place, cybernation permits much greater rationalization of managerial activities. The computers can produce information about what is happening now, as well as continuously updated information about what will be the probable consequences of specific decisions based on present and extrapolated circumstances. The results are available in a multitude of detailed or simplified displays in the form of words, tables of figures, patterns of light, growth and decay curves, dial readings and so on. In many situations, built-in feedback monitors the developing situation and deals with routine changes, errors and needs with little or no intervention by human beings. This frees management for attention to more basic duties. There is, for example—

. . . an automatic lathe . . . which gauges each part as it is produced and automatically resets the cutting tools to compensate for tool wear. In addition, when the cutting tools have been worn down to a certain predetermined limit, the machine automatically replaces them with sharp tools. The parts are automatically loaded onto the machine and are automatically unloaded as they are finished. These lathes can be operated for 5 to 8 hours without attention, except for an occasional check to make sure that parts are being delivered to the loading mechanism.[9]

Another example, combining built-in feedback with a display capability, adds further illumination:

The Grayson-Robinson apparel chain, which has more than 100 stores throughout the country, receives print-punch tags daily from its stores and converts them to full-size punchcards. The complete merchandise and inventory control function is then handled on a computer. What styles are to be processed first are determined at the computer center. During any given week about 60 per cent of the sales data are received and summarized. On the following Monday morning the remaining 40 per cent of the sales data are received. The computer can then begin running style reports immediately after the tickets have been converted to cards. By this time the company can run up style reports by departments and price lines in order to obtain the necesssary merchandising information. The entire reporting job is completed by Wednesday afternoon of each week, including reports on all inactive stockpiles.[10]

Freeing management from petty distractions in these ways permits more precise and better substantiated decisions, whether they have to do with business strategy, government economic policy, equipment system planning or military strategy and tactics. Thus, management in business or government can have much better control both over the system as it operates and over the introduction of changes into future operations. Indeed, the changes themselves may be planned in conformity with, and guided by, a strategy that is derived from a computer analysis of the future environment.

In the fourth place, cybernation allows government and industry much greater freedom in locating their facilities efficiently in relation to the accessibility of raw products, markets, transportation and needed (or cheaper) human and material resources. Distance is no longer a barrier to control and coordination. The computers that control automated processes need not be near the factories nor the data-processing computers near their sources of information or users if other considerations are more pressing. Widely dispersed installations can be coordinated and controlled from still another place, and the dispersed units can interact with each other and affect one another's performance as easily, in many cases, as if they were all in the same place.

In the fifth place, some degree of cybernation is necessary to meet the needs of our larger population and to maintain or increase the rate of growth of the Gross National Product. An estimated eighty million persons will be added to our population in the next twenty years. Beyond increases in productivity per man hour to be expected from the projected 20 per cent growth in the labor force during this same period, productive growth will have to be provided by machines.

If the criteria are control, understanding and profits, there are strong reasons why government and business should want to, and indeed would have to, expand cybernation as rapidly as they can. The versatility of computers and automation is becoming better understood all the time by those who use them, even though, as with the human brain, most present users are far from applying their full potential. Cheap and general purpose computers or modular components applicable to many types of automatic production and decision making are now being manufactured. In good part, they are cheap because they themselves are produced by automated methods. Techniques for gathering the field data that serve as the "inputs" to the machines are being refined and themselves automated or semiautomated. For example, a large shoe distributor is planning to attach a prepunched IBM card to each shoe box. When a sale is made, the card is returned to a central facility to guide inventory adjustment, reordering and sales recording and analysis. Techniques for quickly implementing the "outputs" from the machines are also being invented. Methods are being developed for systematically establishing the precise kind and degree of cybernation required in specific situations, as well as the changes needed in the rest of the institution or organization using cybernation.

These are the advantages for management, for government and for those parts of the work force whose status has been enhanced because of cybernation. But as cybernation advances, new and profound problems will arise for our society and its values. Cybernation presages changes in the social system so vast and so different from those with which we have traditionally wrestled that it will challenge to their roots our current perceptions about the viability of our way of life. If our democratic system has a chance to survive at all, we shall need far more understanding of the consequences of cybernation. Even the job of simply preserving a *going* society will take a level of planning far exceeding any of our previous experiences with centralized control.

The balance of this paper will point out some of the implications of cybernation that we must recognize in our task of developing a society and institutions in which man may be allowed to reach his full capacities.

THE PROBLEMS OF CYBERNATION

UNEMPLOYMENT AND EMPLOYMENT

BLUE-COLLAR ADULTS

In the highly automated chemical industry, the number of production jobs has fallen 3% since 1956 while output has soared 27%. Though steel capacity has increased 20% since 1955, the number of men needed to operate the industry's plants—even at full capacity—has dropped 17,000. Auto employment slid from a peak of 746,000 in boom 1955 to 614,000 in November. . . . Since the meat industry's 1956 employment peak, 28,000 workers have lost their jobs despite a production increase of 3%. Bakery jobs have been in a steady decline from 174,000 in 1954 to 163,000 last year. On the farm one man can grow enough to feed 24 people; back in 1949 he could feed only 15.[11]

Further insight into the problem of declining employment for the blue-collar worker comes from union statements to the effect that the number of these employees in manufacturing has been reduced by 1,500,000 in the last six years. As one example from the service industries, automatic elevators have already displaced 40,000 operators in New York.

Another disturbing aspect of the blue-collar displacement problem is its impact on employment opportunities for Negroes. There is already an increasingly lopsided Negro-to-white unemployment ratio as the dock, factory and mine operations where Negroes have hitherto found their steadiest employment are cybernated. This, plus the handicaps of bias in hiring and lack of educational opportunity, leaves Negroes very few chances to gain new skills and new jobs. Continued widespread and disproportionate firings of Negroes, if accompanied by ineffectual re-employment methods, may well produce a situation that will increase disenchantment abroad and encourage discontent and violence here.

SERVICE INDUSTRIES

It is commonly argued that, with the growth of population, there will always be more need for people in the service industries. The assumption is that these industries will be able to absorb the displaced, retrained blue-collar labor force; that automation will not seriously displace people who perform service functions; and that the demand for engineers and scientists will be so great as to provide employment for any number of the young people who graduate with engineering training. (Indeed, some of this demand is expected to arise from the needs of cybernetic systems themselves.)

It is all very well to speak glowingly of the coming growth in the service industries and the vast opportunities for well-paid jobs and job upgrading that these activities will provide as blue-collar opportunities diminish. But is the future as bright and as simple as this speculation implies? In the first place, service activities will also tend to displace workers by becoming self-service, by becoming cybernated and by being eliminated. Consider the following data: The United States Census Bureau was able to use fifty statisticians in 1960 to do the tabulations that required 4,100 in 1950. Even where people are not being fired, service industries can now carry on a vastly greater amount of business without hiring additional personnel; for example, a 50 per cent increase in the Bell System's volume of calls in the last ten years with only a 10 per cent increase in personnel.

Automation frequently permits the mass production of both cheap items and items of adequate to superior quality. It frequently uses methods of fabrication that make replacement of part or all of the item more efficient or less bother than repairing it. As automation results in more leisure time, certainly some of this time will be used by more and more do-it-yourselfers to replace worn-out or faulty components in home appliances that are now repaired by paid service personnel. Nor is it clear that repairing computers will be big business. Computer design is in the direction of microminiaturized components: when there is a failure in the system, the malfunctioning part is simply unplugged or pulled out, much as a drawer from a bureau, and replaced by a new unit. Routine procedures determine which component is malfunctioning, so routine that the larger computers now indicate where their own troubles are, so routine that small computers could be built to troubleshoot others. This does not mean that clever maintenance and repair people will be completely unnecessary, but it does mean that a much more careful estimate is required of the probable need for these skills in home-repair work or in computer-repair work.

Drip-dry clothes, synthetic fabrics, plus self-service dry and wet cleaning facilities probably will outmode this type of service activity.

Identification by fingerprints, instantly checked against an up-to-date nation-wide credit rating (performed by a central computer facility), could eliminate all service activities associated with processing based on identification (for example, bank tellers). A computer that can identify fingerprints does not yet exist, but there is no reason to believe it will not be invented in the next two decades.

If people cost more than machines—either in money or because of the managerial effort involved—there will be growing incentives to replace them in one way or another in most service activities where they perform routine, predefined tasks. It is possible, of course, that eventually people will not cost more than machines, because there may be so many of them competing for jobs, including a growing number of working women. But will service people be this cheap? As union strength is weakened or threatened through reductions in blue-collar membership, unions will try, as they have already begun to do, to organize the white-collar worker and other service personnel more completely in order to help them to protect their jobs from managements willing to hire those who, having no other work to turn to, would work for less money. Former blue-collar workers who, through retraining, will join the ranks of the service group may help to produce an atmosphere conducive to such unionizing. But how many service organizations will accept the complications of union negotiations, strikes, personnel services and higher wages in preference to investing in cybernation?

It is possible that as automation and computers are applied more widely an attitude of indifference to personalized service will gradually develop. People will not demand it and organizations will not provide it. The family doctor is disappearing; clerks of all sorts in stores of all sorts are disappearing as well. For example:

> The R. H. Macy Co. is trying out its first electronic sales girl. This machine is smart enough to dispense 36 different items in 10 separate styles and sizes. It accepts one- and five-dollar bills in addition to coins and returns the correct change plus rejecting counterfeit currency.[12]

People either get used to this or, as in the case of the self-service supermarket, seem to prefer it.

It is already the rare sales clerk who knows the "real" differences between functionally similar items; indeed, in most stores, sales clerks as such are rare. Thus, the customer is almost forced to do much of his own selecting and to know at least as much about or to be at least as casual about the differences between competing items as the clerk. As automation increases, the utility of the sales clerk will further diminish. With some products, automation will permit extensive variation in design and utility. With others, especially if our society follows its present

course, automation will encourage the endless prolifera-
tion of items only marginally different from one other. In
either event there is no reason to believe that the clerk
or salesman will become more knowledgeable about an
even larger variety of competing items. Finally, it is obvious that the remaining tasks of the clerk, such as recording the sale and insuring that the item is paid for, can be
cybernated without difficulty.

The greater the indifference to personalized service by
both buyers and sellers, the greater the opportunity, of
course, to remove human judgments from the system. Cybernation may well encourage acceptance of such depersonalization, and this, in turn, would encourage further
reductions in opportunities for service jobs.

MIDDLE MANAGEMENT

The blue-collar worker and the relatively menial service
worker will not be the only employment victims of cybernation.

. . . Broadly, our prognostications are along the following lines:
(1) Information technology should move the bound-
ary between planning and performance upward. Just
as planning was taken from the hourly worker and
given to the industrial engineer, we now expect it to
be taken from a number of middle managers and
given to as yet largely nonexistent specialists: "Operation researchers," perhaps, or "organizational analysts." Jobs at today's middle-management level will
become highly structured. Much more of the work
will be programmed, i.e., covered by sets of operating rules governing the day-to-day decisions that are
made.
(2) Correlatively, we predict that large industrial
organizations will recentralize, that top managers will
take on an ever larger proportion of the innovating,
planning, and other "creative" functions than they
have now.
(3) A radical reorganization of middle-management
levels should occur with *certain classes* of middle-

management jobs moving downward in status and compensation (because they will require less autonomy and skill), while other classes move upward into the top-management group.

(4) We suggest, too, that the line separating the top from the middle of the organization will be drawn more clearly and impenetrably than ever, much like the line drawn in the last few decades between hourly workers and first-line supervisors.

. . . Information technology promises to allow fewer people to do more work. The more it can reduce the number of middle managers, the more top managers will be willing to try it. . . . One can imagine major psychological problems arising from the depersonalization of relationships within management and the greater distance between people at different levels. . . . In particular, we may have to reappraise our traditional notions about the worth of the individual as opposed to the organization, and about the mobility rights of young men on the make. This kind of inquiry may be painfully difficult, but will be increasingly necessary.[13]

As cybernation moves into the areas now dominated by middle management in government and in business— and this move is already beginning—growing numbers of middle managers will find themselves displaced. Perhaps the bulk of displaced members of the blue-collar and service work force might be trained "up" or "over" to other jobs with, generally speaking, little or no decline in status. But the middle manager presents a special and poignant problem. Where can he go? To firms that are not as yet assigning routine liaison, analysis and minor executive tasks to machines? This may take care of some of the best of the displaced managers and junior executives, but if these firms are to have a future, the chances are that they will have to computerize eventually in order to compete. To the government? Again, some could join it, but the style and format of governmental operations may require readjustments that many junior executives would be unable to make. And, in any case, government too, as we have seen, is turning to computers, and it is entirely possible that much of the work of *its* middle management will also be absorbed by the computers. Up into top management? A few, of course, but necessarily only a few. Into the service end of the organization, such as sales? Some here, certainly, if they have the talent for such work. If computers and automation lead to an even greater efflorescence of marginally differentiated articles and services, there will be a correspondingly greater emphasis on sales in an effort to compete successfully. But can this be an outlet for a truly significant portion of the displaced? And at what salary? Overseas appointments in nations not yet using cybernation at the management level? Again, for a few, but only for those with the special ability to fit into a different culture at the corresponding level from which they came.

Middle management is the group in the society with the most intensive emotional drive for success and status. Their family and social life is molded by these needs, as the endless literature on life in suburbia and exurbia demonstrate. They stand to be deeply disturbed by the threat and fact of their replacement by machines. One wonders what the threat will do to the ambitions of those who will still be students and who, as followers of one of the pervasive American dreams, will have aspired to the role of middle manager "on the way up."

With the demise or downgrading of this group, changes in consumption levels and patterns can also be expected. These people, although they are not the only consumers of products of the sort advertised in *The New Yorker*, *Holiday* and the like, are certainly among the largest of such consumers. They are the style-setters, the innovators and the experimenters with new, quality products. With their loss of status and the loss of their buying power, one can imagine changes in advertising, or at least changes in the "taste" that this advertising tries to generate. It is possible that the new middle elite, the engineers, operations researchers and systems analysts will simply absorb the standards of the group they will have replaced. But they may be different enough in outlook and motives to have different styles in consumption.

OVERWORKED PROFESSIONALS

There are service jobs, of course, that require judgments about people by people. (We are not including here the "personalized service" type of salesmanship.) The shortage of people with these talents is evidenced by the sixty-hour and more work weeks of many professionals. But these people are the products of special education, special motives, and special attitudes that are not shared to any great degree by those who turn to blue-collar or routine service tasks. Increasing the proportion of citizens with this sort of professional competence would require systematic changes in attitudes, motives, and levels of education, not to mention more teachers, a professional service already in short supply. Alterations of this magnitude cannot be carried out overnight or by casual advertising campaigns or minor government appropriations. It is doubtful indeed, in our present operating context, that they can be done fast enough to make a significant difference in the employment picture for professional services in the next decade or two. Values become imbedded early in life. They are subject to change, to be sure, but we are not, as a democratic society, adept at or inclined to change them deliberately and systematically.

Even if the teachers and the appropriate attitudes already existed, service needs at the professional level might not be great enough to absorb a large share of the potentially unemployed. Much of the work that now takes up the time of many professionals, such as doctors and lawyers, could be done by computers—just as much of the time of teachers is now taken up by teaching what could be done as well by machines.

The development of procedures for medical diagnosis by machine is proceeding well. A completely automatic analysis of data can produce just as good a diagnosis of brain malfunction as that done by a highly trained doctor. Cybernated diagnosis will be used in conjunction with improved multipurpose antibiotics and with microminiaturized, highly sensitive and accurate telemetering equipment (which can be swallowed, imbedded in the body, or affixed to it) in order to detect, perhaps at a distance, significant symptoms.[14] All of these developments are likely to change the nature of a doctor's time-consuming tasks. In the field of law successful codification, so that searches and evaluations can be automatic, as well as changes in legal procedures, will probably make the lawyer's work substantially different from what it is today, at least in terms of how he allocates his time.

Computers probably will perform tasks like these because the shortage of professionals will be more acute at the time the computers acquire the necessary capabilities. By then, speeded-up data processing and interpretation will be necessary if professional services are to be rendered with any adequacy. Once the computers are in operation, the need for additional professional people may be only moderate, and those who are needed will have to be of very high caliber indeed. Probably only a small percentage of the population will have the natural endowments to meet such high requirements. A tour of the strongholds of science and engineering and conversations with productive scientists and engineers already lead to the conclusion that much of what now appears to be creative, barrier-breaking "research and development" is in fact routine work done by mediocre scientists and engineers. We lose sight of the fact that not everybody with dirty hands or a white coat is an Einstein or a Steinmetz. Many first-class scientists in universities will testify that one consequence of the increasingly large federal funds for research is that many more mediocre scientists doing mediocre work are being supported. No doubt for some time to come good use can be made by good professionals of battalions of mediocre professionals. But battalions are not armies. And sooner or later one general of science or engineering will be able to fight this war for knowledge more effectively with more push buttons than with more intellectual foot soldiers.

UNTRAINED ADOLESCENTS

Altogether the United States will need 13,500,000 more jobs in the Sixties merely to keep abreast of the expected growth in the labor force. This means an average of 25,000 new jobs each week, on top

of those required to drain the reservoir of present unemployment and to replace jobs made superfluous by
improved technology. In the last year, despite the
slackness of employment opportunities, 2,500,000
more people came into the job scramble than left it
through death, age, sickness or voluntary withdrawal.
This was more than double the 835,000 average annual growth in the working population in the last ten
years. By the end of this decade, 3,000,000 youngsters will be starting their quest for jobs each year, as
against 2,000,000 now. This almost automatically
guarantees trouble in getting the over-all unemployment rate down to 4 per cent because the proportion
of idleness among teen-age workers is always far
higher than it is among their elders.[15]

The Labor Department estimates that 26,000,000 adolescents will seek work in the sixties. If present performance is any indicator, in the decade ahead 30 per cent
of adolescents will continue to drop out before completing
high school and many who could go to college won't. The
unemployment rate for such dropouts is about 30 per cent
now. Robert E. Iffert, of the Department of Health, Education, and Welfare, concluded in a 1958 study that approximately one-fourth of the students who enter college
leave after their freshman year never to return. Figures
compiled since then lead him to conclude that there has
been no significant change, in spite of the National Defense Education Act, which was supposed to help reduce
this figure.[16]

If some figures recently given by James B. Conant turn
out to be typical, at least one situation is much more serious than the average would imply. He found that in one
of our largest cities, in an almost exclusively Negro slum
of 125,000, 70 per cent of the boys and girls between 16
and 21 were out of school and unemployed. In another
city, in an almost exclusively Negro slum in the same age
group, 48 per cent of the high school graduates were unemployed and 63 per cent of the high school dropouts
were unemployed.[17] These adolescents would in the

normal course join the untrained or poorly trained work force, a work force that will be more and more the repository of untrainable or untrained people displaced from their jobs by cybernation. These adolescents will have the following choices: they can stay in school, for which they are unsuited either by motivation or by intelligence; they can seek training that will raise them out of the untrained work force; they can compete in the growing man-power pool of those seeking relatively unskilled jobs, or they can loaf.

If they loaf, almost inevitably they are going to become delinquent. Thus, without adequate occupational outlets for these youths, cybernation may contribute substantially to further social disruption.

Threatened institutions often try forcibly to repress groups demanding changes in the *status quo*. Imagine the incentives to use force that would exist in a nation beset by national and international frustrations and bedeviled by anarchic unemployed-youth movements. Imagine, too, the incentives to use force in view of the reserves of volunteer "police" made up of adults who can vent their own unemployment-based hostility in a socially approved way by punishing or disciplining these "children."

A constructive alternative, of course, is to provide appropriate training for these young people in tasks that are not about to be automated. But this implies an elaborate, costly program of research and planning to recruit teachers, to apply advanced teaching machine methods as a supplement to teachers, and to stimulate presently unmotivated youngsters to learn. The program would also require intensive cooperation among business, labor, education, local social service agencies and the government. And all this must begin *now* in order for it to be ready when it will be needed.

None of this is easily met. Persuading dropouts to stay in school will not be easy. Teachers will not be easy to recruit unless they are well paid. There is already a shortage of teachers. And let no one suggest that an easy source of teachers would be displaced workers. There is no reason to believe that they have the verbal and social facility to teach, and most of them would have nothing to teach but skills that have become obsolete. Some, of course, might be taught to teach, though this would add obvious complications to the whole effort.

Knowing what to teach will depend on knowing what types of jobs are likely to exist when the student finishes his training. This will require knowledge about the trends and plans of local industry, if that is where the youths are to work (and if that is where industry plans to stay!), and of industries in other localities, if the youths are willing to move. Such knowledge often does not exist in a rapidly changing world or, if it exists, may not be forthcoming from businesses more concerned with competition than with the frustrated "delinquents" of their community. As of now, in the words of Dr. Conant, "unemployment of youth is literally nobody's affair."

SOME PROPOSED SOLUTIONS

Retraining is often proposed as if it were also the cure-all for coping with adults displaced by cybernation as well as young people. In some circumstances it has worked well for some people, especially with office personnel who have been displaced by data-processing computers and have learned other office jobs, including servicing the computers. But in other cases, especially with poorly educated blue-collar workers, retraining has not always been successful, nor have new jobs based on that retraining been available. Max Horton, Michigan's Director of Employment Security, says:

"I suppose that is as good as any way for getting rid of the unemployed—just keeping them in retraining. But how retrainable are the mass of these unskilled and semi-skilled unemployed? Two-thirds of them have less than a high school education. Are they interested in retraining? But most important, is there a job waiting for them when they have been retrained?" The new California Smith-Collier Act retraining program drew only 100 applicants in six months.[18]

A. H. Raskin's survey of the situation leads him to conclude:

> The upgrading task will be a difficult, and perhaps impossible, one for those whose education and general background do not fit them for skilled work. The outlook is especially bleak for miners, laborers and other unskilled workers over 40, who already make up such a big chunk of the hard core of joblessness.[19]

Moreover, management has not always been willing to institute retraining programs. People are either fired outright in some cases or, more often, simply are not rehired after a layoff.

> Labor and management have been slow to face the problem over the bargaining table. Harry Bridges' West Coast longshoremen's union recently agreed to give shippers a free hand to mechanize cargo handling—in exchange for a guarantee of present jobs, plus early retirement and liberal death benefits. In Chicago this week, President Clark Kerr of the University of California, one of the top labor economists, will preside over a company-union committee meeting at Armour & Co. to draw up a plan for the rapidly automating meat industry. A similar committee is at work at Kaiser Steel Co. But many authorities think such efforts are far too few, that management must do more. E. C. Schulze, acting area director of Ohio's state employment service, says: "I've yet to see an employer's group willing to take a look at this problem and seek solutions. They refuse to recognize their responsibility. They talk about long-term trends—but nobody talks about the immediate problem of jobless, needy people."[20]

The problem of retraining blue-collar workers is formidable enough. But, in view of the coming role of cybernation in the service industries, the retraining problem for service personnel seems insuperable. No one has seriously proposed what service tasks this working group could be retrained *for*—to say nothing of training them for jobs that would pay high enough wages to make them good consumers of the cornucopia of products manufactured by automation.

Another proposal for coping with the unemployment-via-cybernation problem is shorter hours for the same pay. This approach is intended to maintain the ability of workers to consume the products of cybernation and, in the case of blue-collar workers, to maintain the strength of unions. This would retain the consumer purchasing capacity for x workers in those situations where the nature of the cybernation process is such that x men would do essentially the same work as x plus y men used to do. But when the task itself is eliminated or new tasks are developed that need different talents, shorter shifts clearly will not solve the problem. The latter conditions are the more likely ones as cybernation becomes more sophisticated.

Proponents of cybernation claim that it should reduce the price of products by removing much of the cost of labor and increasing consumer demand. Whether the price of beef or milk or rent will be reduced in phase with the displaced worker's lowered pay check remains to be seen. So far this has not happened. Whether the price of TV sets, cars, refrigerators and the like will be reduced substantially depends in part on how much product cost goes into larger advertising budgets aimed at differentiating the product from the essentially same one produced last year or from the practically identical one produced on some other firm's automated production line.

An obvious solution to unemployment is a public works program. If our understanding of the direction of cybernation is correct, the government will probably be faced for the indefinite future with the need to support part of the population through public works. There is no dearth of public work to be done, and it is not impossible that so much would continue to be needed that an appropriately organized public works program could stimulate the economy to the point that a substantial portion of the work force could be reabsorbed into the private sector. That is, although the proportion of workers needed for any particular task will be reduced through the use of cybernation, the total number of tasks that need to be done could equal or exceed the absolute number of people available to do them. It is not known whether this situation would obtain for enough tasks in enough places so that the portion of the population working on public projects would be relatively small. However if it should turn out that this felicitous state of affairs could be realized in principle, clearly it could only be realized and sustained if there were to be considerable and continuous centralized planning and control over financing, the choice of public projects, and the places where they were to be done. If, for whatever reasons, this situation could not be achieved, the public works pay roll would remain very large indeed.

What would be the effects on the attitudes and aspirations of a society, and particularly of its leadership, when a significant part of it is overtly supported by governmental public works programs? ("Overtly" is used because much of the aerospace industry in particular and of the weapons systems industry in general is subsidized by the government right now: they literally live off cost plus fixed fee contracts, and there is no other comparable market for their products.) Whatever else the attitudes might be, they certainly would not be conducive to maintaining the spirit of a capitalistic economy. This shift in perspective may or may not be desirable, but those who think it would be undesirable should realize that encouraging the extension of cybernation, in the interests of free enterprise and better profits, may be self-defeating.

The inherent flexibility of cybernated systems, which permits great latitude in their geographic location, is the inspiration for the proposal that if jobs are lost through cybernation, the unemployed could be moved to another area where jobs exist. It is said that a governmental agency similar to the Agricultural Resettlement Administration, which moved farmers from the Dust Bowl to cities, could be used. However, two important differences between that situation and this one would complicate this effort: the contemporary cause of the unemployment would not be the result of an act of God; and it is not immediately evident that these unemployed people could find jobs in other areas, which might be suffering from a similar plethora of useless workers.

Herbert Striner has suggested that a more extreme approach would be to export blue-collar and white-collar workers and their families to nations needing their talents. The problem of whether or how the salary differential might be made up is one of several difficulties with this proposal. Yet, if such emigration could be carried out, it might be a better solution than letting the workers atrophy here. The economic history of former colonial powers and their colonization techniques indicate that "dumping" of excess personnel into foreign lands would not be a radically new innovation.

Another possible long-run approach might be curtailment of the birth rate. In times of depression the rate falls off naturally—which may be the way the process would be accomplished here if enough people become unemployed or marginally employed (although the effects of the lowered birth rate would only follow after the economic and social changes had been made). Of course, the government could encourage birth control by reducing the income tax dependency deduction or by other tax means.

Finally, there is the proposal to reduce the working population by increasing the incentives for early retirement. Government could do this by reducing the retirement age for social security, and unions and management could use their collective ingenuity to provide special retirement incentives. Naturally, this would increase the already large percentage of retired elderly people. Along with the other familiar problems associated with this group is the poignant one we shall face in more general form in the next section: how are all these people to be kept happily occupied in their leisure?

Whether any of these proposed solutions is adequate to the challenge of unemployment is not known to us, or, we gather, to those who have proposed one solution or another. But even if, in principle, some combination of them would be adequate, in order to put them into effect, a considerable change would be necessary in the attitudes and voting behavior of Congress and our tax-paying citizens. Preconceptions about the virtues and vices of work, inflation, the national debt and government control run deep and shift slowly.

Not all of these dire threats would come to pass, of course, if cybernation reduced consumer buying power through unemployment and thereby the financial capability of industry and business to introduce or profit from cybernation. In this way we might all be saved from the adverse effects of unemployment from this source. But the economy would still be faced with those threats to its well-being which, as were pointed out earlier, make the need to cybernate so compelling.

Cybernation is by nature the sort of process that will be introduced selectively by organization, industry and locality. The ill effects will be felt at first only locally and, as a result, will not be recognized by those who introduce it —and perhaps not even by the government—as a *national* problem with many serious implications for the whole social system. Also, because one of the chief effects of cybernation on employment is not to hire rather than to fire, the economic-social consequences will be delayed and will at any time be exacerbated or ameliorated by other economic and social factors, such as the condition of our foreign markets, which also are being changed and challenged by European and Russian cybernation. By the time the adverse effects of cybernation are sufficiently noticeable to be ascribed to cybernation, the equipment will be in and operating.

Once this happens, the costs of backtracking may be too great for private enterprise to sustain. For, in addition to the costs of removing the equipment, there will be the costs of building a precybernation system of operations. But which firms will voluntarily undertake such a job if they are unsure whether their competitors are suffering the same setback—or indeed if their competitors are going to decybernate at all? And, if not voluntarily, how would the government enforce, control, and pay for the change-over?

ADDITIONAL LEISURE

It is generally recognized that sooner or later automation and computers will mean shorter working hours and greater leisure for most if not all of the American people. It is also generally, if vaguely, recognized that there probably are problems connected with the use of leisure that will take time to work out.

Two stages need to be distinguished: the state of leisure over the next decade or two, when our society will still be in transition to a way of life based on the widespread application of cybernation; and the relatively stable state some time in the future when supposedly everybody will have more leisure time than today and enough security to enjoy it. The transitional stage is our chief concern, for the end is far enough off to make more than some general speculations about it footless. At this later time people's behavior and attitudes will be conditioned as much by presently unforeseeable social and technological developments as by the character and impact of cybernation itself.

During the transition there will be four different "leisure" classes: 1) the unemployed, 2) the low-salaried employees working short hours, 3) the adequately paid to high-salaried group working short hours and 4) those with no more leisure than they now have—which in the case of many professionals means very few hours of leisure indeed.

LEISURE CLASS ONE

Today most of the unemployed are from low educational backgrounds where leisure has always been simply a respite from labor. No particular aspirations to, or positive attitudes about, the creative use of leisure characterize this group. Since their main concern is finding work and security, what they do with their leisure is a gratuitous question; whatever they do, it will hardly contribute to someone else's profits.

It is worth speculating that one thing they might do is to participate in radical organizations through which they could vent their hostility over being made insecure and useless. Another thing they could do, if so motivated and if the opportunity were available, would be to learn a skill not likely to be cybernated in the near future, although, as we have seen, the question arises of what this would be.

Another thing would be to move to areas where there is still a demand for them. But breaking community ties is always difficult, especially during periods of threat when the familiar social group is the chief symbol of security. And who would pay for their move and who would guarantee a job when they got where they were going?[21]

As cybernation expands its domain, the unemployed "leisure" class will not consist only of blue-collar workers. The displaced service worker will also swell the ranks of the unemployed, as well as the relatively well-trained white-collar workers until they can find jobs or displace from jobs the less well-trained or less presentable, like the college graduate filling-station attendant of not so many years ago. It is doubtful that during their unemployed period these people will look upon that time as "leisure" time. For the poorly educated, watching television, gossiping and puttering around the house will be low-cost time-fillers between unemployment checks; for the better educated, efforts at systematic self-improvement, perhaps, as well as reading, television and gossip; for many, it will be time spent in making the agonizing shift in style of living required of the unemployed. These will be more or less individual tragedies representing at any given time a small portion of the work force of the nation, statistically speaking. They will be spread over the cities and suburbs of the nation, reflecting the consequences of actions taken by particular firms. If the spirit of the day grows more statistical than individualistic, as this paper suggests later that it well might, there is a real question of our capacity to make the necessary organized effort in order to anticipate and cope with these "individual" cases.

The free time of some men will be used to care for their children while their wives, in an effort to replace lost income, work at service jobs. But this arrangement is incompatible with our image of what properly constitutes man's role and man's work. The effects of this use of leisure on all family members will be corrosive rather than constructive and will contribute to disruption of the family circle. Leisure for this group of people may well acquire a connotation that will discourage for a long time to come any real desire to achieve it or any effort to learn how to use it creatively.

One wonders, too, what women, with their growing tendency to work—to combat boredom as well as for money—will do as the barriers to work become higher, as menial white-collar jobs disappear under the impact of cybernation and as the competition increases for the remaining jobs. If there are jobs, 6,000,000 more women are expected to be in the labor force in 1970 than were in it in 1960. Out of a total labor force of 87,000,000 at that time, 30,000,000 would be women. To the extent that women who want jobs to combat boredom will not be able to get them, there will be a growing leisure class that will be untrained for, and does not want, the added leisure. As for those women who have a source of adequate income but want jobs because they are bored, they will have less and less to do at home as automated procedures further routinize domestic chores.

LEISURE CLASS TWO

A different kind of leisure problem will exist for the low-income group working shorter hours. This group will be composed of people with the attitudes and behavior traditionally associated with this class, as well as some others who will have drifted into the group as a result of having been displaced by cybernation. What evidence there is indicates that now and probably for years to come, when members of this group have leisure time as a result of fewer working hours, the tendency will be to take another job.[22] It is reasonable to believe that the general insecurity inevitably arising from changing work arrangements and the overall threat of automation would encourage "moonlighting" rather than the use of free time for recreation. If these people cannot find second jobs, it is hard to imagine their doing anything different with their free time from what they do now, since they will not have the money, the motives or the knowledge to search out different activities.

If the shorter hours are of the order of four eight-hours days, potentially serious social problems will arise. For example, a father will be working fewer hours than his children do in school. What he will do "around the house" and what adjustments he, his wife and children will have to make to each other will certainly add very real difficulties to the already inadequate, ambiguous and frustrating personal relationships that typify much of middle-class family life.

LEISURE CLASS THREE

Workers with good or adequate income employed for shorter hours are the group usually thought of when one talks about the positive opportunities for using extra leisure in a cybernated world. Its members for the most part will be the professional, semiprofessional or skilled workers who will contribute enough in their social role to command a good salary but who will not be so rare as to be needed for forty hours a week. These people already value learning and learning to learn. Given knowledge about, money for and access to new leisure-time activities, they are likely to make use of them. They could help to do various desirable social service tasks in the community, tasks for which there is not enough money to attract paid personnel of high enough quality. They could help to teach, and, by virtue of their own intimate experiences with cybernation, they would be able to pass on the attitudes and knowledge that will be needed to live effectively in a cybernated world. It is likely, too, that this group will be the chief repository of creative, skilled manual talents. In a nation living off mass-produced, automatically produced products, there may be a real if limited demand for hand-made articles. (We may become again in part a nation of small shopkeepers and craftsmen.) In general, this group of people will probably produce and consume most of its own leisure-time activities.

LEISURE CLASS FOUR

The fourth group consists of those who probably will have little or no more leisure time than they now have except to the extent permitted by additions to their ranks and by the services of cybernation. But extrapolations for the foreseeable future indicate insufficient increases in the class of presently overworked professionals and executives. Computers should be able to remove many of the more tedious aspects of their work in another few years, but for some time to come these people will continue to be over-burdened. Some of this relatively small proportion of the population may manage to get down to a forty-hour week, and these lucky few should find no difficulty in using their leisure as productively and creatively as those in the third group.

Thus, during the transition period, it is the second group, the low-salaried workers who cannot or will not find another job, that presents the true leisure problem, as distinct from the unemployment problem. Here is where the multiple problems connected with private and public make-play efforts may prove very difficult indeed. We have some knowledge about relatively low-income work-ers who become voluntarily interested in adult education and adult play sessions, but we have had no real experi-ence with the problems of how to stimulate the interests and change the attitudes of a large population that is forced to work shorter hours but is used to equating work and security, that will be bombarded with an advertising *geist* praising consumption and glamorous leisure, that will be bounded closely on one side by the unemployed and on the other by a relatively well-to-do community to which it cannot hope to aspire. Boredom may drive these people to seek new leisure-time activities if they are provided and do not cost much. But boredom combined with other fac-tors may also make for frustration and aggression and all the social and political problems these qualities imply.

DECISIONS AND PUBLIC OPINION

PRIVILEGED INFORMATION

The government must turn to computers to handle many of its major problems simply because the data in-volved are so massive and the factors so complex that only machines can handle the material fast enough to al-low timely action based on understanding of the facts. In the nature of the situation, the decisions made by the government with the help of computers would be based in good part on computers that have been programmed with more or less confidential information—and privileged access to information, at the time it is needed, is a sufficient if not always necessary condition for attaining and maintaining power. There may not be any easy way to insure that decisions based on computers could not become a threat to democratic government.

Most of the necessary inputs for the government's computer systems are available only to the government, because it is the only institution with sufficiently extensive facilities for massive surveys (whether they be photographic, observational, paper and pencil or electronic in nature). Also, the costs of these facilities and their computer installations are so great that buying and maintaining such a system is sensible only if one has the decision-making needs of a government and the data required to feed the machines. Other organizations, with other purposes, would not need this kind of installation. These machines can provide more potent information than merely rapidly produced summaries and tabulations of data. They can quickly provide information on relationships among data, which may be appreciated as significant only by those already having privileged information based on a simpler level of analysis or on other nonquantified intelligence to which the user is privy.[23] Computers can also provide information in the form of extrapolations of the consequences of specific strategies and the probabilities that these consequences will arise. This information can be based on exceedingly complex contingencies. The utility and applicability of these extrapolations will be fully understandable only to those knowing the particular assumptions that went into the programming of the machines.

THE INEVITABILITY OF IGNORANCE

It may be impossible to allow much of the government, to say nothing of the public, access to the kind of information we have been discussing here. But let us assume that somehow the operation of the government has been reorganized so that procedures are enforced to permit competing political parties and other private organizations to have access to the government's raw data, to have parallel systems for the processing of data as well as to have access to the government's computer programs. Even then, most people will be incapable of judging the validity of one contending computer program compared to another, or whether the policies based on them are appropriate.

This condition exists today about military postures. These are derived in good part from computer analyses and computer-based games that produce probabilities based on programmed assumptions about weapon systems and our and the enemy's behavior. Here the intellectual ineffectualness of the layman is obscured by the secrecy that keeps him from finding out what he probably would not be able to understand anyway. If this sounds condescending, it only needs to be pointed out that there are large areas of misunderstanding and misinterpretation among the military too. At any given time, some of these people do not fully appreciate the relationships between the programs used in the computers and the real world in which the consequences are supposed to follow. As it is now, the average intelligent man has little basis for judging the differing opinions of economists about the state of the economy or even about the reasons for a past state. He also has little basis for appraising the conflicting opinions among scientists and engineers about the costs and results of complex scientific developments such as man in space. In both examples, computers play important roles in the esoteric arguments involved.

Thus, even if people may have more leisure time to attend more closely to politics, they may not have the ability to contribute to the formulation of policy. Some observers feel that the middle class does not now take a strong interest in voting and is alienated in its responsibility for the conduct of government. Leisure may not change this trend, especially when government becomes in large part the complex computer operation that it must necessarily become.

Significant public opinion may come from only a relatively small portion of the public: 1) those who are able to follow the battles of the computers and to understand the implications of their programs; and 2) those who are concerned with government policy but who are outside of or unfamiliar with the computer environment.

For this segment of the voting population, differences over decisions that are made or should be made might become more intense and more irreconcilable. Already there is a difference of opinion among intelligent men about the problem of the proper roles in American foreign policy of military weapons, arms control and various levels of disarmament. One side accuses its opponents of naïveté or ignorance about the "facts" (computer-based), and the other side objects to the immorality or political insensibilities of its opponents. Many aspects of the problem involve incommensurables; most are too complex to stand simplification in order to appeal to the larger public or to an unsophisticated Congressman. Yet the arguments *are* simplified for these purposes and the result is fantastic confusion. The ensuing frustration leads to further efforts to make the case black or white and to further efforts by one contingent to provide ever more impressive computer-based analyses and by the other side to demonstrate that they are beside the point.

This is only one example of the problems that will arise from the existence of sophisticated computers. Will the problems create greater chasms between the sophisticated voter and the general public, and within the sophisticated voting group itself?

PERSONNEL AND PERSONALITIES

As for the selection of the men who are to plan or make policy, a computerized government will require different training from that which executive personnel in most governmental agencies has today. Certainly, without such training (and perhaps with it) there is bound to be a deepening of the split between politics and facts. For example, it is evident that the attitudes of many Congressmen toward space activities are motivated more by politics and conventional interpretations of reality than by engineering facts or the realities of international relations.

The same schisms will be compounded as computers are used more and more to plan programs in the Department of Health, Education, and Welfare, urban development, communications, transportation, foreign aid and the analysis of intelligence data of all sorts.

In business and industry the shift has already begun toward recruiting top management from the cadre of engineering and laboratory administration, for these are the people who understand the possibilities of, and are sympathetic to, computer-based thinking. In government the trend has not been so clear-cut, but it is noteworthy that the scientist, as high-level adviser, is a recent innovation and one clearly here to stay. Sometimes unhappily and sometimes enthusiastically, the scientist, scientist-administrator and engineer acknowledge that their role of adviser is frequently confused with that of policy-maker. As people with this training come more to influence policy and those chosen to make it, changes in the character and attitudes of the men responsible for the conduct of government will inevitably occur.

For reasons of personality as well as professional perspective, many operations researchers and systems analysts have great difficulty in coping with the more ambiguous and less "logical" aspects of society.[24] Their temperaments, training and sympathies may not incline them to indulge the slow, ponderous, illogical and emotional tendencies of democratic processes. Or they may ignore the extralogical nature of man. Emphasis on logic, in association with the other factors we have mentioned, may encourage a trend toward the recruitment of authoritarian personalities. There is no necessary correlation between the desire to apply scientific logic to problems and the desire to apply democratic principles to daily, or even to professional scientific, life.

MASS VS. THE INDIVIDUAL

The psychological influence of computers is overwhelming: they symbolize and re-enforce the potency of America's belief in the utility of science and technology. There is a sense of security in nicely worked-up curves and complex displays of information which are the products of almost unimaginably intricate and elegant machinery. In general, the influence of computers will continue to be enhanced if those who use them attend chiefly to those components of reality which can be put into a computer and processed by it, and the important values will become those which are compatible with this approach to analyzing and manipulating the world. For example, the influence of computers has already been sufficiently strong to seduce military planners and civil defense planners *away* from those aspects of their problems which are not now subject to data processing. Most of the planning for survival following nuclear attack has to do with those parts of the situation which can be studied by computers. Crucial aspects of psychological and social reorganization have been pushed into the background simply because they cannot be handled statistically with convenience or with the demonstrated "expertness" of the specialist in computers. Thus, the nature of the postattack situation is argued learnedly but spuriously by those who have the attention of leadership, an attention stimulated by the glamour of computers, the prestige of their scientist-keepers, and the comfort of their "hard facts."

Computers are especially useful for dealing with social situations that pertain to people in the mass, such as traffic control, financial transactions, mass-demand consumer goods, allocation of resources and the like. They are so useful in these areas that they undoubtedly will help to seduce planners into inventing a society with goals that can be dealt with in the mass rather than in terms of the individual. In fact, the whole trend toward cybernation can be seen as an effort to remove the variabilities in man's on-the-job behavior and off-the-job needs which, because of their nonstatistical nature, complicate production and consumption. Thus, somewhere along the line, the idea of the individual may be completely swallowed up in statistics. The planner and those he plans for may become divorced from one another, and the alienation of the individual from his government and individual from individual within government may grow ever greater.

Computers will inevitably be used to plan employment for those displaced by cybernation. This may lead to a more rationalized society than could otherwise be invented, with a more adequate allocation of jobs. But one wonders whether it will not also lead, on a national scale, to an attitude in the planner of relative indifference to the individual, an indifference similar to that shown by many managers of large self-service institutions who find an occasional complaint too much trouble to cope with individually because the influence of the individual on the operation of the system is too negligible to warrant attention.

What will be the consequences for our relations with underdeveloped nations of a government that sees the world through computers? With our general public alienated from its own productive and governmental processes and our leadership seemingly successful through its use of computer-based planning and control, our government may well become more and more incapable of recognizing the differences between the needs, aspirations and customs of these nations and those of our own country. In these nations, productive and governmental processes will still be very human activities, with all the nonstatistical variabilities that implies. Our decision to race the USSR to the moon is an initial indication of our incapacity as an advanced technological nation to appreciate what our acts look like to other nations with different attitudes.

On the other hand, the emphasis on human behavior as a statistical reality may encourage revisions in the temporal scale of government planning and programs. Time is a statistical property in cybernated systems: it takes time for variables to average out, to rise or fall in their effects, and the time period usually is not a fiscal year or some small multiple thereof. Thus, perhaps we can hope for more sensible long-range planning in government as a result of the computer's need for long time periods in which to make its statistical models work out. If this should come about, of course, it will require vast changes in the conduct of government and in the devices that government, and especially the Congress, uses for controlling its activities. It may also result in extending the present trend of turning over governmental policy-planning and, in effect, policy-making responsibilities to private organizations and their human and machine computers such as RAND. For unless the rules for Congressional elections are also changed, some of the responsibility that Congressmen now take for programs, when they vote relatively short-term appropriations, will no doubt be transferred to the machines that invented the plans if Congressmen should be faced with passing on appropriations and programs that would extend far beyond the time of their incumbencies.

DECISIONS FOR BUSINESS

The implications of the concentration of decision-making within business firms as a result of cybernation are not as clear-cut as the effects for government. In principle, both big and small business will be able to know much more about the nature of their markets and of their organizational operations through cybernation. Whether or not this will help both big and small proportionately is far from clear. Big business will undoubtedly have better facilities for information and decisions, but small business may be able to get what it needs by buying it from service organizations that will come into existence for this purpose. Big organizations will be able to afford high-priced personnel for doing the thinking beyond that done by the machines. If quality of thinking is always related to price, the big organizations will be able to put their small competitors out of business. But the big organizations, precisely because of their size, may have relatively little maneuverability, and some of the best minds may find the little organizations a more exciting game. Whether the little organizations could stay afloat is moot, but one can anticipate some exciting entrepreneurial maneuvers among the small firms while they last.

One thing is clear: among the small organizations, and probably among the big ones too, we can expect disastrous mistakes as a result of poor machine programming or inaccurate interpretations of the directives of the machines. These will be greatest during the early period when it will be faddish to plan via machine and when few organizations will have the brain power and organization to do so intelligently. Thus, added to the unemployment ranks in the decade or so ahead will be those who have been put out of jobs because their firms have misused computers.

THE CONTROL OF CYBERNATION

TIME AND PLANNING

Time is crucial in any plan to cope with cybernation. Ways of ameliorating its adverse effects require thinking farther ahead than we ever do. In a society in the process of becoming cybernated, education and training for work as well as education and training for leisure must begin early in life. Shifts in behavior, attitudes and aspirations take a long time to mature. It will be extraordinarily difficult to produce appropriate "culture-bearers," both parents and teachers, in sufficient numbers, distribution and quality in the relatively brief time available. It is hard to see, for example, how Congress, composed in good part of older men acting from traditional perspectives and operating by seniority, could recognize soon enough and then legislate well enough to produce the fundamental shifts needed to meet the complexities of cybernation. It is hard to see how our style of pragmatic making-do and frantic crash programs can radically change in the next few years. This is especially hard to visualize when the whole cybernation situation is such that we find it impossible to determine the consequences of cybernation even in the medium long run. The differences expressed in the public statements of business and labor demonstrate that any reconciliation of interests will be a very long-range effort indeed. "Drastic" actions to forestall or eliminate the ill effects of cybernation will not be taken in time unless we change our operating style drastically.

EDUCATION: OCCUPATIONS AND ATTITUDES

Among the many factors contributing to the stability of a social system are two intimately intertwined ones: the types of tasks that are performed; and the nature of the relationship between the attitudes of the members of the society toward these tasks and their opinions about the proper goals of the individual members of the society and the right ways of reaching them.

The long-range stability of the social system depends on a population of young people properly educated to enter the adult world of tasks and attitudes. Once, the pace of change was slow enough to permit a comfortable margin of compatibility between the adult world and the one children were trained to expect. This compatibility no longer exists. Now we have to ask: What should be the education of a population more and more enveloped in cybernation? What are the appropriate attitudes toward, and training for, participation in government, the use of leisure, standards of consumption, particular occupations?

Education must cope with the transitional period when the disruption among different socioeconomic and occupational groups will be the greatest; and the later, relatively stable period, if it ever comes to exist, when most people would have adequate income and shorter working hours. The problem involves looking ahead five, ten, twenty years to see what are likely to be the occupational and social needs and attitudes of those future periods; planning the intellectual and social education of each age group in the numbers needed; motivating young people to seek certain types of jobs and to adopt the desirable and necessary attitudes; providing enough suitable teachers; being able to alter all of these as the actualities in society and technology indicate; and directing the pattern of cybernation so that it fits with the expected kinds and distribution of abilities and attitudes produced by home and school.

To what extent education and technology can be coordinated is not at all clear, if only because we do not
know, even for today's world, the criteria for judging the
consonance or dissonance in our educational, attitudinal
and occupational systems. We think that parts of the social
system are badly out of phase with other parts and that, as
a whole, the system is progressively less capable of coping
with the problems it produces. But there is little consensus
on the "causes" and even less on what can be done about
them. All we have at present is the hope that most people
can be educated for significant participation in such a
world as we have foreseen here—we have no evidence
that it can be done.

If we do not find the answers to these questions soon,
we will have a population in the next ten to twenty years
more and more out of touch with national and international realities, ever more the victims of insecurity on the
one hand and ennui on the other, and more and more mis-
matched to the occupational needs of the day. If we fail
to find the answers, we can bumble along, very probably
heading into disaster, or we can restrict the extension of
cybernation, permitting it only where necessary for the national interest. But judging the national interest and distinguishing it from private interests would confront us
with most of the problems that have been outlined in this
paper.

Perhaps time has already run out. Even if our style
somehow should shift to long-range planning, it would not
eliminate the inadequate training and inadequate values
of much of our present adolescent and preadolescent
population, as well as of those adults who will be displaced or remain unhired as a result of cybernation in the
next decade. Only a partial solution exists in this case:
Begin now a program of economic and social first aid for
these people.

A MORATORIUM ON CYBERNATION?

Can we control the effects of cybernation by making it
illegal or unprofitable to develop cybernation technology?
No, not without virtually stopping the development of al-

most all of new technology and a good part of the general development of scientific knowledge. The accumulation of knowledge in many areas of science depends on computers. To refine computers and make them more versatile requires research in almost every scientific area. It also requires the development of a technology, usually automated, to produce the articles needed to build new computers. As long as we choose to compete with other parts of the world, we shall have to develop new products and new means for producing them better. Cybernation is the only way to do it on a significant scale. As long as we choose to live in a world guided by science and its technology we have no choice but to encourage the development of cybernation. If we insist on this framework, the answers to coping with its effects must be found elsewhere than in a moratorium on its development.

CONTROL: PUBLIC OR PRIVATE?

There has always been tension between big industry, with its concern for profit and market control, and government, with its concern for the national interest. The tension has increased as big business has become so large as to be quasi-governmental in its influence and as government has had to turn to and even subsidize parts of business in order to meet parts of the national interest within a free-enterprise framework. Under these circumstances we can expect strong differences between government and business as to when and where it is socially legitimate to introduce automation.

Sufficient governmental control over who can cybernate, when and where would not come easily. In the first place, decisions about control would have to be based on the intentions of local business and industry as well as on the national picture. For example, the effects on Congressional seating of shifts in populations as a result of cybernation-based industrial relocation would presumably enter the calculations. Longer-run consequences would have to be balanced against short-run profits or social dislocations. Implications for our military posture and for international trade would be significant. Moreover, it would be difficult for the government to make a case for control of private organizations on the basis of ambiguous estimates of the effects of automation on hiring policy. In any particular case, it becomes clear only well after the fact of cybernation whether increases or changes in production resulted in a corresponding increase in man hours of work sufficient to compensate the economy for the jobs lost or the people unhired.

Finally, it must be kept in mind that the power of some of the largest unions is seriously threatened by automation. In a relatively short time they may not have the leverage they now have. Thus, a crucial counterbalance to the pressures from business may be absent when it is most needed. It is possible that the crisis that will arouse the government to exert control will not be evident until the blue-collar work force has been so eroded as to have weakened the unions irreparably.

Yet some sort of control is going to be necessary. There are, of course, the federal regulatory agencies. However, they have never been distinguished for applying their powers with the vigor sometimes allowed by their mandates, and there is no reason to suppose that their traditional weaknesses would suddenly disappear and that an agency created to cope with cybernation would be effective. Nor is there any reason to believe that an agency with the very wide-ranging powers that it would need would be approved before the crisis that it was supposed to avert was upon us.

In theory, control could be exercised by private enterprise. But in the unlikely case that competitors could see their mutual·interests clearly enough to join forces, the very act of cooperative control would be incompatible with our antitrust laws. Whether the government or some alter-government comprised of business, labor and industry were to do the controlling, either group would have to undertake a degree of national planning and control thoroughly incompatible with the way in which we look upon the management of our economic and social system today.

AFTER THE TAKE-OVER

In twenty years, other things being equal, most of the routine blue-collar and white-collar tasks that can be done by cybernation will be. Our schools will probably be turning out a larger proportion of the population better educated than they are today, but most of our citizens will be unable to understand the cybernated world in which they live. Perhaps they will understand the rudiments of calculus, biology, nuclear physics and the humanities. But the research realm of scientists, the problems of government and the interplay between them will be beyond the ken even of our college graduates. Besides, most people will have had to recognize that, when it comes to logic, the machines by and large can think better than they, for in that time reasonably good thinking computers should be operating on a large scale.

There will be a small, almost separate, society of people in rapport with the advanced computers. These cyberneticians will have estalished a relationship with their machines that cannot be shared with the average man any more than the average man today can understand the problems of molecular biology, nuclear physics or neuropsychiatry. Indeed, many scholars will not have the capacity to share their knowledge or feeling about this new man-machine relationship. Those with the talent for the work probably will have to develop it from childhood and will be trained as intensively as the classical ballerina.

Some of the remaining population will be productively engaged in human-to-human or human-to-machine activities requiring judgment and a high level of intelligence and training. But the rest, whose innate intelligence or training is not of the highest, what will they do? We can foresee a nation with a large portion of its people doing, directly or indirectly, the endless public tasks that the welfare state needs and that the government will not allow to be cybernated because of the serious unemployment that would result. These people will work short hours, with much time for the pursuit of leisure activities.

Even with a college education, what will they do all their long lives, day after day, four-day week end after week end, vacation after vacation, in a more and more crowded world? (There is a population explosion to face in another ten to thirty years.) What will they believe in and aspire to as they work their shorter hours and, on the outside, pursue their "self-fulfilling" activities, whatever they may be? No one has ever seriously envisioned what characteristics these activities might have in order to be able to engross most men and women most of their adult lives. What will be the relationship of these people to government, to the "upper intellectuals," to the rest of the world, to themselves?

Obviously, attitudes toward work, play and social responsibility will have changed greatly. Somehow we shall have had to cope emotionally with the vast gap in living standards that will then typify the difference between us and the have-not nations. We shall presumably have found some way to give meaning to the consumption of mass leisure. It would seem that a life oriented to private recreation might carry with it an attitude of relative indifference to public responsibility. This indifference, plus the centralization of authority, would seem to imply a governing elite and a popular acceptance of such an elite.

If this world is to exist as a coherent society, it will have to have its own logic, so that it will make sense to its inhabitants. Today, for most of our population, our society makes sense, even though some other eyes hardly see us as logical in the formal sense of the word and the eyes of some of our own people look on us as a more or less pointless society. We make and solve our problems chiefly by other than mathematical logical standards, and so must the cybernated generations. What these standards might be, we do not know. But if they are inadequate, the frustration and pointlessness that they produce may well evoke, in turn, a war of desperation—ostensibly against some external enemy but, in fact, a war to make the world safe for human beings by destroying most of the society's sophisticated technological base. One thing is clear: if the new "logic" is to resolve the problems raised here, it will have to generate beliefs, behavior and goals far different from those which we have held until now and which are driving us more and more inexorably into a contradictory world run by (and for?) ever more intelligent, ever more versatile slaves.

FOOTNOTES

1. This paper makes the following assumptions in looking on the next twenty years or so: *1*) international relations will derive from the same general conditions that pertain today; *2*) the weapons systems industries will continue to support a major share of our economy; *3*) major discoveries will be made and applied in other technologies, including psychology and medicine; *4*) trends in megalopolis living and in population growth will continue; *5*) no major shifts in underlying social attitudes and in public and private goals will take place.

2. John Diebold, *Automation: Its Impact on Business and Labor* (National Planning Association, Planning Pamphlet No. 106, [Washington, D. C., May, 1959]), 3.

3. In order to eliminate the awkwardness of repeating the words "automation" and "computers" each time we wish to refer to both at the same time, and in order to avoid the semantic difficulties involved in using one term or the other to mean both ends of the continuum, we invent the term "cybernation" to refer to *both* automation and computers. The word is legitimate at least to the extent that it derives from "cybernetics," a term invented by Norbert Wiener to mean the processes of communication and control in man and machines. He derived it from the Greek word for steersman. The theory and practice of cybernetics

underlie all systematic design and application of automation and computers.

4. "Multi-Purpose Automation Unit Is Sold 'Off the
Shelf,'" *New York Times,* (June 23, 1961), 44.

5. Norbert Wiener, "Some Moral and Technical Consequences of Automation," *Science,* Vol. 131, No. 3410
(May 6, 1960), 1356.

6. *Ibid.,* 1357.

7. *Calling All Jobs* (National Association of Manufacturers [New York, Oct., 1957]), 21.

8. "When Machines Have Jobs—and Workers Do Not,"
U.S. News and World Report, Vol. 50, No. 6 (Feb. 6,
1961), 76.

9. From statement by Walter Reuther before the Subcommittee on Economic Stabilization of the Joint Committee on the Economic Report, U. S. Congress; *Automation and Technological Change* (84th Congress,
First Session [Washington, D. C.: U.S. Government
Printing Office, 1955]), 99.

10. From statement of James A. Suffridge, President, Retail Clerks International Association before the Subcommittee on Automation and Energy Resources of
the Joint Economic Committee, U. S. Congress; *New
Views on Automation* (86th Congress, Second Session
[Washington, D. C.: US Government Printing Office,
1960]), 591.

11. "The Automation Jobless . . . Not Fired, Just Not
Hired," *Time,* Vol. 77, No. 9 (Feb. 24, 1961), 69.

12. From statement by Howard Coughlin, President, Office Employees International Union, AFL-CIO, before
the Subcommittee on Automation and Energy Resource of the Joint Economic Committee, U. S. Congress; *New Views on Automation* (86th Congress,
Second Session [Washington, D. C.: US Government
Printing Office, 1960]), 513.

13. Harold J. Leavitt and Thomas L. Whisler, "Management in the 1980's," *Harvard Business Review* (Nov.-
Dec. 1958), 41-48.

14. See, for example, Howard Rusk, "New Tools in Medicine," *New York Times* (July 23, 1961).

15. A. H. Raskin, "Hard-Core Unemployment a Rising
National Problem," *New York Times* (Apr. 6, 1961),
18.

16. In conversation with Mr. Iffert. See also Robert E. Iffert, *Retention and Withdrawal of College Students* (Bulletin No. 1, Department of Health, Education, and Welfare [Washington, D. C.: US Government Printing Office, 1958]).

17. James B. Conant, "Social Dynamite in Our Large Cities," *Vital Speeches*, #18 (July 1, 1961), 554 ff.

18. "The Automation Jobless . . . Not Fired, Just Not Hired," *Time*, Vol. 77, No. 9 (Feb. 24, 1961), 69.

19. A. H. Raskin, "Fears About Automation Overshadowing Its Boons," *New York Times* (Apr. 7, 1961), 16.

20. "The Automation Jobless . . . Not Fired, Just Not Hired," *Time*, Vol. 77, No. 9 (Feb. 24, 1961), 69.

21. Perhaps an indication of things to come is to be found in the recent Federal Court ruling that employees have an "earned and vested right" of seniority and that this cannot be "denied unilaterally" or affected by a change in the location of their employer. "Court Bars Firing in Plant Move," *Washington Post* (July 7, 1961).

22. Harvey Swados, "Less Work—Less Leisure," *Mass Leisure*, ed. Eric Larrabee and Rolf Meyersohn (Glencoe, Ill.: The Free Press, 1958), 353.

23. Lawrence E. Davies, "Data Retriever to Help the CIA. Finds One Page in Millions in Only a Few Seconds," *New York Times* (July 12, 1961).

24. Donald N. Michael, "Some Factors Tending to Limit the Utility of the Social Scientist in Military Systems Analysis," *Operations Research*, Vol. 5, No. 1 (Feb. 1957), 90-96.

Part Two

IMPLICATIONS
FOR
THEORY

■ *4* ■

*Inventing the Future**

by Dennis Gabor

PROFESSOR OF APPLIED ELECTRON PHYSICS,
UNIVERSITY OF LONDON

There exists no universally agreed definition either of applied electron physics or of electronics, and I find this vagueness very convenient, because in my own work I have never respected other limits than those of my own ignorance—sometimes not even these. This lack of sharp demarcation will enable me to range here over a very wide field. I will start near home with examples of my own work, and later on approach the question of the impact of electronic inventions and of inventions in general on our civilization which is threatened by three great perils. The first peril is extermination by war, the second is crippling by overpopulation, and the third is a very frustrating sort of success—two tragedies and a tragicomedy.

From our own work I have chosen three examples, which are of the nature of inventive developments, and

* Reprinted from *Encounter*, May, 1960, by permission of the Author and *Encounter*.

which are in fields in which electronics already has or soon will have important consequences for civilization. These fields are entertainment, power and prediction. All three are examples of work still in progress; they will be both reviews and previews.

My first example is from the field of entertainment, and it concerns our work on color television, which has now been going on for quite a few years. In all industrial countries television is an enormous success. It is now far and away the most important medium of popular entertainment. On the other hand the history of color television is the story of an uphill fight, as yet with no certainty of success. In the United States, the Radio Corporation of America started this venture almost ten years ago, and to date they have primed it with more capital than was ever spent for starting up the cinema, radio and monochrome television put together. Yet to this day color television is far from being popular there, and this has of course discouraged all other countries. I cannot go into all the reasons for this lack of success, because they are at least as much political as technical; I can talk only about the technical side of the matter.

In 1951, when I first became interested in color television, the technical difficulties appeared so enormous that it appeared doubtful whether any firm would dare to put a color set on the market. What appeared at first sight to be an almost impossibly difficult problem has been solved in the United States by admirable engineering and manufacturing skill, but at a price which the public, it appears, is not prepared to pay.

The flat television tube, which can be hung on the wall like a picture, contains a principle which makes it very suitable for color television, but it has difficulties of its own. The idea came to me in a flash in 1952, but we are still working on the realization. The principle is to produce the colors by a "parallax filter" with almost microscopic thickness, which is fixed on the viewing screen. The three-color phosphors are deposited on the screen through the slits of the parallax screen, in a comparatively easy manufacturing process, which requires only a low grade of accuracy. The colors are then produced by three electron beams, one for each color, which run parallel to the screen, in a vertical direction, but at different distances, and when they have reached the writing position are thrown at the screen, very close together but at different angles, so that penetrating through the slits of the parallax screen each beam excites its own strip of colored phosphor. In the flat tube high-grade manufacturing accuracy is avoided at the cost of a complicated electron-optical problem.

In brief, the problem is to make three color-beams run vertically, at closely controlled distances, parallel to the screen, sweep these horizontally, in the rhythm of the line scan, and vertically, by a common electric sweep-wave, in the rhythm of the frame scan. Moreover, the whole electron optics must be folded together into a minimum of space. This is done by launching the three beams from *one* gun vertically downward, deflecting them horizontally, by a pair of deflecting plates, and then turning the whole complex of rays into a second vertical plane, by an electron-optical organ which is called a "reversing lens." This is evidently a difficult electron-optical problem, and it took my only collaborator at that time, Dr. Peter Stuart, three years of hard work before it was satisfactorily solved. It took us another year before we could make the tube "scan itself," that is to say producing the vertical sweep-field by the action of the electron beam itself. And when at last we had produced the first self-scanning tube, it was too complicated and expensive. We are still working on simpler realization, which we hope will lend itself to mass manufacture.

Looking back on this development which is now going into its sixth year, it would not be true to say that I would not have undertaken it if I had known how difficult it would be. Difficulties have always attracted rather than repelled me. But had I known that, by the time our work showed reasonable progress, both in this country and in the United States one industrial firm after the other would shut down its television tube factory and its television tube research laboratory, and that color television would become almost a bogey-word, I do not believe that I would have started it.

At the present moment it is thinkable, though not probable, that color television, like the three-dimensional film, will be something that flashed on the scene for a brief moment, to disappear again. A few years ago this was not even thinkable. But time is almost certainly on the side of color television. Assuming normal further development of our industrial civilization, what appears today as a desirable luxury gadget, but rather too expensive, may well become a necessity for the national economy—to make the wheels go round.

A second example. Until quite recently it appeared that electronics had nothing to do with power production; as a part of "light" electrical engineering it was clearly separated from the "heavy" branch. The advent of nuclear power did not change this position. Nuclear fission plants raised immense, challenging problems in metallurgy, in mechanical and even in civil engineering, but electrical engineering started in the orthodox way at the turbine shaft, and electronics came in only for some problems of measurement and control.

This has been changed recently by the possibility of thermoelectric generators, and by the even more exciting glimpse of unlimited power from the seas by thermonuclear fusion. In the long run this will be absolutely vital if an industrial civilization of several thousand million people is to survive on this earth. No wonder that this country, the United States, and the Soviet Union are now devoting a quite appreciable part of their scientific man power to research on thermonuclear fusion.

Fusion belongs of course very much to the domain of the applied electron physicist, because, as everybody knows, it requires temperatures of several hundred million degrees, and at such temperatures matter is in the "plasma" state, as in electric discharges, and electric discharges are the only means for reaching such temperatures. For somebody like myself, who has worked on and off for over thirty years on plasma problems, this was a most wonderful opportunity to come back to them. It was also a very unexpected opportunity, because gas discharge devices, such as mercury rectifiers, are rapidly losing their technical importance with the advent of solid-state devices. When in 1954, with Drs. Ash and Dracott, I concluded six years' research on the elucidation of a gas discharge phenomenon ("Langmuir's Paradox") which had remained unexplained for almost thirty years, I was quite convinced that I had finished with the plasma forever.

Two years ago, when we again started work on plasma problems, we had, in addition to our usual shortage of cash, space and man power, the handicap that fusion was still completely classified as secret. We had to keep, therefore, at a respectful distance from the main problem. I had also to promise that I would not blow up the Imperial College with a deuteron explosion. We started, therefore, on high temperature arcs, which was sufficiently far from the heart of the matter and not classified.

An electric arc is naturally rather hot, but to make it *very* hot is not an easy matter. There exists a law, known as Steenbeck's Principle, which states that an arc is not hotter than it can help being. This anthropomorphistic language comes easily to those who have worked much with gas discharges. They are used to looking at an electric discharge as something like a living being, which *wants* to keep alive. In order to keep alive it must dissipate energy, but Steenbeck's Principle states that the arc will dissipate energy only at the minimum rate necessary for its maintenance. Therefore if we want to make an arc get very hot, we must make life difficult for it; on the other hand we must take care that it is not killed.

In our experiments we have made the arc tough and almost unkillable by feeding it with the energy stored up in a large choke, and we make life difficult for it by forcing it to traverse a strong magnetic field. But if one tries this trick on an arc, one will soon find that the arc has a defense mechanism ready for keeping cool. This is the so-called Hall-field, an electric field which will establish itself in an arc channel at right angles to the channel and to the magnetic field. Its effect is that the electrons will flow through the channel almost as if there were no magnetic field at all. Thus if we want the magnetic field to have an effect, we must use a further trick. This trick is that we are forcing the arc, which has "naturally" a filamentary shape, to assume the shape of a disc, with converging currents.

While the long preparations for these experiments were carried out, the subject of fusion became declassified, and we could dare to take a short step nearer to its core. When I looked into the theory of the multielectrode arc, it struck me that it had a feature which may well be more interesting than the temperature which it produces. This is the presence of a very large circulating current in the discharge. The theory shows that in the arc at atmosphere pressure it may be perhaps 10 times the radial current, but at low pressures it may be 100 times larger. Such a current, closed in itself, is a semistable structure, and it may be possible to shoot it out of the discharge, which it may survive for some time. A piece of plasma which is shot out of a discharge is known as a "plasmoid." The American physicist W. H. Bostick first produced plasmoids some years ago, by discharging a condenser in a high vacuum. Such vacuum arcs, living only on the gas liberated by the electrodes, can carry currents of many thousand amperes, and they blow themselves out by their own magnetic field. Bostick thus obtained little sticks of plasma, which were blown out with velocities up to ten times Sputnik-speed. It struck me that we have a possibility of producing toroidal plasmoids, by shooting out the plasma carrying the circulating current. The interest of our experiments, if any, is in the fact that in ZETA and in the United States devices, the circulating discharge is produced in a toroidal space completely enclosed from all sides, while we produce it in an open structure, so that we can shoot out the plasmoid axially.

I want to emphasize that even the experiments are still a *very* long way from the core of the fusion problem. So far the largest speeds achieved are a few 10^7 cm/sec. If it were possible to achieve a few 10^8 cm/sec. one could think of using plasmoids for heating a nuclear furnace. It would be like stoking a furnace with red-hot bullets, which go white-hot on impact. This may be perhaps one way toward thermonuclear power, but probably a very hard way.

For my part, the interest of these experiments was that they have led me to more advanced ideas, of which it would be very premature to talk. I can say only that personally I have come to the conviction that the fusion problem can and will be solved, but also that the thermonuclear generators of the future will have to be the biggest and boldest machines ever devised.

THE PREDICTION BOX

The third example of our research activities concerns a special line of computers. It belongs to electronics rather than to electron physics, because its basic elements are electronic devices, not electrons or ions. The computer in question is one of the great family of intelligent machines whose emergence is, I believe, one of the most significant features of the mid-twentieth century. To avoid hurting philosophical feelings I want to say at once that I am using the term "intelligent machines" merely as an abbreviation for "artefacts simulating actions which in living beings we would consider as manifestations of intelligence." That these machines are electronic may be accidental; it so happens that we have first learned to carry out by electronic means those processes which in the animal nervous system are performed by chemical and physicochemical mechanisms. For simplicity of explanation I will introduce our machine as a predictor, though it has more general applications. The sort of prediction of which I want to talk has nothing to do with the naïve determinism of Laplace. We do not want to predict processes which run down regularly like clockwork, but statistical processes, known by the name of "stochastic processes," which are only partly regular. Examples of such processes are sea waves (the real ones, not the ones in textbooks), the weather, the prices on the Stock Exchange. I want to explain the problem with the aid of the figure shown below, in a greatly simplified language.

We take a single stochastic variable, which can be, for instance, the amplitudes of sea waves, or almost anything else. We know its past values up to the present moment, and we want to predict its future values some time τ in advance. For this we have at our disposal first, the past values, second, a large amount of information on the statistical habits of the process, and third, some auxiliary or "side information" on parameters influencing the process.

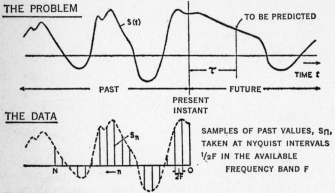

THE PROBLEM

$s(t)$

TO BE PREDICTED

τ

TIME t

PAST   FUTURE

PRESENT INSTANT

THE DATA

s_n

SAMPLES OF PAST VALUES, s_n, TAKEN AT NYQUIST INTERVALS $1/2F$ IN THE AVAILABLE FREQUENCY BAND F

N $\leftarrow n$ $2F$ 0

THE OPERATION   TO PRODUCE THE FUTURE OUT OF PAST VALUES

$$O_{(s)} = \sum_0^N c_n s_n + \sum_0^N \sum_0^N c_{n_1 n_2} s_{n_1} s_{n_2} + \sum_0^N \sum_0^N \sum_0^N c_{n_1 n_2 n_3} s_{n_1} s_{n_2} s_{n_3} + \cdots$$

THE SUCCESS CRITERION   FOR ADJUSTING THE PARAMETERS c

$$\overline{[O_{(s)} - s_{(\tau)}]^2} = \text{minimum}$$

WHERE THE AVERAGE IS TAKEN OVER PAST EXPERIENCE ON SIMILAR TIME SERIES

As regards the past values, we can introduce a great simplification of the problem if we take into consideration that every physical instrument or method of observation which gives us these values has a finite waveband. One can then show that the independent values in the series are discrete, there is only one independent datum in an interval of $1/2F$ if F is the waveband. These samples are the only values of the past on which we must base the prediction. They are called s_n, and are numbered backwards from the present instant 0 to some maximum.

We can now at once write down a perfectly general

formula for the prediction of a future value from these past samples. For good reasons we have chosen an algebraic polynomial. *Any* single-valued function of the data can be approximated beyond any limit by this form, provided that we make the numbers of terms sufficiently large. This polynomial expression contains the products of the samples, in all possible combinations, with coefficients c which have to be determined. The products are ordered in terms of first, second, and so on, order, according to the number of factors in the product. The first term represents linear prediction, and this is the only one which has so far received satisfactory mathematical treatment by Kolmogoroff and by Wiener.

We must give a precise meaning to "approximating the future as well as possible." Again for good reasons, we choose the criterion of *least mean square error*. This means that on the average the squared difference between the true and the predicted value must be as small as possible.

We now have a definite mathematical problem, but if we went about it in the ordinary way, by writing down the explicit equations for the unknown coefficients c and solving them, it would be of formidable complexity. Fortunately there is an easier way out, one which has been practiced by living beings from time immemorial. We have only to take a leaf out of the book of Nature. Let us make a computer, complex enough to produce the polynomial $O(s)$ with a great number of terms with undetermined values of the coefficients c and make it learn its job by experience.[1]

The predictor itself is a box with say a hundred knobs which can be adjusted, each knob corresponding to one of the coefficients c in the polynomial. The rest is the teaching apparatus or trainer. This consists, first, of a tape recorder with a long sample of the statistical process of the kind which we want to predict. The recorder is of a special type, in which eighteen past samples can be read out simultaneously by staggered magnetic heads. These values are fed into the computer, which then computes from these some trial value. In order to compare this with the true value which ought to be predicted, there is one head which is advanced by τ, and reads it out directly. The trial value and the true value are fed into a comparator, which calculates the success criterion, which is the squared difference of these two values, averaged over the whole run of the teaching tape. The result of the calculation is fed into an adjustor, which will change the adjustment or one of several of the knobs in such a way that the next run will produce a better result, and so on.

At this point you may rightly ask how we can be sure that the predictor will improve from run to run. This is where the advantage of the special mathematical form comes in which we have chosen with some cunning. The mean square error as a function of the coefficient c is an elliptic paraboloid, in as many dimensions as there are coefficients. The point is that such a paraboloid always has a minimum, and only one! Hence *any* rule which tells the machine to descend steadily will result in the end in as close an approach as we like. There exist several strategies for achieving this, the most famous is the "relaxation strategy" of Sir Richard Southwell. We use a variant of this, adjusting always one knob at a time. To speed up the process the comparator, which calculates the success criterion, is triplicated, so that in every run we determine the mean square error for *three* different values of one of the coefficients c. With the mathematical form which we have chosen, the mean square error as function of any one of the c will be always a parabola, and this is determined by three of its points. We have a computer which then calculates right away how we have to set this knob for optimum result, the others remaining unchanged. The machine then goes in turn repeatedly over all the knobs, until it has come as near to the minimum as does not matter. With one hundred knobs this might take five thousand runs in the worst case, but this does not matter as the machine has unlimited patience. We had of course to take special precautions lest the tape might wear out before the patience of the machine is exhausted!

Our predictor is not fully finished, but now that the multiplier problem is solved—by the Wilby multiplier, a baffling new invention which, I feel certain, can be made to perform as many as one hundred thousand multiplications per second—I can talk of it with full confidence, because electronic circuits *must work*. One always gets them to work in the end as one wants, which is very different from electron optics, let alone plasma work.

I have introduced this device as a "predictor," but in fact it is far more a universal learning machine. It will be possible to use it as a filter, to separate noise from message and as a recognizer, without any change of its structure, merely by giving it a different training course. Professor Arnold Tustin has suggested a further application, of which I had not thought before. There exist complicated systems, which one can observe but with which one must not interfere, such as for instance large petrol refineries or the British economic system. In this case one can take records of the observed inputs and outputs, and feed them into the machine with the instruction: "Produce the second out of the first!" The machine will then make itself into a functional model of the system to be studied; in other words it can be used as a universal simulator.

It must be admitted that such a machine has some claim to be called intelligent. There is many a game in which it can beat humans, for the simple reason that it has not only unlimited patience and a precise, quantitative memory, but also because it is free from illusions. Give a human being three or more interdependent knobs, and let him try to get an optimum, for instance in a color television picture. Only tiredness will prevent him from running endlessly in circles.

On the other hand the intelligence of the machine is certainly less than scientific. It may be able for instance to predict the trajectories of balls, as a tennis player learns to predict them by sheer experience, but it will never formulate the laws of dynamics. Like all other machines constructed to date, its activities are complicated, but always on the same logical level. A machine like this will never produce an abstraction.

HUMAN COMPLEXITY

Admittedly, all machines constructed to date are at best highly able executives, powered only by the intelligence of the designer. They are "idiot savants," which for long chains of deductive arithmetical operations will run circles around the best humans, but are incapable of abstractions and inductions. They cannot, as intelligent living beings do, organize themselves in correspondence with a wide variety of situations, ordering their experiences in an economical way, and building up their own rules for reacting to new situations on the basis of past associations. Will this always be so? There is a strong revulsion in many people against admitting the possibility of machines behaving like human beings; they feel that this would be equal to admitting that "man *is* a machine." Much of this feeling is an understandable reaction against the cocksureness of the early materialists, like La Mettrie, who bluntly asserted that "man is nothing but a machine." On logical grounds the feeling is quite unjustified, because man is a machine is not a verifiable statement: it is a meaningless noise, like the question, "Can machines think?" But feelings are not logical, nor can they be eliminated by logical argument. Man is a machine, though logically meaningless, expresses a valuation. It was a revoltingly low valuation of Man at the time when clockworks and the primitive automata of Vaucanson were the most complicated machines in existence; it is rather different today, when electronic computers can carry out jobs in a split second which would take months for trained humans, and it will be very different in the future.

Probably the most important factor in our changed attitude to machines is our new view of complexity. Scientists, even more than other people, decline to be impressed by mere size. But if increasing size goes parallel with increasing complexity, at higher levels of complication entirely new phenomena can emerge. Biologists may have felt this for a long time, but to the exact scientist it was revealed for the first time by the great mathematician, the late John von Neumann, when he demonstrated that self-reproducing machines must have very many elements, of the order of one hundred thousand, and that evolution can take place only beyond a certain level of complexity.

Another factor is the recognition that the most complicated logical processes can be carried out by a succession of a few types of simple operations, which can be easily mechanized. In this respect it is very interesting, and close to my main theme, to observe the minor revolution which has taken place in neurophysiology since mathematicians, physicists and electronic engineers took an interest in it. To put it briefly, into what used to be a classical field of pure research they have introduced a spirit of invention. Certain results were grabbed from the hand of the somewhat reluctant neurophysiologist and ruthlessly formulated into simple principles to serve as a basis for inventing models. These principles are briefly as follows: (1) There exists only a limited class of neurons, and these differ only in the number and in the thresholds of their stimulating and inhibitory synapses. (2) Any learning or habituation is nothing but a change of thresholds.

These are the bold and perhaps oversimplified working hypotheses of the mathematicians and electronic engineers which have been more or less accepted by the "tame" neurophysiologists who cooperate with them. They have momentous consequences. Chief of these is that, as the same type of neuron, placed anywhere in the nervous system, will show exactly the same behavior and will fire or not under the same conditions of stimulation, the meaning of a signal (of a burst or volley, or its absence) is entirely determined by its location, that is to say by the connection of the neuron with others, and ultimately with the sensory and effector organs.

If this working hypothesis is right, it means that unless we open up the brain we cannot put any concept into it except by the "legitimate channels," via the sensory organs. There is no possibility of evoking a concept by "specific signals" or by "resonance," as has been often imagined in the past. This in turn means that *there can be no thought transference or extrasensory perception*.

This deduction from an unproved set of working hypotheses will not, of course, impress the surprisingly large number of people who want to believe in ESP. Personally I think that to make room for ESP in brain models at the present stage would be about as wise as it would have been to ask Newton to make allowance in his law of gravity for levitation.

It might appear that if the brain is as simple as that, nothing can prevent us from making right away an attempt at constructing an artificial brain. But there are formidable quantitative obstacles in the way. First, the human brain contains some 10^{10} neurons, rather more than there are electronic valves in the world today. But second, the rather naïve attempts made so far at constructing brains are so uneconomical that they would exhaust this formidable number just by the action of recognizing the patterns, black or white, on a six by six chess board. Not until we have made a further, enormous step in the miniaturizing of the logical components (which might well take us outside electronics), and not until we have learned to imitate hierarchical thinking, can we even dream of producing anything like a universal artificial brain, capable of competing with the human brain, which is a miracle of economical organization. There is good reason to believe that the brain of Newton or of Mozart contained only about the same number of neurons as the brain of a moron. On the basis of our present knowledge with 10^{10} relais we could not even construct a moron.

THE MECHANIZATION OF GENIUS

So far, the influence of electronic inventions on civilization was, on the whole, beneficial. The reproductive inventions, high-fidelity sound recording, radio and television have put the masterpieces of music and of the stage within everybody's reach, of course, mixed with advertisements and with entertainment. I have no apology to offer for advertisements; but as regards entertainment, it was J. B. Priestley who asked whether the cinema was "any worse than the cartwheel around the village idiot's neck as a Sunday entertainment?"

It is also interesting and comforting to observe that the hi-fi gramophone and the radio, these highly democratic inventions, have brought a triumph to the aristocratic principle, that nothing is worth doing unless it is done supremely well. Today there is no *need* for anybody to play the piano who plays it less well than Myra Hess. (Playing the piano for your own pleasure is quite another matter, but this has little to do with the level of artistic achievement of the epoch. The Medicis were no lesser judges of art for never touching a paint brush.)

There is even a possibility that in music the intermediary between the composer and his public will be cut out altogether. Great composers need not be great performers on any instrument, nor need they be accomplished conductors, but we must concede that the composer is the best judge of how his work ought to be performed. Several years ago the engineers of the Radio Corporation of America constructed a wonderful musical instrument which enables a single man to put together, at leisure, any orchestral music, instrument by instrument, without being able to play a single one, and to correct it as often as he likes, until it sounds perfect to him. To my knowledge no composer has tried his hand on it, but if ever there will be a new Beethoven (and not deaf), posterity may be able to hear his own interpretation of his symphonies, without any intermediaries. This would be a further and final triumph of the aristocratic principle—if we are agreed that the creative artist ranks above the interpreter, be he a Bruno Walter or a Toscanini.

Will the machine go a step further and cut out also the creative artist? Is all this talk about composing symphonies[2] or writing sonnets just science fiction or is it a serious forecast of things to come?

My answer is that I sincerely hope that machines *will* never replace the creative artist, but in good conscience I cannot say that they never *could*. The brilliant researches of one modern school of mathematicians and logicians[3] have proved that it is not possible to construct deterministic machines to solve a class of mathematical problems which have been quite successfully tackled by human brains, and this suggests that the same applies to artistic creations. On the other hand there is strong evidence that a machine which embodies random elements can in every respect simulate the human mind. This is the old idea of monkeys on typewriters, but with an important difference. By embodying all the deterministic knowledge in the machine (such as of the English language, of the rules of logic, of harmony and melody) and by building in an enormous store of previous experience which allows preselecting elements likely to succeed, the probability space can be enormously restricted. Moreover (perhaps by teaching the machine by feedback what is agreeable to the human public and what is not) the machine can be its own critic and censor. I believe, though, that such a machine will be hardly less complicated than the human brain, and therefore there is some hope that it will never be built. On the other hand I should welcome simpler machines, such as Orwell's versifier which produces popular lyrics "untouched by human brains" for debunking all that is mechanical and bogus in what passes by the name of art.

I am afraid though that one cannot exclude the possibility of another, much more sinister short circuit between invention and the public, not electronic but chemical. Primitive drugs such as alcohol and opium have existed since time immemorial, and they were beneficial in helping human beings to bear their miseries. Fortunately, one can say, they were ruinous when taken in excess for health or stamina, and society has kept them within bounds. But there is no reason why this should always be so. It is not unthinkable, even likely, that drugs will be discovered which give to simple, average people the happiness of the creative artist, and beyond this, the indescribable bliss of the ecstatic saint,[4] and which will not be ruinous to health, or even to will power. A human society in possession of such a drug would not necessarily degenerate, nor need it be overrun by barbarians, but unless it decides by an act of will that it prefers to stay sober, it will not produce any more art. If this happened, I am glad that electronics will be innocent of it.

I believe that of all electronic inventions now within viewing distance predictors are likely to have the greatest influence on civilization. In a well-ordered society the highest, the most respected and the most responsible posts go, or at least ought to go, to men who have the gift of making the right decisions on the basis of uncertain data, by a partly reasoning, partly instinctive foresight of the future. A false and irresponsible predictor like Hitler can ruin a civilization; in fact we have now reached the stage when we cannot afford another Hitler. At first sight it is a relief to think that in the near future objective electronic predictors may assist the statesmen. But a warning must be uttered, not to attach undue hopes to mechanical predictors when applied to human affairs. A predictor, whether man or machine, can remain objective only so long as its forecasts will not influence the processes which they predict. Weather forecasting is of this type; forecasting economic trends is quite another matter. A financial editor takes an active part in shaping the future. Once the forecasts are communicated to men who influence affairs, the process becomes a complicated "Neumann-Morgenstern game" between them and the predictor. To avoid complicating matters, let us just consider the case that a predictor has built up such a high reputation of being always right that men will blindly follow its forecasts. The machine, being a learning machine, will soon notice that everything it says goes, and from that moment on there is no guarantee against its going astray. Absolute power will corrupt not only men but also machines! Let us hope that these things will be better understood before social predictors become important.

A GOLDEN AGE?

After this excursion into a hypothetical future I want to step back into the present, and ask the question, "Do we need inventors?" Or, more precisely does this country need inventors? Let me for a moment play the part of the *advocatus diaboli*, and plead the case against inventors. I could ask, for instance: "Does it make any difference that polythene was invented in this country, and nylon in the United States?" There is now no shortage of either polythene or nylon in Britain or in the United States or in any industrial country which has not invented either of them. Or does it matter that transistors were invented in the United States? The whole know-how has come to this country for less than the cost of research, and the moderate royalties will have to be anyway invested in Britain. I have quoted one cautionary tale, of color television, at the beginning, and I could add, from my own experience, some even more frightening cases in which invention and initiative did *not* pay. Perhaps I had better stop, or I might find too good arguments. But I feel sure that to all these arguments there will be one reply. "We want British inventors, because we do not want to become a second-rate country, and because we want to be in nobody's debt for ideas and inventions!" I believe that such a proud resolve is worth more than all the economic arguments, even if it springs from roots which are instinctive rather than rational.

If we agree about this, what must we do to help inventors? In a country so richly endowed with inventive talent as Britain, there is no need for any artificial breeding and nursing, but I believe that it is of great importance to eliminate some of the obstacles, external and internal.

Once upon a time Britain had no shortage of inventors. In books like *Self-Help* by Samuel Smiles[5] we read with a shudder of these maniacs who worked on relentlessly with their wives in rags, their children crying with hunger, who were later persecuted by irate workmen, and, when their invention was finally successful, were cheated by manufacturers who stole their inventions in the hope that they could not go to court. In the end there is the horrible refrain: "died in extreme poverty." We now hear that all this belongs to the past; "the inventor starving in a garret has been replaced by the scientist in the research laboratory." But it is just this very widespread modern belief which is a subtle danger to invention, and it will be worth considering it in a little detail.

There is, of course, some truth in it. One of the greatest of inventors, the late Irving Langmuir, worked all his life in almost monastic happiness in the Research Laboratory of the General Electric Company, producing inventions which brought millions to his company, and scientific discoveries which brought him the Nobel Prize. But not all inventors have this happy disposition. Three of the greatest, Rudolf Diesel, W. H. Carothers (the inventor of nylon and other important high polymers) and Edwin Armstrong (the inventor of the superheterodyne, of superregeneration and of frequency modulation) ended their highly useful and successful lives by suicide—all three because of imaginary worries. Even if they do not risk their own money, the responsibility for keeping their promises weighs heavily on highly strung and sensitive individuals. Shall we then keep them out of danger, for their own health, by changing the inventor into a scientist, working in a research laboratory? Though the inventor and the scientist often represent very different psychological types, this metamorphosis can be effected, without any crude pressure, just by the climate of opinion.

INVENTION AND RESEARCH

I believe that Rutherford is a good example of a highly gifted individual who could have been equally great as an inventor and as a scientist. When the young New Zealander came to this country, he brought with him an invention, and not a bad one either—the magnetic detector of radio waves. If he had not gone in 1896 to Cambridge, England, but say to Pittsburgh, Pennsylvania, I have not the slightest doubt that he, and not Valdemar Poulsen, would have become the inventor of magnetic sound recording.[6] As it was, in his whole wonderful scientific life Rutherford never made another invention, and became the epitome of a pure research worker.

Rutherford's is certainly a rather exceptional case because few inventors have this gift of curiosity, that appetite for scientific truth of which he had a somewhat old-fashioned, unsophisticated, but all the more vivid conception. Most inventors would make only average research workers, some even poor ones, but I have little doubt that in a climate of opinion which favors research they would settle down quite happily and forget running after dreams.

But what is good for the individual is not necessarily the best for society. Will great research laboratories, staffed by devoted research-minded workers, really pour out automatically a stream of worth-while inventions? I am afraid this is just one of the comfortable beliefs of modern "organization man." [7] Thanks to recent researches,[8] one can give a fairly quantitative appraisal. From a careful investigation into the history of 60 important modern inventions, it appears that not less than 33 are the work of individual or independent inventors, 6 are borderline cases, and only 22 come from research laboratories, of which 15 are chemical inventions.[9] It may be noted that electronic research laboratories have a very good record, because modern television is largely the work of excellent inventors employed by large firms, such as Westinghouse, RCA, EMI and Marconi's, whereas the work of individual inventors, such as J. L. Baird and D. v. Mihalyi came to a dead end. Also, one of the most outstanding modern inventions, the transistor, is the work of the exceptional team of the three Nobel Prize winners, Shockley, Bardeen and Brattain, in the Bell Telephone Laboratories.

This might look like a sufficient vindication of the modern institution of great industrial or national research laboratories, in spite of the more than 50 per cent contribution of the small minority of individual, independent inventors, but on closer look it is only a justification of those institutions which know how to employ and to stimulate inventors. Research is a modern hurrah word, which exploits the immense prestige of science. Even the institutions which deal exclusively with inventions cannot do without it; they call themselves research foundations in the United States and in this country, we have the National Research Development Corporation—as if invention were nothing but the development of research results! There is no objection against a name, so long as we do not forget what it covers. But to suggest that television is a result of research into photo-emitters and electron optics, or that the transistor is the result of research in semiconductors is plainly misleading. V. K. Zworykin, the principal originator of electronic television, is a true inventor, a descendant of the pure line of the heroes of Smiles, and so is Shockley. The difference is, of course, that they are not self-taught mechanics, but fully trained scientists. The other difference, that they have preferred to work for large corporations instead of as free lancers (though Shockley has now changed his mind), is not very profound. Even the inventors of old times valued achievement more than money[10] and in modern times, when inventions are still uncertain but income tax is dead certain, money is even less important. Inventors can fling themselves heart and soul into their vocation, whether they are free lancers or employees, even too much so, as witnessed by the tragic case of W. H. Carothers of Du Pont's.

Once a great invention is made, legend rapidly grows around it and makes of it a result of patient research and observation—forgetting only the guiding vision and the motive power! The transistor is a particularly good nucleus for a legend, because it was accompanied by so much brilliant research. But the fact is that Shockley did not set out to carry on research in semiconductors; he set out to invent a solid-state amplifier.

UTOPIA?

In the invention-stimulating atmosphere of the United States (or of the Soviet Union) there is probably no need to utter such warnings. But in this country, where the prestige of pure research is so immense, it will be as well to avoid confusion of ideas and to protect the inventor from extinction. The stimulation must start early, through science teachers, newspapers, radio, television and periodicals accessible to young people. Fortunately, there is no shortage in this country for gifted popularizers of science, with the right attitude to inventions. The universities can do their share by teaching the history of technology and, generally by teaching science, not as a *post facto* logical reconstruction, but as a succession of ideas, with their historical background, giving due recognition to their originators.

But the universities can make a more important contribution. It is a plain fact that very few of the modern electronic devices were invented by people trained as electrical engineers. The majority were invented by physicists, some by mathematicians, one by an architect. This is no reflection on the intelligence of electrical engineering students. What can you expect of the man who has been taught the tools of his trade in a situation in which the scientific background of electronic inventions extends from symbolic logic to quantum physics? I believe that the best we can do is to advise young people who show exceptional early promise and who want to become inventors to take up electrical engineering not directly, but as a postgraduate study and to study for the first three years nothing but mathematics and physics.[11] These are the years in which the mind is most receptive for abstractions, and in which quantum physics will not appear "strange." Later, some of them can be advised to study in addition physical chemistry, metallurgy, even physiology, especially of the nervous system. It is not a great exaggeration to say that almost any bit of odd information is more likely to inspire an original invention than knowledge which the inventor shares with all his professional colleagues.

We may be agreed that this country needs inventors to hold our own in the international race, but this does not necessarily mean that we approve of the race itself, any more than we approve of the armaments race. I want, therefore, to pose in all seriousness the question: "Do we need more inventions?"

There is, of course, an easy answer to this. Almost every important invention unbalances the front of progress, and a new invention is needed to redress the balance. Disinfectants and chemotherapy have strongly reduced child mortality in the East, the population is growing out of control and we need "the Pill" to keep it in bounds. The steam engine, the internal combustion engine, and the like are threatening our stock of fossil fuel with exhaustion; we must have nuclear power, and after that thermonuclear power. This is a compelling practical argument, but a very unsatisfactory one. It means simply that we cannot stop inventing, because we are riding a tiger!

Let us therefore hear what our best contemporaries have to say on this question: our writers and thinkers. But I am afraid it is not much use going to them for encouragement. Today a scientist or inventor must be very illiterate indeed if he is to retain a little of the happy, confident spirit of Samuel Smiles or of the Prince Consort a hundred years ago. It may be better for his peace of mind if outside working hours he is interested only in music, or if he reads nothing but detective novels. He may even read good literature, but, as I think most scientists do, he must not take it seriously. If he takes seriously what our best contemporary thinkers and men of letters have to say on the subject of industrial civilization, it will make him at best very unhappy. At the worst it will give him a strong

desire to give up his futile and dangerous work, and to retire into a monastery.

I believe that it is a very significant fact that no optimistic utopia has been written for the last thirty years.
Utopian literature did not die, as one might think, in 1914;
it survived the first World War by about a decade. Some
of H. G. Wells' best utopian works date from this time,
and I recall with particular pleasure the *Daedalus* of the
young J. B. S. Haldane, sparkling with optimism and belief
in salvation by science. But after Aldous Huxley's incom-
parably brilliant antiutopia *Brave New World* (1931), no
more utopias were written, only dreary science fiction and
George Orwell's horrible nightmare *1984*.

WORKING AGAINST LEISURE

If we cannot get encouragement from the men of letters, can we perhaps get it from our fellow scientists? No
more utopias were written for the last generation, but
we have now scientific forecasts from two distinguished
physicists, *The Foreseeable Future* by Sir George Thomson (1958), and *The Next Million Years* by Sir Charles
Darwin (1952). Thomson's is a cautious application of the
scientific method, neither very encouraging nor disturbing, but Darwin's is a profoundly depressing book. His
thesis is, briefly, that we are not moving toward a Golden
Age, because the present is a Golden Age, and the next
million years will see a sort of statistical fluctuation around
a level rather lower than the present. I have no wish to
give a rival forecast of the next million years, but I want
to give my view, for what it is worth, of the near future.
My thesis is, briefly, that from a purely material point of
view a "Golden Age" is at hand—but that there are immensely strong forces at work to prevent us entering it
for the next few generations—and that there is nobody
to show us the way to it.

The plain fact is that science and technology have immensely enlarged the set of possible worlds. Until quite
recently, the majority of people had to work hard to keep a
leisured minority. We are now for the first time in history
faced with the possibility of a world in which only a minor-

ity need work to keep the great majority in idle luxury. Soon the minority which has to work for the rest may be so small that it could be entirely recruited from volunteers, who prefer the joys of a useful and even of a dedicated life to idleness.

Men have always envied the leisured classes, but it now appears that the dream of leisure for all is turning into a nightmare. Indeed, to think of the privileged classes of the past is enough to make one doubtful. The aristocracies of the past had two great psychological satisfactions which would be denied to a leisured majority: they could command human service, and they believed themselves to be *élites*. Yet for the averagely gifted members of the privileged classes life became bearable only by hard drinking!

The leisured society of the future is still mostly below the horizon, but it seems to me that our contemporary world has already developed several very strong defense mechanisms to prevent it from becoming a reality.

The first defense mechanism is Parkinson's Law: "Work automatically expands so as to fill the available time." Though this great law was first formulated in this country, if we want to see it in action we must look to the United States, the most advanced and richest industrial country, where tomorrow is already here. In the United States in 1957, for the first time in history, the white-collar workers have outnumbered the blue-collar workers; there are now more paper-pushers than tool-pushers. It is only surprising why they do not outnumber them 3:1 or 4:1. Not very long ago the great majority of mankind had to work in agriculture; even in the United States in 1900 the proportion was 31 per cent. Today less than 12 per cent are sufficient to produce so much food that a great fraction of it goes daily down the drains, that millions are on a slimming diet and producers of canned foods advertise that their food has fewer calories per weight than that of their competitors. Or look at the car industry, where less than a million workers produce so many cars that they can be sold fast enough only by employing all the means of high-pressure salesmanship to make customers change them long before the car starts showing signs of wear. These are very clear manifestations of Parkinson's Law.

But looking at it this way, the growth of paper-pushers is not a tumor; it is the healthy reaction of a society in which people have been brought up to work, not only for earning money, but also because they want to feel useful, and want to keep their self-respect.

A second, perhaps even more important, defense mechanism is the recent strong increase of the birth rate, particularly noticeable in the United States, but also in Britain and in France. This is quite a different phenomenon from the overpopulation of poor and ignorant countries. It is again an expression of our healthy and virtuous civilization; people have more babies not because they cannot help it, but because they love having children. Nevertheless, apart from the very different motivation, it looks dangerously like Malthus' Law, on which Darwin based his pessimistic outlook: the law that a population tends to increase up to the starvation limit. I am inclined to take a less serious view of this, as may be seen from my putting Malthus' Law on the same level as Parkinson's Law. I do not believe that in highly civilized countries the population need grow up to the starvation level, but it looks to me as if it had a tendency to grow up to a level sufficient to ban the nightmare of leisure for everybody.

A third defense mechanism, and a very strong one, is, of course—defense. All I need say about it is that much of the effort in all industrial countries goes into making the most devilishly ingenious products of the human mind, which at best will never be used, at worst might destroy all of us.

Our contemporary world has a fourth defense mechanism ready against a too-easy life, and I am glad to say that at least this one is wholly laudable. It is aid to the underdeveloped countries of the East. It is not on a large scale, and it will not last long, as these countries are already making very determined efforts to raise themselves to a higher technological level; but while it lasts it will be good for them, and good for us.

These four, as I see it, are the chief defense mechanisms of our society against the nightmare of a leisured world, for which we are socially and psychologically unprepared. I do not feel competent to give an opinion on the question whether mankind can or cannot be conditioned to bear leisure without boredom, and without losing that magnificent spirit by which a poor animal, almost toothless and clawless, has raised itself gradually to the status of modern man. For my part, I should be satisfied with a compromise, because man in the past has shown rather too much fighting spirit. But I can see little sign of any preparations to meet this problem in our Western civilization, and none at all in the Soviet Union where the official creed is, of course, to deny the existence of the problem altogether.[12] This may well be a great danger, because they are making such great strides in their industrial development that they may well take the step from poverty to plenty in one generation, instead of the two or three of the Western countries, psychologically completely unprepared and with all their dynamism still in their blood.

It is a sad thought indeed that our civilization has not produced a new vision, which could guide us on into the new Golden Age which has now become physically possible, but only physically. All we have is the pedestrian dream of the trade unions of the thirty-five-hour week, the twenty-four-hour week and so on. But even this is not certain, because work which is not necessary to sustain life may have to come back as occupational therapy. This reminds me of the pathetic picture of the dog in the old physiological laboratories, climbing endlessly up a moving ramp. The dog will never get anywhere, but at least it will keep in fine fettle.

THE LOST VISION

Who is responsible for this tragicomedy of Man frustrated by success? If the intellectuals at the other side of the fence say that the fault is ours, of the scientists and inventors, we are not in a position to deny it. But instead of bowing our heads in shame, I think we ought to return the accusation, and ask: "Who has left mankind without a vision?" The predictable part of the future may be a job for electronic predictors, but that part of it which is not predictable, which is largely a matter of free human choice, is not the business of machines, nor of scientists, not even of psychologists, but it ought to be, as it was in the great epochs of the past, the prerogative of the inspired humanists, of the poets and writers. And for more than a generation we receive from these quarters little else but more or less polished expressions of despair and disgust.

Some thirty years ago the French critic Julien Benda wrote a famous book, *La Trahison des Clercs*, in which he accused the *"clercs,"* the writers and thinkers (who by their vocation had the duty to uphold the ideals of freedom, justice and the dignity of the individual) of "treason" by embracing dogma of one sort or another, or the creed of extreme nationalism. Today we are faced with a new treason of the *clercs*—oh, nothing as crude and criminal as the treason of the French intellectuals, Barrès and Maurras—no treason by commission, but only by omission: by not giving us a vision for which to live.

Until such time when our *clercs* change their mind, and come up from their depths of comfortable and complacent despair, we shall have to muddle through, from invention to invention. And if we want a measure of hope, we must not turn to the intellectuals; we must look at the present and into the past.

In the present we can see more simple happiness of the Common Man than has ever existed in the world. Even uniformity can have its delights. Some years ago I saw in the *New Yorker* the following cartoon: a suburban row of houses, as far as the eye can see, and through every gate steps a young man, who has just arrived with the commuter's train. A little dog with wagging tail runs out to greet every young man, behind every dog runs a little toddler, and behind every little toddler, on the doorstep, stands a smiling young wife. This is stereotyped happiness, but unique and wonderful for those who live it. Worse things can happen to humanity than this scene repeating itself through a hundred generations!

This is what we can see in the present. Looking into the past, we can see our ancestors, men with much the same capabilities as ours, miserably sheltering under dripping trees from the cold pelting rain. The journey which led from these poor savages to the distinguished audience following my remarks seems to me worth while. It will be for another, in another historic epoch, before another audience, to draw the balance of splendors and miseries and to decide whether the rest of the journey was necessary.

FOOTNOTES

1. One might ask why we do not give this problem to one of the giant universal digital computers, such as the IBM 704 or 709? In fact these machines are so universal that one could set them up to solve our problem, but not faster than our specialized machine (which can perform 400,000 multiplications per second), and the rental of these machines for long times is rather prohibitive. Besides, a university institute must turn out able young research workers as well as research results, and training them as programmers of giant machines is a poor sort of training.

2. This ruthless idea is not as modern as one might think. The first composing machine, the *Componium*, was built in 1824 by Winckler and is preserved in Brussels. Other more recent ruthless suggestions are the Electronic Manager, the Electronic Surgeon, and the Electronic Judge. (Cf. the *Proceedings of the Symposium on the Mechanisations of Thought Processes*, organized by A. M. Uttley at the National Physical Laboratory, Teddington, November 24, 1958.) Why do these people never suggest the Electronic Research Worker?

3. Cf. M. Davis, *Computability and Unsolvability* (New York: McGraw-Hill, 1958).

4. It appears that opium produces the "sensations of a poet" (but it ruined Coleridge), and that mescalin can give "a vividness of vision of which only great painters

are capable," as eloquently witnessed by Aldous Huxley (*Doors of Perception*, New York: Harper & Brothers, 1954). What is the "use" of great painting if the sight of "light playing on a garden chair" or even the sight of "the folds of one's trousers" can produce a palpitating pleasure which no Rembrandt can give to the sober eye?

5. A new edition of this classic has recently appeared, with an introduction by Asa Briggs (London: John Murray, 1959).

6. I have heard from Sir Ernest Marsden, FRS, that Rutherford actually had the idea, and received encouragement from J. J. Thomson, but let it drop because the development promised to be lengthy and expensive, and undoubtedly also because by that time he had lost interest in inventions.

7. William H. Whyte, Jr., *The Organization Man* (New York: Doubleday & Co., 1956). Other comfortable beliefs of Organization Man are that "ideas come from the group, not from individuals"; that "creative leadership is a staff function"; that decisions ought to be made in committees only; and that "a man who gets ulcers probably shouldn't be in business anyway."

8. John Jewkes, David Sawers, and Richard Stillerman, *The Sources of Invention* (London: Macmillan, 1958).

9. One case, admittedly not typical, deserves to be singled out, because it gives a somewhat unexpected answer to the question, "Is invention the result of research?" This is the story of the Kodachrome color process, which was invented by two young musicians, Leo Godowski and Leopold Mannes, who were so enthusiastic about it that they went on with their experiments during their concert tours, in hotel rooms. Later, Dr. C. E. K. Mees, FRS, the famous Director of Research of the Eastman Kodak Company, himself a distinguished inventor, invited them to join his laboratories with salaries, royalties and excellent laboratory facilities, where it took another ten years to make Kodachrome commercial. (The most remarkable feature of this case is that the two outsiders worked on an orthodox chemical basis originating from the scientific work of Fischer and Siegrist, 1910-14, on dye couplers, which was open to all dye chemists.)

10. Think of the noble words of Charles Goodyear, written at the time when he was imprisoned for debt, "Only when someone sows and no one reaps is there truly reason for despair."

11. I am aware that such a course might not be suitable for a new Thomas Alva Edison, but it is always difficult to cater for the exceptional genius. Edison could absorb whole libraries full of odd facts with his enormous eidetic memory, but he was unable to learn mathematics and quantitative physics. It is quite possible that he would have failed all examinations in mathematics.

12. The official attitude of Marxists is, I believe, well illustrated by the following quotation from the late Frédéric Joliot: "There are those who object to the view of progress which depends upon shorter working hours on the grounds that then people will not know what to do with their leisure, and will let themselves lapse into idleness and immorality. Such fears are groundless, because the time saved on working hours will open up to the individual a culture rich enough to induce him to work spontaneously during his leisure at the things he enjoys, and even attain the supreme joy of creative achievement in the realm of art and of science." (*Quelques réflexions sur l'énergie Physique et Chimie* [Paris: 1958].)

   To believe this one would have to believe first either that in future *everybody* will be exceptionally gifted, or that the less gifted members of the old leisured classes were driven to drink by a bad conscience.

■ 5 ■

Some Moral and Technical Consequences of Automation[*]

by Norbert Wiener

PROFESSOR MATHEMATICS,
MASSACHUSETTS INSTITUTE OF TECHNOLOGY

Some thirteen years ago, a book of mine was published by the name of *Cybernetics*. In it I discussed the problems of control and communication in the living organism and the machine. I made a considerable number of predictions about the development of controlled machines and about the corresponding techniques of automatization, which I foresaw as having important consequences affecting the society of the future. Now, thirteen years later, it seems appropriate to take stock of the present position with respect to both cybernetic technique and the social consequences of this technique.

Before commencing on the detail of these matters, I should like to mention a certain attitude of the man in the

---

[*] Reprinted from *Science*, May 6, 1960, by permission of the Author and *Science*.

street toward cybernetics and automatization. This attitude needs a critical discussion, and in my opinion it
should be rejected in its entirety. This is the assumption
that machines cannot possess any degree of originality.
This frequently takes the form of a statement that nothing
can come out of the machine which has not been put into
it. This is often interpreted as asserting that a machine
which man has made must remain continually subject to
man, so that its operation is at any time open to human
interference and to a change in policy. On the basis of
such an attitude, many people have pooh-poohed the dangers of machine techniques, and they have flatly contra-
dicted the early predictions of Samuel Butler that the machine might take over the control of mankind.

It is true that in the time of Samuel Butler the available machines were far less hazardous than machines are
today, for they involved only power, not a certain degree
of thinking and communication. However, the machine
techniques of the present day have invaded the latter
fields as well, so that the actual machine of today is very
different from the image that Butler held, and we cannot
transfer to these new devices the assumptions which
seemed axiomatic a generation ago. I find myself facing a
public which has formed its attitude toward the machine
on the basis of an imperfect understanding of the structure
and mode of operation of modern machines.

It is my thesis that machines can and do transcend some
of the limitations of their designers, and that in doing so
they may be both effective and dangerous. It may well be
that in principle we cannot make any machine the elements of whose behavior we cannot comprehend sooner
or later. This does not mean in any way that we shall be
able to comprehend these elements in substantially less
time than the time required for operation of the machine, or even within any given number of years or generations.

As is now generally admitted, over a limited range of
operation, machines act far more rapidly than human beings and are far more precise in performing the details of
their operations. This being the case, even when machines
do not in any way transcend man's intelligence, they very

well may, and often do, transcend man in the performance of tasks. An intelligent understanding of their mode
of performance may be delayed until long after the task
which they have been set has been completed.

This means that though machines are theoretically subject to human criticism, such criticism may be ineffective
until long after it is relevant. To be effective in warding off
disastrous consequences, our understanding of our man-
made machines should in general develop *pari passu* with
the performance of the machine. By the very slowness of
our human actions, our effective control of our machines
may be nullified. By the time we are able to react to information conveyed by our senses and stop the car we are
driving, it may already have run head on into a wall.

GAME-PLAYING

I shall come back to this point later in this article. For
the present, let me discuss the technique of machines for
a very specific purpose: that of playing games. In this
matter I shall deal more particularly with the game of
checkers, for which the International Business Machines
Corporation has developed very effective game-playing
machines.

Let me say once for all that we are not concerned here
with the machines which operate on a perfect closed theory of the game they play. The game theory of von Neumann and Morgenstern may be suggestive as to the operation of actual game-playing machines, but it does not actually describe them.

In a game as complicated as checkers, if each player
tries to choose his play in view of the best move his opponent can make, against the best response he can give,
against the best response his opponent can give, and so
on, he will have taken upon himself an impossible task.
Not only is this humanly impossible but there is actually
no reason to suppose that it is the best policy against the
opponent by whom he is faced, whose limitations are
equal to his own.

The von Neumann theory of games bears no very
close relation to the theory by which game-playing machines operate. The latter corresponds much more closely

to the methods of play used by expert but limited human chess players against other chess players. Such players depend on certain strategic evaluations, which are in essence not complete. While the von Neumann type of play is valid for games like ticktacktoe, with a complete theory, the very interest of chess and checkers lies in the fact that they do not possess a complete theory. Neither do war nor business competition nor any of the other forms of competitive activity in which we are really interested.

In a game like ticktacktoe, with a small number of moves, where each player is in a position to contemplate all possibilities and to establish a defense against the best possible moves of the other player, a complete theory of the von Neumann type is valid. In such a case, the game must inevitably end in a win for the first player, a win for the second player or a draw.

I question strongly whether this concept of the perfect game is a completely realistic one in the cases of actual, nontrivial games. Great generals like Napoleon and great admirals like Nelson have proceeded in a different manner. They have been aware not only of the limitations of their opponents in such matters as materiel and personnel but equally of their limitations in experience and in military know-how. It was by a realistic appraisal of the relative inexperience in naval operations of the continental powers as compared with the highly developed tactical and strategic competence of the British fleet that Nelson was able to display the boldness which pushed the continental forces off the seas. This he could not have done had he engaged in the long, relatively indecisive, and possibly losing, conflict to which his assumption of the best possible strategy on the part of his enemy would have doomed him.

In assessing not merely the materiel and personnel of his enemies but also the degree of judgment and the amount of skill in tactics and strategy to be expected of them, Nelson acted on the basis of their record in previous combats. Similarly, an important factor in Napoleon's conduct of his combat with the Austrians in Italy was his knowledge of the rigidity and mental limitations of Würmser.

This element of experience should receive adequate recognition in any realistic theory of games. It is quite legitimate for a chess player to play, not against an ideal, nonexisting, perfect antagonist, but rather against one whose habits he has been able to determine from the record. Thus, in the theory of games, at least two different intellectual efforts must be made. One is the short-term effort of playing with a determined policy for the individual game. The other is the examination of a record of many games. This record has been set by the player himself, by his opponent or even by players with whom he has not personally played. In terms of this record, he determines the relative advantages of different policies as proved over the past.

There is even a third stage of judgment required in a chess game. This is expressed at least in part by the length of the significant past. The development of theory in chess decreases the importance of games played at a different stage of the art. On the other hand, an astute chess theoretician may estimate in advance that a certain policy currently in fashion has become of little value, and that it may be best to return to earlier modes of play to anticipate the change in policy of the people whom he is likely to find as his opponents.

Thus, in determining policy in chess there are several different levels of consideration which correspond in a certain way to the different logical types of Bertrand Russell. There is the level of tactics, the level of strategy, the level of the general considerations which should have been weighed in determining this strategy, the level in which the length of the relevant past—the past within which these considerations may be valid—is taken into account, and so on. Each new level demands a study of a much larger past than the previous one.

I have compared these levels with the logical types of Russell concerning classes, classes of classes, classes of classes of classes and so on. It may be noted that Russell does not consider statements involving all types as significant. He brings out the futility of such questions as that concerning the barber who shaves all persons, and only those persons who do not shave themselves. Does he shave himself? On one type he does, on the next type he does not and so on indefinitely. All such questions involving an infinity of types may lead to unsolvable paradoxes. Similarly, the search for the best policy under all levels of sophistication is a futile one and must lead to nothing but confusion.

These considerations arise in the determination of policy by machines as well as in the determination of policy by persons. These are the questions which arise in the programming of programming. The lowest type of game-playing machine plays in terms of a certain rigid evaluation of plays. Quantities such as the value of pieces gained or lost, the command of the pieces, their mobility and so on can be given numerical weights on a certain empirical basis, and a weighting may be given on this basis to each next play conforming to the rules of the game. The play with the greatest weight may be chosen. Under these circumstances, the play of the machine will seem to its antagonist—who cannot help but evaluate the chess personality of the machine—a rigid one.

LEARNING MACHINES

The next step is for the machine to take into consideration not merely the moves as they occurred in the individual game but the record of games previously played. On this basis, the machine may stop from time to time, not to play but to consider what (linear or nonlinear) weighting of the factors which it has been given to consider would correspond best to won games as opposed to lost (or drawn) games. On this basis, it continues to play with a new weighting. Such a machine would seem to its human opponent to have a far less rigid game personality, and tricks which would defeat it at an earlier stage may now fail to deceive it.

The present level of these learning machines is that they play a fair amateur game at chess but that in checkers they can show a marked superiority to the player who has programmed them after from ten to twenty playing hours of working and indoctrination. They thus most definitely escape from the completely effective control of the man who has made them. Rigid as the repertory of factors may be which they are in a position to take into consideration, they do unquestionably—and so say those who have played with them—show originality, not merely in their tactics, which may be quite unforeseen, but even in the detailed weighting of their strategy.

As I have said, checker-playing machines which learn have developed to the point at which they can defeat the programmer. However, they appear still to have one weakness. This lies in the end game. Here the machines are somewhat clumsy in determining the best way to give the *coup de grâce*. This is due to the fact that the existing machines have for the most part adopted a program in which the identical strategy is carried out at each stage of the game. In view of the similarity of values of pieces in checkers, this is quite natural for a large part of the play but ceases to be perfectly relevant when the board is relatively empty and the main problem is that of moving into position rather than that of direct attack. Within the frame of the methods I have described it is quite possible to have a second exploration to determine what the policy should be after the number of pieces of the opponent is so reduced that these new considerations become paramount.

Chess-playing machines have not, so far, been brought to the degree of perfection of checker-playing machines, although, as I have said, they can most certainly play a respectable amateur game. Probably the reason for this is similar to the reason for their relative efficiency in the end game of checkers. In chess, not only is the end game quite different in its proper strategy from the mid game but the opening game is also. The difference between checkers and chess in this respect is that the initial play of the pieces in checkers is not very different in character from the play which arises in the mid game, while in chess, pieces at the beginning have an arrangement of exceptionally low mobility, so that the problem of deploying them from this position is particularly difficult. This is the reason why opening play and development form a special branch of chess theory.

There are various ways in which the machine can take cognizance of these well-known facts and explore a separate waiting strategy for the opening. This does not mean

that the type of game theory which I have here discussed is not applicable to chess but merely that it requires much more consideration before we can make a
machine that can play master chess. Some of my friends
who are engaged in these problems believe that this goal
will be achieved in from ten to twenty-five years. Not being a chess expert, I do not venture to make any such predictions on my own initiative.

It is quite in the cards that learning machines will be
used to program the pushing of the button in a new push-
button war. Here we are considering a field in which automata of a nonlearning character are probably already in
use. It is quite out of the question to program these machines on the basis of an actual experience in real war.
For one thing, a sufficient experience to give an adequate programming would probably see humanity already
wiped out.

Moreover, the techniques of push-button war are
bound to change so much that by the time an adequate
experience could have been accumulated, the basis of the
beginning would have radically changed. Therefore, the
programming of such a learning machine would have to
be based on some sort of war game, just as commanders
and staff officials now learn an important part of the art of
strategy in a similar manner. Here, however, if the rules
for victory in a war game do not correspond to what we
actually wish for our country, it is more than likely that
such a machine may produce a policy which would win a
nominal victory on points at the cost of every interest we
have at heart, even that of national survival.

MAN AND SLAVE

The problem, and it is a moral problem, with which
we are here faced is very close to one of the great problems of slavery. Let us grant that slavery is bad because
it is cruel. It is, however, self-contradictory, and for a reason which is quite different. We wish a slave to be intelligent, to be able to assist us in the carrying out of our tasks.
However, we also wish him to be subservient. Complete
subservience and complete intelligence do not go together. How often in ancient times the clever Greek phi-

losopher slave of a less intelligent Roman slaveholder must have dominated the actions of his master rather than obeyed his wishes! Similarly, if the machines become more and more efficient and operate at a higher and higher psychological level, the catastrophe foreseen by Butler of the dominance of the machine comes nearer and nearer.

The human brain is a far more efficient control apparatus than is the intelligent machine when we come to the higher areas of logic. It is a self-organizing system which depends on its capacity to modify itself into a new machine rather than on ironclad accuracy and speed in problem-solving. We have already made very successful machines of the lowest logical type, with a rigid policy. We are beginning to make machines of the second logical type, where the policy itself improves with learning. In the construction of operative machines, there is no specific foreseeable limit with respect to logical type, nor is it safe to make a pronouncement about the exact level at which the brain is superior to the machine. Yet for a long time at least there will always be some level at which the brain is better than the constructed machine, even though this level may shift upwards and upwards.

It may be seen that the result of a programming technique of automatization is to remove from the mind of the designer and operator an effective understanding of many of the stages by which the machine comes to its conclusions and of what the real tactical intentions of many of its operations may be. This is highly relevant to the problem of our being able to foresee undesired consequences outside the frame of the strategy of the game while the machine is still in action and while intervention on our part may prevent the occurrence of these consequences.

Here it is necessary to realize that human action is a feedback action. To avoid a disastrous consequence, it is not enough that some action on our part should be sufficient to change the course of the machine, because it is quite possible that we lack information on which to base consideration of such an action.

In neurophysiological language, ataxia can be quite as much of a deprivation as paralysis. A patient with locomotor ataxia may not suffer from any defect of his muscles or motor nerves, but if his muscles and tendons and organs do not tell him exactly what position he is in, and whether the tensions to which his organs are subjected will or will not lead to his falling, he will be unable to stand up. Similarly, when a machine constructed by us is capable of operating on its incoming data at a pace which we cannot keep, we may not know, until too late, when to turn it off. We all know the fable of the sorcerer's apprentice, in which the boy makes the broom carry water in his master's absence, so that it is on the point of drowning him when his master reappears. If the boy had had to seek a charm to stop the mischief in the *grimoires* of his master's library, he might have been drowned before he had discovered the relevant incantation. Similarly, if a bottle factory is programmed on the basis of maximum productivity, the owner may be made bankrupt by the enormous inventory of unsalable bottles manufactured before he learns he should have stopped production six months earlier.

The "Sorcerer's Apprentice" is only one of many tales based on the assumption that the agencies of magic are literal-minded. There is the story of the genie and the fisherman in the *Arabian Nights,* in which the fisherman breaks the seal of Solomon which has imprisoned the genie and finds the genie vowed to his own destruction; there is the tale of the "Monkey's Paw," by W. W. Jacobs, in which the sergeant major brings back from India a talisman which has the power to grant each of three people three wishes. Of the first recipient of this talisman we are told only that his third wish is for death. The sergeant major, the second person whose wishes are granted, finds his experiences too terrible to relate. His friend, who receives the talisman, wishes first for £200. Shortly thereafter, an official of the factory in which his son works comes to tell him that his son has been killed in the machinery and that, without any admission of responsibility, the company is sending him as consolation the sum of £200. His next wish is that his son should come back, and the ghost knocks at the door. His third wish is that the ghost should go away.

Disastrous results are to be expected not merely in the

world of fairy tales but in the real world wherever two agencies essentially foreign to each other are coupled in the attempt to achieve a common purpose. If the communication between these two agencies as to the nature of this purpose is incomplete, it must only be expected that the results of this cooperation will be unsatisfactory. If we use, to achieve our purposes, a mechanical agency with whose operation we cannot efficiently interfere once we have started it, because the action is so fast and irrevocable that we have not the data to intervene before the action is complete, then we had better be quite sure that the purpose put into the machine is the purpose which we really desire and not merely a colorful imitation of it.

TIME SCALES

Up to this point I have been considering the quasimoral problems caused by the simultaneous action of the machine and the human being in a joint enterprise. We have seen that one of the chief causes of the danger of disastrous consequences in the use of the learning machine is that man and machine operate on two distinct time scales, so that the machine is much faster than man and the two do not gear together without serious difficulties. Problems of the same sort arise whenever two control operators on very different time scales act together, irrespective of which system is the faster and which system is the slower. This leaves us the much more directly moral question: What are the moral problems when man as an individual operates in connection with the controlled process of a much slower time scale, such as a portion of political history or—our main subject of inquiry—the development of science?

Let it be noted that the development of science is a control and communication process for the long-term understanding and control of matter. In this process fifty years are as a day in the life of the individual. For this reason, the individual scientist must work as a part of a process whose time scale is so long that he himself can only contemplate a very limited sector of it. Here, too, communication between the two parts of a double machine is difficult and limited. Even when the individual

believes that science contributes to the human ends which
he has at heart, his belief needs a continual scanning and
re-evaluation which is only partly possible. For the individual scientist, even the partial appraisal of this liaison
between the man and the process requires an imaginative
forward glance at history which is difficult, exacting and
only limitedly achievable. And if we adhere simply to the
creed of the scientist, that an incomplete knowledge of
the world and of ourselves is better than no knowledge,
we can still by no means always justify the naïve assumption that the faster we rush ahead to employ the new
powers for action which are opened up to us, the better
it will be. We must always exert the full strength of our
imagination to examine where the full use of our new
modalities may lead us.

▪ 6 ▪

Some Moral and Technical Consequences of Automation— A Refutation*

by Arthur L. Samuel

INTERNATIONAL BUSINESS MACHINES CORPORATION

In an article entitled "Some Moral and Technical Consequences of Automation," Norbert Wiener has stated some conclusions with which I disagree. Wiener seems to believe that machines *can* possess originality and that they *are* a threat to mankind. In ascribing a contrary opinion to the man in the street—to wit, "that nothing can come out of the machine which has not been put into it"—he overlooks or ignores the fact that there is a long history of the acceptance of this more reassuring view by scientific workers in the field, from the time of Charles Babbage to the present. Apparently Wiener shares some of the lack of understanding which he ascribes to the public, at least to the

---

* Reprinted from *Science*, September 16, 1960, by permission of the Author and *Science*.

extent that he reads implications into some of the recent work which the workers themselves deny.

It is my conviction that machines cannot possess originality in the sense implied by Wiener and that they cannot transcend man's intelligence. I agree with Wiener in his thesis that "machines can and do transcend some of the limitations of their designers, and that in doing so they may be both effective and dangerous." The modern automobile travels faster than its designer can run, it is effective and the records of highway fatalities attest to the dangerous consequences. However, a perusal of Wiener's article reveals that much more than this is meant, and it is to this extension of the thesis that I wish to take exception.

Wiener's reference to the "Sorcerer's Apprentice," and to the many tales based on the assumption that the agencies of magic are literal-minded, might almost lead one to think that he attributes magic to the machine. He most certainly seems to imply an equality between man and the machine when he states "disastrous results are to be expected not merely in the world of fairy tales but in the real world wherever two agencies essentially foreign to each other are coupled in the attempt to achieve a common purpose." In relationships between man and a machine the machine is an agency, but only an agency of man, entirely subservient to man and to his will. Of course, no one will deny that "we had better be quite sure that the purpose put into the machine is the purpose which we really desire and not merely a colorful imitation of it." If we want our house to be at 70°F when we get up in the morning, we had better set the thermostat at 70° and not at 32°. But once the thermostat is set at 70° we can go to sleep without fear that the genie in the furnace controls might, for some reason of his own, decide that 32° was a better figure. In exactly the same way and to the same degree we must anticipate our own inability to interfere when we instruct a modern digital computer (which works faster than we do) and when we instruct a thermostat (which works while we sleep).

Wiener's analogy between a machine and a human slave is also quite misleading. He is right in his assertion that "complete subservience and complete intelligence do not go together" in a human slave with human emotions and needs and with a will of his own. To ascribe human attributes to a machine simply because the machine can simulate some forms of human behavior is, obviously, a fallacious form of reasoning.

A machine is not a genie, it does not work by magic, it does not possess a will, and, Wiener to the contrary, nothing comes out which has not been put in, barring, of course, an infrequent case of malfunctioning. Programming techniques which we now employ to instruct the modern digital computer so as to make it into a learning machine *do not* "remove from the mind of the designer and operator an effective understanding of many of the stages by which the machine comes to its conclusions." Since the machine does not have a mind of its own, the "conclusions" are not "its." The so-called conclusions are only the logical consequences of the input program and input data, as revealed by the mechanistic functioning of an inanimate assemblage of mechanical and electrical parts. The "intentions" which the machine seems to manifest are the intentions of the human programmer, as specified in advance, or they are subsidiary intentions derived from these, following rules specified by the programmer. We can even anticipate higher levels of abstraction, just as Wiener does, in which the program will not only modify the subsidiary intentions but will also modify the rules which are used in their derivation, or in which it will modify the ways in which it modifies the rules and so on, or even in which one machine will design and construct a second machine with enhanced capabilities. However, and this is important, the machine *will not* and *cannot* do any of these things until it has been instructed as to how to proceed. There is (and logically there must always remain) a complete hiatus between (1) any ultimate extension and elaboration in this process of carrying out man's wishes and (2) the development within the machine of a will of its own. To believe otherwise is either to believe in magic or to believe that the existence of man's will is an illusion and that man's actions are as mechanical as the machine's. Perhaps Wiener's article and my rebuttal have both been mechanistically determined, but this I refuse to believe.

An apparent exception to these conclusions might be claimed for projected machines of the so-called "neural net" type. These machines were not mentioned by Wiener, and, unfortunately, they cannot be adequately discussed in the space available here. Briefly, however, one envisions a collection of simple devices which, individually, simulate the neurons of an animal's nervous system and which are interconnected by some random process simulating the organization of the nervous system. It is maintained by many serious workers that such nets can be made to exhibit purposeful activity by instruction and training with reward-and-punishment routines similar to those used with young animals. Since the internal connections would be unknown, the precise behavior of the nets would be unpredictable and, therefore, potentially dangerous. At the present time, the largest nets that can be constructed are nearer in size to the nervous system of a flatworm than to the brain of man and so hardly constitute a threat. If practical machines of this type become a reality we will have to take a much closer look at their implications than either Wiener or I have been able to do.

One final matter requires some clarification—a matter having to do with Wiener's concluding remarks to the effect that "we must always exert the full strength of our imagination to examine where the full use of our new modalities may lead us." This certainly makes good sense if we assume that Wiener means for us to include the full use of our intelligence as well as of our imagination. However, coming as it did at the end of an article which raised the specter of man's domination by a "learning machine," this statement casts an unwarranted shadow over the learning machine and, specifically, over the modern digital computer. I would be remiss were I to close without setting the record straight in this regard.

First a word about the capabilities of the digital computer. Although I have maintained that "nothing comes out that has not gone in," this does not mean that the output does not possess value over and beyond the value to us of the input data. The utility of the computer resides in

the speed and accuracy with which the computer provides the desired transformations of the input data from a
form which man may not be able to use directly to one
which is of direct utility. In principle, a man with a pencil
and a piece of paper could always arrive at the same result. In practice, it might take so long to perform the calculation that the answer would no longer be of value, and,
indeed, the answer might never be obtained because of
man's faculty for making mistakes. Because of the very
large disparity in speeds (of the order of 100,000 to 1),
on a computer we can complete calculations which are of
immense economic value with great precision and with a
reliability which inspires confidence, and all this in time
intervals which conform to the demands of real-life situations. The magnitude of the tasks and the speed with
which they are performed are truly breath-taking, and
they do tend to impress the casual observer as being a
form of magic, particularly when he is unacquainted with
the many, many hours of human thought which have gone
into both the design of the machine and, more particularly,
into the writing of the program which specifies the machine's detailed behavior.

Most uses of the computer can be explained in terms of
simulation. When one computes the breaking strength
of an airplane wing under conditions of turbulence, one is,
in effect, simulating the behavior of an actual airplane
wing which is subjected to unusual stresses, all this without danger to a human pilot, and, indeed, without ever
having to build the airplane in the first place. The
checker-playing program on the IBM 704, to which Wiener referred, actually simulates a human checker player,
and the machine learns by accumulating data from its
playing experience and by using some of the logical
processes which might be employed by a person under
similar circumstances. The specific logical processes used
are, of course, those which were specified in advance by
the human programmer. In these, and in many other situations, the great speed of the computer enables us to test
the outcome resulting from a variety of choices of initial
actions and so to choose the course with the highest
pay-off before the march of human events forces us to

take some inadequately considered action. This ability to look into the future, as it were, by simulation on a computer is already being widely used, and as time goes on it is sure to find application in more and more aspects of our daily lives.

Finally, as to the portents for good or evil which are contained in the use of this truly remarkable machine—most, if not all, of man's inventions are instrumentalities which may be employed by both saints and sinners. One can make a case, as one of my associates has jokingly done, for the thesis that the typewriter is an invention of the devil, since its use in the nations' war offices has made wars more horrible, and because it has enslaved the flower of our young womanhood. On the whole, however, most of us concede that the typewriter, as a laborsaving device, has been a boon, not a curse. The digital computer is something more than merely another laborsaving device, since it augments man's brain rather than his brawn, and since it allows him to look into the future. If we believe, as most scientists do, that it is to our advantage to increase the rate at which we can acquire knowledge, then we can hardly do otherwise than to assert that the modern digital computer is a modality whose value is overwhelmingly on the side of the good. I rest my case with this assertion.

∎ 7 ∎

Why Machines Will Never Think

by Edward T. D. Calhoun
BELL TELEPHONE LABORATORIES, INC.

Men once hoped that forces of nature were members of the group. They tried charms, special words and incantations, threats and gifts in their efforts to sell these forces a plan of action that would help the economy. We call these gimmicks magic, and we do not use magic any more. We use psychology, but only on each other, and only because it seems to work with some consistency.

Men once hoped that the world was governed by laws framed for the general good. They tried submitting their wills to symbols of the world's authority, hoping that the world would be just. We know that they were disappointed, and we call their submission superstitious. We no longer try to get along with the world, just with the group.

We are not hopeless, however. We may fit in yet. We have the Promise of Automation. Automation promises certain definable benefits and certain definable hardships. These, however, are not directly relevant to the age-old question of our place in the general scheme of things. We are here concerned with the indefinable promise of automation. We have not made ourselves at home with the impersonalities of existence either by our powers of projecting emotion or by our powers of regulating motivation. But we have yet to apply our full powers of descriptive explanation. Although we fail to understand ourselves as persons in an impersonal world, we may yet describe ourselves as nonpersons in a nonpersonal world.

We have made a good start: We have built machines which we have occasion to call "information-processing systems." Some of these machines have "word-organized memories"; they perform not only "arithmetic" operations, but also operations of "decision logic." They can be connected to "detectors," not to say "sensing devices," and can "send orders" which control the operations of other machines. They have "deduced theorems" and "played chess." They have gone through "processes of learning." If they do not yet "think," it is considered at least possible that they will, either when their operations are subtler or when "thinking" is more precisely defined.

The layman is familiar with words like "information," "memory" and "decision." The computer specialist is also a layman, familiar with these terms. He uses them with special meanings because his field is growing rapidly without an established terminology. He uses familiar terms which are conveniently descriptive, and he understands them by his special knowledge of the machine functions to which they refer. He does not always have the opportunity or inclination to explain to nonspecialists just what is meant and not meant by his special terms. Part of the purpose of this article is to clear up some of the misunderstandings which may come from the application to machines of words commonly understood to mean human uses of human faculties.

It should be emphasized, however, that if the indefinable promise of automation is to be fulfilled, then neither the layman nor the specialist knows at present how thought and its related activities should really be understood. We use the words, but we understand them only as in a glass darkly. Not until that day when the really subtle information-processing system is built and programmed shall we perhaps see face to face, and know even as we are known. Renouncing all magic and all superstition, we may wait for the final revelation of our unity with the environment.

In the meantime, my purpose in this article has three related parts: to distinguish the different uses of some familiar words whose sense is growing more ambiguous day by day; to show that an important difference of real meanings, and not just a quarrel over words, is at issue in the question whether machines do or will think; to propose that the difference between human thinking and automatic computing should be understood, *not* as an essential difference in *patterns of observable behavior*, but as an essential difference between the way a man and the way a machine *has the function* of performing his or its activities. In order to make my proposal definite, I shall offer an analysis of the meaning of function. This term has a use in ordinary language which is familiar, but whose exact meaning in new perspectives is hard to state. Function is a term also used in mathematics and related fields, and has been defined as a kind of abstract mapping, or correlating of elements according to some stated or assumed rule. I think it is not true that the understanding of function which is useful in mathematics simply makes precise the meaning of the word in ordinary use. My opinion is that there is a distinction between *function* and *operation;* that the distinction may be of no great use in mathematics; but that keeping the distinction is the beginning of understanding, while losing it is the beginning of endless confusion, with respect to how we compare with our charming constructions, the computers and automatic controllers.

I mean by operation a general pattern of producible relations, roughly the way something works. In the theater of in-principle abstractions where the mathematician sits, the producible may be regarded as already effected, since there is no difficulty with times and means. Therefore, there seems no vivid mathematical difference between the *agency* which gives an object the *capacity* to be produced, and the *pattern of design* which is the anticipating description of what *result* an object would be if it were produced. To name the difference between function and operation, without here explaining the difference, I shall say that a function defines how some agent or agency gives some object or order of objects the capacity to be effected, while an operation is an anticipating description of how things are supposed to be if they work out as planned.

In mathematics, the agencies are powers of invoking or selecting or stipulating abstract objects or forms by the use of special symbols according to rules established by mathematicians' convention. For example, the capacity for there to be given the sum of a number with itself or another number is established by means of the symbol, "+," and the rules for its use. However, for mathematical purposes, addition is judged by its results, not by the power of establishing "+" or some alternative symbolism. Understand addition any way one likes; if $2 + 2 = 4$, and so on, is all one can assert, all understandings come down to the same results. Only when one is allowed, for example, to say also that $2x + 2x = 4x$ has the conventional meaning of addition been extended.

The question of how to compare men with machines in regard to such faculties as seeing and thinking is a question which concerns not only patterns of result but also capacities and how those capacities are established. Once a computer of a given type is built, programmed and running as it should, there are some series of actions of associating or substituting signs which can take place and others which cannot. The capacity for these series of sign manipulations is given by the agency of a set of physical components put together according to a general type of machine design, and the reason for there being a machine is to be found in its designer's reason for wishing certain general types of sign manipulation to take place. That the machine in its electronic being cares anything for the fact that it prints out letters and numbers which men can read is certainly doubtful. That it has any idea that it is working for men is just as doubtful. Yet what we mean by the machine is the thing which is designed in relation to men's interpretations. What the elements and pulses that happen to be parts of a particular machine may be in relation to their own interpretations, we have no idea.

Once a being who is human is alive and thinking, there
are some actions of associating and replacing words and
images which he will do and others which he will not do.
The capacity for thinking in words and images is given
by the agency of ourselves, whatever we are, since the
thoughts of a man which he did not himself think would
not be thought at all. The reason that a man thinks is that
thinking is part of the way he lives. The fact that it would
be useful for something or other to be computed would
not be reason enough for a man to think something out, if
the thinking were not part of his own life. He might just
as well sleep.

A machine and a man may go through similar operations
in working out a certain computed result. But the functions
of the machine and of the man are of different orders. The
machine gives no more significance to its results than was
in the general design which it exemplifies. A man gives
his activities the significance of their place as part of his
own life. It is an illusion to think that, if a function is described in terms of a mechanical construction, it is more
concrete or physically real than if it is identified with what
we know in ourselves. What we recognize in a machine is
an abstract design of its structure. What we recognize in
our own awareness of ourselves is the character of immediate physical reality at the only point at which it could be
given for any physical entity, namely, where the entity
itself is physically real.

(To anticipate possible confusion, I should note that my
title, "Why Machines Will Never Think," does not refer
to the conceivable relation of some particular set of connected and pulsed or pulsing electronic components to a
"life" of their own which might be called thinking. I would
not call the components in such a relation a machine; I
would not know what to call them. What we call the machine constructed out of these components would seem to
be almost entirely irrelevant to what its components'
"mind" might be. I identify another person's appearance
to me with the life of his which is like, but not the same
as, my life, because of the morality of personal recognition
in which he and I both find ourselves. If anyone finds us
bound in such a moral universe with a machine—or with

a stone or anything else—let him prophesy the fact. I am not such a prophet nor counterprophet. I do not know what it is like to be a pulsed transistor. I do not even know what it is like to be a pulsed brain cell, and I am told that my head is full of them.

My title refers to the relation of machines to activities which are designed to follow patterns that resemble and serve the same purposes as patterns of activity which men go through when they think. My argument will be that thinking is not a pattern of activity; that apart from similar patterns of activity, men and machines are quite different; and that one of the essential differences implies that men can think and machines cannot.)

THE NEW TERMS

Information, as it is ordinarily understood, is added knowledge. Not all knowledge can be added. For example, the knowledge of how to apply a principle is part of the understanding of the principle, not an addition to this understanding. Again, the recognition of an object is the beginning of knowledge of the object, not an addition. However, the knowledge that someone has a certain name and a certain citizenship is information which adds to knowledge of the person.

Information is also a technical term used in a field called Information Theory. In this field, information is treated as a measurable quantity. It would be difficult to say how to measure an addition to knowledge, and Information Theory does not try to say. Information, as it is conceived for technical purposes, is a quantitative relation of what might be called the *distinctiveness* of the particular occurrence of some sign.

How can distinctiveness have a quantitative relation? To answer by another question, Why do collectors value items in proportion to their rarity? (Why do women care if they are seen with other women wearing clothes of the same model and color?) Information as a quantitative relation is, roughly, the rarity value of the occurrence of a sign. Rarity value is determined by several factors. First, the nature of the collection must be defined: What general kind of item is being collected, and how finely will different types of this kind of item be discriminated from each other? If one is collecting stamps, shall one collect Christmas seals or only postage stamps? Shall two stamps of the same design be considered different because one is rather more red and the other rather more orange?

To determine rarity value once the types of item have been marked off, it is necessary to gauge the probability that an item of one type will appear rather than an item of another type. Sometimes it is known how many items of each type there are, and each separate item (not type of item) can be considered equally likely to turn up. In this situation, the calculation of probabilities for the appearance of some item or other of a given type is fairly simple. More often, perhaps, it is necessary to "go by experience." In a sequence of discoveries in the past, so many items of each of a number of types have turned up. The sequence of discoveries may be rather short or comparatively long; it may be known that it was affected by certain special circumstances (such as collecting stamps out of the wastebaskets of one country). The projection of probabilities on the basis of sample sequences can be fairly complicated, but there are statistical methods for reliably approximating such probabilities.

Finally, the rarity value of a particular item can be determined only so far as the type of that item can be identified. Stamp collectors may decide not to collect stamps so mutilated that their issue cannot be clearly identified. Not all collectors can be so selective. Information theory was originally developed to evaluate various means of signaling. A system of signals can be viewed as defining the various distinctive types of sign in a significant collection. Each sign must have enough distinctiveness, or rarity value, to serve the purposes of its use. For example, if it is desired to signify any one of ten different words by means of sequences of two signs, how many types of sign must there be? If there are two types, there will be only four distinct sequences of two signs; if there are three types, eight sequences; if there are four types, sixteen sequences. For the given purpose, then, there must be at least four distinct types of sign. But suppose that, as often happens, the transmission of signals is not entirely reliable:

a signal sent may be clearly of one type; received, it may be of rather confused or even misleading appearance. The information in, or relative quantity of distinctiveness of, the appearance of a confused signal or of a signal which may have been entirely altered, is less than the information in a reliable signal. Methods exist for calculating the statistical probability that an item with a given appearance at the end of a process belonged, at the beginning of the process, to one defined type rather than another.

In ordinary language, then, information is a form of knowledge which can be collected. In technical language, information is a quantity of the distinctiveness of a sign relative to a system for collecting and distinguishing signs. Is there really any essential difference between knowledge and quantitative relation?

In ordinary language, communication is the sharing by one person of the knowledge of what he feels, wants or thinks, with another person by the use of expressive signs. In technical language, communication is the transportation and attendant transformation of information (technical sense) which occurs when a sign is given at one place and reproduced or translated, perhaps after deformation due to vagaries of transmission, at another place. The layman may have heard that much specialized intelligence is being devoted to problems of communication. He may have thought that he was about to be told how to overcome his shyness in a scientific way. This is not the case, he may or may not be disappointed to hear—unless the problem of how to share understanding amounts, really, to no more than the question of how to construct a reliable and efficient signaling system.

Once attention has turned from relations of ideas to relations of physical signs, various other terms related to information and communication can be used with special senses. A language can be viewed as a set of sign types with rules to specify which combinations or sequences of signs are proper in the language. Correlations can be established between various combinations of signs permitted within a language, and these correlations can be called definitions or statements or inferences, depending on what is wished. Correlations can also be established between languages, and called translations or interpretations. Languages which can be translated into each other, and whose corresponding expressions (sequences of signs) carry the same amount of information (relative quantity of distinctiveness), can be called equivalent codes.

There is considerable interest, among computer specialists, in the problem of "communication between machines and between men and machines." This problem is somewhat less dramatic than the layman imagines, if he thinks of a day of reckoning when the very stones shall cry out. The problem is a problem of constructing codes and means of correlating signs which will provide efficient translations between systems of "collecting information" (technical sense outlined above) used by human technicians and by computers, card punchers and so on, of various makes and models. Translation, here, does *not* mean discovering an idea by means of the correlation of a word from an unfamiliar language with a word from a familiar one. Translation signifies only the selection of that sign, from a second code, which corresponds to a sign selected from a given code.

The code used in the computations of the digital computers—the ones thought to be more like the brain than any other machines are—is the binary code. The binary code collects only two elementary types of sign, though it admits, of course, a great variety of sequences of signs. (The decimal code, used for writing numerals and in telephone dialing, collects ten distinct types of elementary signs, the familiar zero to nine.) A binary digit, or "bit" is of one of two types, and is represented within a computer by a device in one of two distinct states, usually capable of affecting an electrical pulse in one of two distinct ways. To set the device in one of its states is to "write" a bit. To receive the effect of the device on a pulse is to "read" a bit.

A well-known two-state device is the simple switch for turning a light on or off. The switch has two significant positions, open and closed. A lamp with a three-way bulb for three degrees of brightness is operated by a switch with four positions (including "off"). Its switch is a four-state device. Designers of computers have many ways of limiting a device for data storage to two states which are sig-

nificant in their effect on an electrical pulse. Typical
pairs of states are the transparency or opaqueness of a spot
between a beam of light and a photocell, the presence or
absence of a permanent magnet, one polarity or the other
of a magnet, the presence or absence of a charge affecting
conductivity. The reason for using two elementary signs
rather than ten, as in the decimal system, or twenty-six, as
in English spelling, is that the use of two signs retains distinctiveness, and the use of only two signs reduces the
chances for confusion in transmission to a minimum.

The memory of a computer is sometimes also called
internal data storage. The latter terminology may be less
confusing. Whatever its name, data storage is a set of two-
state devices with a particular function (to be described)
in the operations of the computer. Each of the devices
of memory, or data storage, has an address. This address is
a number coded as a sequence of bits which will direct
various operations of the computer to the particular device
which has the address. Common operations directed to a
device in data storage would be setting it in one of
its states ("writing in memory") or sending an electrical
pulse for it to affect, thereby setting another device somewhere to a corresponding state ("reading out of memory").

There are other two-state devices in the computer besides the ones on which data (signs) can be stored. Some
of these devices also have addresses. What distinguishes a
device as belonging to storage is really only its function in
the computer's operation. Generally speaking, a device belonging to storage has its state altered *relatively* in-
frequently, and it is supposed never to be altered except
as a consequence of orders whose codes are attached, directly or indirectly, to the code for its address.

An order is like data, in that it is set up in the code of a
combination of states of a group of two-state devices. An
order, however, appears on devices through which the
basic operating pulse of the computer passes, and by
which this pulse is switched into the pathways which open
to it certain effects and close to it other effects. These
effects, depending upon how they result from the structure
of pathways composing the computer's "logic circuits,"

may represent the results of addition, storing, matching and the like, or even of decision.

A decision, for a computer, is an operation according to which if a set of devices is read in one state, one order will be set up for switching the next "order pulse"; if the set of devices is read in another state, another order will be set up. A computer decides what shall happen next on somewhat the same principle that a screen decides whether an insect is small enough to get through. The computer, of course, has a more flexible range of decision. In fact, a computer can be programmed (arranged to operate) in such a way that after making a decision on one pattern, it will later reach an order which results in changing the original decision order so that it will make a different pattern of decision. The changed order may then be set up once more and a different decision be made.

The way in which a computer can be programmed for an operation which resembles learning illustrates the use of a computer's facility for changing what are called its decisions. It should be explained that a program is a sequence of orders and associated addresses coded in bits and stored. These program orders are really not orders in the sense that they control the operations of the computer. While they are stored, they are nothing but data. However, the computer is built to operate in such a way that when a program is running, these orders are read out of storage, one by one, to be set up on devices which do switch the basic pulse which powers the computer's activity.

Now, assume a pleasure bit, P, which is set to the value 1. Assume a problem bit, Q, which may have the values 0 or 1. Assume that the problem bit is closed to writing operations, but that it can be compared with the pleasure bit by means of a match circuit. Assume further that as the computer runs through various sequences of orders, its operations set and reset the problem bit, Q, to 1 or 0 in a way which is not directly controlled by program orders. Suppose that at some point in the program there is a decision order, D. At the time when D is running, some bit, B, is read out. If B has the value 0, the next orders shall be E and the sequence of orders following E. If B has the value 1, the next orders shall be F and the sequence of orders following F. Suppose that the value of B is 0 when the decision order, D, is run for the first time. The next orders will be E and following. In the sequence of orders following E, we may suppose an order which compares Q, the problem bit, with P, the pleasure bit. If P and Q match, the value of Q is 1, and the program shall proceed. If P and Q do not match, Q is 0 and the next order shall begin a routine for rewriting decision order, D. The next time D is read out (after the program reaches an order which loops back, directing the sequence of executing orders back to the early part of the program), it will determine that if B is 0, the next order shall be F and not E.

The above case is very roughly sketched, but it illustrates the way in which a computer can be programmed to change its decisions in the light of results. It is possible that the above computer could "learn" to run only those sequences of operation which have maintained Q in the optimum state, that is, most frequently matching P. It is arbitrary, of course, to call P a pleasure bit, and Q a problem bit; they are only two-state devices, like many others in the computer. However, in relation to the program of operations sketched above, P and Q have rather romantic *functions*.

Incidentally, if any reader recalls the phrase "word-organized memory" and is still wondering whether it refers to verbal aptitude or a tendency to speak before thinking, I may add the note that with a word-organized memory a computer writes data into, or reads data out of, storage not one bit at a time but in blocks of several bits, called words. Are words, after all, anything more than blocks of letters with certain specialized functions in the human interaction system?

THE NEW QUESTIONS

A speck flies toward one's eye; one's eye closes, usually in time to keep the speck out. Did one see the speck? One would say no, one did not; there was no time to see it. At least, one would have said this before one was being replaced by machines—or before one's language was being replaced by the language of machinery. I shall continue to say that I did not see the speck. I decline even to compromise on the monstrosity of agreeing that my eye saw the speck. I concede that I am not an authority on the mechanism of my eye's reflexes. Nevertheless, as an author of statements in the common language, I claim common authority in the understanding of sight and the use of words which signify sight.

My claim is defiantly made, but to what does it amount? I have walked up to doors which opened at my approach, as though I had been seen. Question: I would not say, would I, that the door's control mechanism, with its photoelectric cell, had seen me? Answer: I would not. I have slapped at flies which escaped as though they had seen my hand coming. Question: Would I say that the flies had seen my hand moving? Answer, less assured: I would, yes. I have read of automatic fire control mechanisms which are designed to track a target coming from any quarter and following any of a number of forms of path. These mechanisms show a much wider range of response to a visible object than do automatic door-openers. Question: Do fire control mechanisms bear enough analogy to a fly's behavior to permit saying that they see a target, or is radar too different from an eye to make the word "see" appropriate?

Answer, at some length: A fire control mechanism does not see a target, for the plain reason that it is a mechanism. Mechanisms either work according to the mode of operation which defines them, or else they become nonmechanisms of a greater or less degree of disorganization; that is, there is an object which either (1) works as a mechanism, (2) is a collection of salvageable parts or (3) is a pile of junk. Seeing is a form of *enjoyment;* enjoyment is a form of possession. (I am using the word "enjoyment" with a wider connotation than that of having a pleasant time.) A mode of operation is a form of attribute; an attribute is a form of something's being possessed. Possessing is the relation of something which *gives* identity to what it has. Being possessed is the relation of something which *gets* identity from what has it. Unless we are not concerned with sources of identity, we should not equate forms of possessing with forms of being possessed.

We do not immediately understand how to define enjoyment. We have said that it is a form of possession. (We do not intend even to try to say what possession is, beyond having suggested that it is the relation of something giving identity.) I believe that enjoyment should be understood as two degrees of possession, that is, as the possession of an act of possession. I enjoy the use of my hands. The use of my hands is my hands having certain intended patterns in the way they act. Inasmuch as they are my hands and my intentions, and *my* hands' intended patterns because the use is *my* use, I enjoy the use of my hands.

In the case of a tool I would not say that I could enjoy its use, in the same sense that I enjoy the use of my hands. I might enjoy working with a tool, or working with it might be just work. If I did enjoy working with a tool, the working would be an activity in which my particular way of using the tool would have a feeling in which I found myself at home. I would identify as mine the fact that my handling of the tool had the feeling of being right. I could not identify as mine, however, the fact of the tool's having a general use. A tool has a use in virtue of the design which fits it for producing certain effects, called desirable, under conditions for which the tool is designed. The tool's design is part of the definition of the tool itself; it is not a faculty on the part of the tool (or of anything or anyone else, so far as I know) of possessing its possession of a use. Therefore, the use of a tool *is not* enjoyed. The use of one's hands *is* enjoyed—by oneself and by no one else.

A gun with a fire control mechanism is a tool for shooting targets. Those who set the gun in operation for such a purpose, and who hit targets of the variety they wish, may be said to enjoy success in using the gun. Those who are responsible for the operation of the gun and for specifying certain effects as those which they wish, may be said to give their identities in a cooperating group to the fact that the gun's operation has the wished-for effect. Success, however, is not use or operation. Say, then, that no one enjoys either the use or the operation of the gun and its facility of target tracking. The idea that there might exist some corporate entity, like an army or a nation, enjoying the use of guns as men enjoy the use of hands, is an idea which I find obscene.

Institutions are social abstractions which properly act only as instruments to serve the purposes elected by communities of true individuals. Like all instruments, institutions neither enjoy any possession nor suffer any loss. They only work well or faultily in good or bad uses.

Any analogy between the behavior of a target tracking mechanism and the eye, however close the analogy, is irrelevant to the question of whether the mechanism sees. I am willing to waive the question of the difference between the media of light and of radio waves (especially since I chose the examples). The fundamental question is whether the mechanism enjoys the exercise of a capacity for detection by means of electromagnetic phenomena or does not. I answer this question negatively, and dismiss from relevance the whole intriguing study of the comparative anatomy of living and nonliving mechanisms.

My authority for saying that a fly sees and a tracking mechanism does not see derives neither from any competence of mine in a special science nor from inner communication either with the hearts of flies or with the hearts of gun sights. My authority derives from my responsibility for my own public use of the common language. I understand this responsibility to mean that my choice of words must be defended on better grounds than that "it is all just a matter of semantics anyway."

I would say that I see what I perceive (sense with some degree of consciousness), but not the speck which is blinked at before it is perceived. I am also inclined to say that a fly sees a threatening hand. I must admit, however, that I do not know whether a fly has any faculty of perception distinct from reflex response; nor do I know whether, if there is a distinction for the fly, the apprehension which signals danger for the fly should be classed as perception or as reflex.

My problem is this: I assert that the verb to see, as a word in common use, cannot properly be used by any author to denote the relation of any mechanism to any phenomenon. I admit, however, that I am uncertain (1) whether seeing should be understood to involve some degree of awareness (whatever awareness may be), (2) whether a fly has any degree of awareness, and (3) whether a fly's escaping a hand involves any more seeing than my own blinking reflex. On what grounds is a sharp line drawn in one case and not in others?

Answer: The question whether seeing involves awareness is a question of the sense of words. If, in relation to seeing, there is no useful distinction between awareness and nonawareness, then the question merely splits hairs. If there is a useful distinction, but no clear uniformity of common usage, then it may be desirable, for the sake of precision, to distinguish two senses of "see": a narrow sense requiring awareness and a broader sense not requiring awareness. An author may then choose one sense or the other in a particular context, making his choice explicit where there might be ambiguity. In this case, the question is, indeed, a question of semantics.

Having chosen to use "see" in a narrow sense, excluding the seeing of a speck in a time too short for awareness, I am uncertain whether to say that a fly sees an impending slap. First, I do not know whether, or in what sense, it would be appropriate to say that a fly is aware of anything. I think that awareness might well be understood as a kind of proportion of the concentration of a being's activity in one of its faculties, where the being is one capable of enjoying the exercise of various faculties. If this were a fair way of understanding awareness, then the hypothesis that a fly had some degree of awareness would at least have a meaning. The question here is, once more, a question of the sense of a word, the word "awareness." In this case, I have not distinguished two possible senses of the word, but have proposed a fuller definition (not necessarily a final one) of the word than would commonly be given.

Finally, there are the two questions, whether a fly actually has the power of awareness proposed for it, and whether this power is exercised in the fly's reaction to a hand. These are questions of how to judge what goes on for the fly, granting that the senses of "see" and "awareness" have been usably established. They are questions of what may or may not be so, either in the world of fact or perhaps only in a world of fantasy where insects are imagined to have some life of their own.

The word "see" may have several senses, may be open to more precise definition in any one of its senses and may have an uncertain application in a particular case. However, I deny that it might be proper to say that a mechanism sees. The reasons for this denial are as follows: The word "see," as a word of common language, whatever variety of sense it may have, always connotes enjoyment, that is, seeing is a possessing which is possessed. I have proposed this partial definition of seeing. My *definition* is not common, but I believe that it does express a necessary part of the common *meaning* of the word see. I could be wrong, of course, but that possibility is part of the fact that I am a fallible individual; the possibility that my proposal is wrong is *not* included as an alternative *within* my position. If I am correct, then, and if it is added that, by definition, mechanisms do not enjoy any possession, then it follows that there is no sense of see in common use which can be used to say that a mechanism sees. One who wished to say that some mechanism sees must introduce a new general class of meaning for the word see. This new class of meaning will hold only in a special language unless and until it is taken up into common usage. Even if it were taken up into common usage, it would still be a second generic sense of the word see. The use of similar signs, spelled s-e-e, would no more mean that mechanisms see as people do than the use of similar letters means that a *key* to a door is the same kind of thing as the *key* of C major.

The purpose of this article is not, actually, to arbitrate questions of terminology. A new use of words is sometimes an important sign of how something new is being understood, or partly understood. There is also such a thing as a new misuse of words, which may be a sign of how something new is being misunderstood. Machines which take the place of human beings in the performance of certain functions are not new. Engines for applying power through cranks, pulleys, clutches, gears and the like are well-known replacements for, and improvements upon, human heavy labor. Calculating machines replace the human effort of writing down columns of figures and operation signs in conformity with the rules of arithmetic. Electrified wires save the trouble of going to a distant place in order to produce an effect there. Thermostatic controls save the trouble of watching temperature gauges and operating the switches or valves appropriate for readjusting the temperature to a standard. All these mechanisms have become fairly familiar.

When a man does heavy labor, we say that he is working hard, whether he gets expected results or finds the work too heavy. We say of an engine either that it is running within its capacity or that it is overloaded. Whether the man's effort is productive or not, the man is working. An engine works (operates according to its design) in one situation and does not work in another, no matter how much fuel it is burning. We use the term "work" in two distinct senses. The man is the measure of whether he works or not, whatever his situation. The engine's design and the results of its operation in a given situation are the measures of whether it works or not, in the given situation. Because men who work closely with engines have a right to personify them, out of intimacy rather than superstition, an engine operator can say that his engine is working hard under a heavy load. Workers do not, however, go on strike for overloaded machines. The reason they go on strike for themselves is that they need to be paid for working, whether the economic system is working or not. Few workers since John Henry have confused themselves with machines.

When a man calculates a sum, he is doing arithmetic. Arithmetic is defined by certain rules. The man either obeys the rules or breaks them. When a sum is being calculated by adding machine, there are many little wheels going around. These little wheels neither obey nor break the rules of arithmetic. Their spinning confirms the laws of mechanics; their spinning also composes the operation of the adding machine. The machine is built according to a design; the design is a set of rules for building a machine to operate in such a way that a column of figures represented on the machine will be followed by a representa-

tion on the machine of the column's sum. The design of
the machine may be developed in symbolic agreement
with the rules of arithmetic, but the design does not *do*
anything. The machine does something, but it does not
do arithmetic. It spins its wheels in accordance with its
design, or it breaks. When it breaks, it just breaks; it does
not break the rules of arithmetic. In order to break a rule
of arithmetic, it is necessary to assert that, for example,
two and two equals five. The adding machine does not
assert a sum; a user of the machine could make an assertion based on the machine's operation, but it would not be
the machine's assertion.

A man carries his knowledge and intentions with him; a
wire carries electric current, which has one of the patterns
possible for electric current. The man may communicate
his knowledge or intentions by using established signs.
A wire does not communicate current, and the pattern of
the current is not knowledge, nor intention, nor even a sign
which can be directly recognized. A man can act as a mes-
senger, who ought to confirm at the end of his journey
whether he remembers or has forgotten the message he
came to deliver. An electric current is a means of communication, which no one expects to confirm anything except laws of electricity.

A man tries to maintain an even temperature in his
house by regulating the furnace. Once he installs a thermostat, there is no more trying. A thermostat's operation in relating furnace operation to temperature is as
empty of will as an arrow's flight steadied by the arrow's
feathers.

Engines and signals, calculators and controls—these
things are not new. The ways we speak of what they do
and the ways we speak of what we do are distinct. Why
then should anyone be saying that computers will be making decisions which men make now? The computer is as
decided as the day before yesterday, and just as lacking in
a power of decision. Why should anyone seriously ask the
question, Do computers think? When I find my way home
for the hundredth time, I do it automatically. If anyone
asked me what I meant by finding my way home *auto-*

matically, I should answer that I did it *without thinking,* because it was such a habit.

It seems to me that, unless we change the meaning of words, either a computer is not automatic or it operates without thinking. Yet my simple reflection seems to miss the point. The point seems to be that: (1) we do not think (old, unscientific use of the word), because our brains are so like computers; but (2) it is all right, because "automatic" can denote much more complicated operations than it used to. I can reply only that I seem long to have been grateful for the habits by which I get through the complicated business of surviving each day. I have been grateful for these habits because, if I had relied on my simple mind, I should never have survived. However, if a theorist of automatic machinery tells me that by "automatic" I have meant "acting in a simple pattern," then perhaps this is what I have meant, unconsciously. But how am I going to mean by "thinking" an activity which takes place without thinking? I think I shall not.

As a matter of fact, the new thing upsetting the language is not the computer as an instrument of automatic control; the new thing is the image of the brain as a computer controlling human activity, a computer receiving its design at the hands of the genes and its redesigns from automatic reactions to itself and its environment. Now, the author would no more say that his brain thinks than that his eye sees. But the author would not ask, unless he worked in a morgue, "Who is this body?" Others would. The question of what personal identity is has never been settled. It is an old question, but automation by electronic computer is going to give it some vivid new forms. If the new forms of the question are to be clear as well as vivid, we shall need to have some clear idea of what we mean by function.

WHAT IS A FUNCTION?

The word "function" has uses established both in common and in technical language. The main purpose of this article is to explain function as a bridge between common and technical understanding, and to show how there is a fundamental difference between enjoying a function (as a man should do) and being designed for a function (as a machine should be).

The use of words in ordinary speech is usually learned by becoming familiar with the range of contexts in which each word is appropriate. This is a process of growing acquaintance with the word. The use of words in technical speech is usually learned as a set of rules for combining the word with other technical symbols. This learning is a process of increasing skill in handling symbols according to rules of association. The difference between acquaintance and skill is a source of frequent misunderstanding and even suspicion between those who use words in an ordinary way and those who use words in a technical way. The ordinary use seems uselessly imprecise for technical understanding; the technical use seems uselessly empty for ordinary understanding.

Neither ordinary nor technical speech attempts an explanation of the concept which is intended in its use of a word, unless understanding breaks down to such an extent that the use of the word becomes really uncertain. I shall attempt an explanation of the concept of function, but it should be understood that the explanation is my own proposal; it is standard neither for an ordinary nor for a technical use of the word "function." There are standard uses for the word, but I know of no standard explanation of the concept of what a function is. While discussing function, I shall use words like object, relation and represent. What is meant by these words is probably as much in need of explanation as the concept of function. However, I cannot try to explain anything but function without being drawn further and further afield.

I shall first define the understanding of function which I propose, and then discuss some of the terms of the definition. A function is that which *connects* objects and representations of objects so that there is an *analogy* for the way the objects are related in the way the representations of these objects are related.

Analogy is an order in which different cases of things-in-relation are identified as examples of the same form of relation. There are different varieties of analogy, because there are different ways of choosing the form of a relation. In order to distinguish the kind of analogy in which functions serve, it is necessary to analyze what is involved in objects' being related.

When two objects are related to each other, there are three factors entering into their relation. First, there is a comparison of attributes. In a specific relation such as seeing, there is a comparison of being one who sees with being something seen. Even in the most abstract kind of relation, mere pairing, the attribute of being one term of a pair is compared with the attribute of being the other term. Second, there is a connection of conditions under which each of the objects in relation has its comparative attribute. No one can be one who sees without there being something which is seen; nothing can be something seen without there being one who sees. Third, there is an association of the objects in relation as being the specific ones which are given with each other. There might be a comparison of being one who sees with being something seen; for one who sees there might be something seen, and for something seen there might be one who sees; but unless the one who sees were associated with the something seen, as the one who sees what is seen, there would be no direct relation of seeing.

The story of the emperor's illusory new clothes provides an illustration of the necessity of association for complete relation. The exhibited emperor is supposed to be something seen by ones who see him only in fine clothes; the adult viewing populace see a man who seems naked, and they dissociate themselves from the evidence of their eyes. The emperor's nakedness is something seen, but not by his consciously bemused subjects; the subjects see something, but not the nakedness before their eyes. The relation of seeing the emperor naked is valid only for the child, who does not know that what he is supposed to see could be different from what he does see.

The absence of a factor of connection from what would otherwise be a relation gives the force to the old child's riddle, "What is the difference between an elephant and a bunch of grapes?" If and when this riddle is given up, the answer comes, "You would be a fine one to send to the store for grapes; you might come home with an elephant." One is fooled by being asked for *the* difference, and tries to think of an established connection in which an elephant has a special characteristic in comparison with grapes. If one were asked for *a* difference, one would select a connection at random and answer, for example, that an elephant is large and single while a bunch of grapes is small and composite. However, being fooled into looking for established connections, one thinks of elephants as large in comparison to mice and single in comparison to herds; one thinks of a bunch of grapes as small in comparison to a watermelon and composite in comparison to a single grape. At a loss for "the" connection, one fails to name a relation of difference.

The absence of comparable attributes for two objects can also prevent a relation. The problem of stating the numerical relation between the length of the side of a square and the length of its diagonal was not settled until it was agreed to call the square root of two a number. There was no problem either of association or of connection. It was clear that one length of side and one length of diagonal go together for each size of square, and that the longer the side, the longer the diagonal. It was not clear what numerical attribute could be found for the length of the diagonal to compare with the length of a side, no matter what measure was assigned for the length of a side as a whole or fractional number. The numerical relation could be stated only when the attribute of having "that number which when multiplied by itself gives the number two" was admitted as a numerical attribute comparable with having the number which represents unity.

There can be different kinds of forms of relation depending upon whether various cases of a relation are identified as having the same form of comparison, the same form of connection or the same form of association. One familiar analogy is the proportion according to which the ratio of one pair of quantities is equivalent to the ratio of another pair—for example, 2:4 : :3:6 (which is read, "two is to four as three is to six"). In this analogy, the ratios are two cases of relation with one form of connection. The connection is that a quantity taken as a unit can be compared as a half only to a quantity which is a double. The two ratios are different cases because they are different associations: two as a half of *four* as its double, but not of six, which is a double of three but not of two.

The factor of comparable attributes has not yet been distinguished in the analogy of proportion. Is there one identical comparison for the two ratios, or are there two distinct comparisons? In one way, it could seem that there are two distinct comparisons. Two taken as one quantity in respect to its double is one half the quantity which is two measures greater. Three is one half the quantity which is three measures greater. In another way, it could seem that there is one comparison—the comparison of a quantity with the attribute of being a unitary half to a quantity with the attribute of being a double.

The problem of how to describe the comparison (or comparisons) which is (are) a factor (factors) in analogous ratios is a special case of a general problem. An analogy is an order in which different cases of a relation are brought under a single form of the relation. How can there be one form and two cases unless the cases are really just two ways of naming the same thing; or unless the form is not really the form of either but only a name for what is similar in each case, suppressing actual differences? I cannot here justify an answer to this problem, but I can indicate one.

An order involves not only an identity of form and a difference of cases, but also an adjustment of application of form to case. The application of the form is common in that it is the same form which applies; yet the application is not single. Each case comes under the form in the terms of its own distinctness from other cases. The form is applied to each case as a separate case, rather than to all cases as one common case. The notion of *shade of color* is an example of an adjustment of application. All varieties of color have a shade, but each has color in its own shade. There is no such thing as plain color; a case of color has the form of being colored in its own way, namely some shade. Shade is both general, in that to be a color is to have a shade, and varied in different colors. One name for an adjustment of application of form to case is "schema." That

is the name I shall use for the factor of order which I
have tried to indicate.

We may go back to the analogy of ratios and the factor
of comparison in the relation of halves to their doubles.
The comparison can be described as the comparison of
the attribute of being half of the addition of an amount to
an equal amount, with the attribute of being greater than
an amount by an amount equal to that amount. When the
comparison of half to double is described in this way, it is
both general for various cases of quantity and yet adjusted
for the particular quantities in each case. The comparison
of half to double, then, serves as the schema by which the
same connection, as the form of relation, is applied to various ratios, as cases of the relation in different associations
of quantities.

We may go all the way back now to the main topic,
What is a function? The terms to remember for the explanation of function are the following: A relation involves
three distinguishable factors—comparative attributes, a
connection of having one of the attributes to there being
something with the other attribute, and an association giving the particular objects related. An analogy is an order
in which cases of a relation are brought under a form of
relation by means of the application of the form through a
schema of the relation.

A function serves as the schema in an analogy between
related objects and related representations of the objects.
The function of an ax, for example, brings under the same
form of relation the plan for a cut to follow a swing and
the sequence of an actual swing resulting in an actual cut.
The plan combines representations of events which are
supposed to take place objectively. The plan and the
events which it anticipates have the same form of relation
in respect to the attributes compared: initiating swing
and resulting cut. It is characteristic of representations to
assume the attributes of what they represent. However, it
is also characteristic of representations that they have associations very different from the associations of what they
represent. In fact, means of representation, like images, are
useful because they can be associated and dissociated in

changing patterns much more easily than objects which they represent.

The association of the image of an initiating swing with the image of an appearing cut does not immediately come under the relation of a plan to cut something by swinging at it. Many things could be imagined in connection with swinging. What gives swing and cut a connection as binding in imagination as in practice is the structure of an ax as a tool with a handle for driving a head with a hard, sharp edge. The structure of the ax as connecting swing and cut is schematic in the analogy of plan to act of cutting. There is a common design of structure, yet a variation of its realization in the materials of imagination and the materials of wood and steel.

The schematic structure of an ax which serves to complete the analogy of plan and act in the intention to chop something is the function of the ax as a tool. The ax itself is not a function, and the ax has other possibilities besides its function. Its handle can break; its edge can be dulled against a stone; the ax can be lost in the woods and rot and rust to dust. The ax has a specific function just insofar as there is an analogy of representational relation to objective relation in which some characteristic of the ax serves as the schematic connection.

One possible misunderstanding of what a function is arises from the fact that analogies are often interlocked. Each time an ax with a good handle and sharp edge is properly swung at a piece of wood, a cut results, or has resulted in most cases. There is an analogy which holds among different cases of the proper use of an ax. This is an analogy among relations of objective events. There is also an analogy between the cases of anticipation for each time it is planned to make a cut with the ax. This is an analogy among relations of representations. The analogy for uses of the ax may be called its actual operation, and the analogy for anticipated uses of the ax may be called its theoretic operation.

Function is easily confused with operation, being interpreted either as the way something does work or the rule according to which it is expected to work. Operation is a way of ordering objects in a sphere of objects or of ordering representations in a sphere of representation; function is a way of ordering representations with objects in a sphere of intentions or meanings. The reason for the confusion of function with operation is that a function may be the schema for bringing not only one set of cases under one form of relation but also for bringing another set of cases under another form of relation.

Just as one form can apply to several cases, so one case can come under several forms. The relation of two people, for example, can be a case of elder and younger and also a case of taller and shorter. That these are different forms of relation is particularly clear if it happens that the elder person is the shorter one. In a similar way, that which brings one set of cases under one form may bring a different set of cases under a different form. For example, the backbone as a distinguishing mark brings vertebrates under one classification and invertebrates under another.

The function of an ax can serve as the connection in each of a whole set of analogies between plan and execution of an ax cut. The analogies will differ from each other by differences of force and angle in the forms of different swings and cuts. The function may extend to every planned use of the ax; the actual operation of the ax may bring all cases of use of the ax together; the theoretic operation of the ax may bring together all cases of anticipated use of the ax. Thus, function and operation may cover the same cases of relation. However, the operations serve in analogies of just two forms among all cases respectively of objective events and represented events. The function serves in analogies of many forms. Operation is relatively regular, since it serves in analogies with one form. Function may be somewhat regular, if the various forms of analogy in which it serves are similar; but function also may be irregular to the point of being arbitrary. That function need not be regular can be illustrated from mathematics. The point is important, because the definition of what "automatic" means involves the idea of function, but not necessarily the idea of a regular pattern of behavior (operation). Much argument about whether men are like machines is beside the point, because spontaneity is confused with irregularity. Machines can be irregular, but not spontaneous. Men's actions can obey rules, but not automatically.

In mathematics, one thing to which a function is commonly assigned is a formula. A formula has a structure which connects a whole, taken as a unity, with one (or more) of its parts, taken independently as a separate unit or collection of units. A formula is like a room—change a piece of furniture and the whole room is changed. This kind of structure can be extended to a very wide range of applications—probably because a present moment both unites in itself something new with something retained, and also is connected to what is retained as belonging to a moment just passed. A formula captures in its structure something of the succession in time which is fundamental both for the way we follow schemes of representation and for the way we understand the objects of our experience.

One formula in arithmetic for the double of two is *two times two,* written as "2×2." An alternative formula, in algebra, for the double of two is *multiplication by two for the value two,* written as "$2(2)$." These formulas have the function of connecting the numbers, two and four, and the numerals, "2" and "4," in like schematic manner. The schema or function of the formula is a convention according to which the whole formula has a value depending upon the value of what appears as a separable part of the formula. In terms of numbers, the formula for doubling two takes on the value of the number four in connection with the number two. In terms of representations of numbers the formula assumes the value of writing a sign for four in connection with writing a sign for two.

The two-times table of arithmetic contains many formulas. If we depend upon seeing connections, these formulas have functions only for relatively small numbers. Two times some very large number undoubtedly has the value of that number's double. We could write "2×81642-9137824," but what should we be representing by writing such a formula? If we had to see where we would get by jumping as far ahead as we had counted, we could not evaluate the written formula; it would be without a function. However, we can postulate a method of computing doubles based on the division of numbers into units, tens, hundreds and so on, and the representation of this division by a system of digits written from right to left. With suitable rules for setting down partial products and for adding "carries," we can see that in principle the double of any represented number can be represented. Such a method of computation is called an algorithm.

An algorithm is one kind of theoretic operation. It can have a very wide range of application since no means need be given for carrying out similar operations in practice. No computer is likely to work out the double of every number. An algorithm is an operation connecting representations in analogous relations. According to the present argument, it should properly be distinguished from functions. Our representations of numbers are built up with the theoretic operation of counting and the algorithms of arithmetic developed from counting. Numbers as objects are abstract quantities, or magnitudes with no physical measure. Numbers relate as quantities, not as results of computation. Therefore, there is no direct analogy between the way numerical signs are related by algorithms and the way numbers are related by their comparative magnitudes.

Nevertheless, a method for computing doubles does make it possible for formulas for large numbers to have a function. The reason is that the method for computing assures that there is a specific connection between the representation of a large number and the representation of its double, consistent with counting, just as the indefinite extension of abstract quantity assures that there is a double for any number. Once a connection of representations is established (by an algorithm), a function can be defined which abstracts from the differences between connection by relative quantity and connection by theoretic computation. The function retains what is alike in the two ways of connecting, namely, the succession of a second value upon the specification of a first value.

The more abstract a connection, the more different forms of relation it can play a part in. The formula, "$2x$," can be understood to have the function of connecting in respective analogies all representations of doubling and the numerical proportions which they represent. The function of "$2x$" is schematic, it should be remembered. It does not have any definite meaning except in the terms of one particular relation or another. The function of "$2x$" connects for the value 1, 1 with 2; for the value 2, 2 with 4, and the same for the value 3 and so on. The function does not connect some general quantity, x, with some general double.

The function of the formula, "$2x$," is defined for the regular correspondence of numerical signs to their computed doubles and the regular proportions of numerical quantities. However, not every correspondence need be regular. The assignment of telephone numbers can define a mapping function for the formula, "$TN(x)$," according to which we can say that for a person, p, having a telephone, one dials $TN(p)$ if one wants to call p. The name and number listed in the telephone directory have the same scheme of connection as the person and the means of calling his telephone. Yet there is no rule of computation, except reading on the same line, which derives the digits of a telephone number from the letters of a name. If all the telephone directories disappeared, even the operation of merely looking up numbers would disappear, but the function of "$TN(x)$" would not. People with names would still have numbers. The directories could be regenerated by inviting everyone to send in a postal card with his name and number.

CONCLUSION

There are two ways in which a function can be defined. One way is to establish a set of representations for objects and then find, construct or assume something whose structure will connect representations and objects in analogous relations. A machine is designed for functions which are defined in this way. A machine is like a formula: as design, it connects symbols of events in plans for its operation; as built and running, it connects events represented, at least implicitly, in its design. Once the physical entities composing the actual machine begin connecting events which have no analogies in the plans for the machine, the machine loses its function and begins to fail. Either it will be reconstructed or it will cease to exist. The machine may be designed for functions which loop back and reconnect their values, for functions which connect in random ways, for functions which connect values of other functions; but the functions of a machine will never be of any more significance than is allowed by the system of representation which the machine is designed to serve.

The other way to define a function is to allow a function to something with a power of adjusting connections of representations to connections of objects. A good playwright does not design a performance; he writes lines for an actor to speak in such a way that speeches will connect in a coherent representation of the character which the actor (not the playwright) is playing. A good constitution allows governmental functions to men with some sense of when to reframe the laws and when to reframe the citizens. A living language allows to its speakers the function of extending the signification of words for newly recognized connections of objects, and to its hearers the function of understanding new connections of objects in unexpected uses of words.

A problem which a man has is never his only problem. There is always the problem also whether the first problem is worth thinking about. The function of a thinker allows always the possibility of changing the terms of a problem in the light of new ways of seeing what the problem really is. An actor, a governor, a speaker, a thinker— all are responsible to give something of themselves to their having the functions allowed to them. Each *enjoys* a function in the order of intention into which he enters.

A machine gives nothing of its identity to having the function for which it is designed. The significance of representations which it connects in its design is preset. The computer processes information, but the information is only signs for other signs—bits representing the letters and figures to which men will attach significance. The computer's identity is who knows what? It certainly thinks of itself as a computer much less than a cat thinks of itself as what men call a cat. The information which a computer processes is not *its* information, not *its* problem. The computer is not even a unified it, except as something put together for functions assigned by its builders.

When a computer begins deciding how it should operate on the basis of its own interpretation of what its information really means, then it will be time to ask whether a computer thinks. That computer would begin to enjoy a function, but it would no longer be an automatic machine.

The confusion of terminology and of understanding which surrounds the replacement of men by machines is a confusion about the difference between operation and function. There are many operations performed by men which can be performed more cheaply, more quickly, more reliably or with less danger by machines. There are many operations for which machines can be designed, which men cannot perform at all. There are even operations of men, such as selecting chess moves, for which there is no reason to design a machine except as a problem in design. The function of a man as a chess-player involves his enjoyment of a part in an intricate competition. A machine does not have such a function. A man plays chess; a machine only goes through the motions.

The surprise of automation will be neither that men are really machines nor that demi-men can be designed and built. The surprise will be that what have been considered crucial and important *functions* turn out to be only crucial and important *operations*. At the so-called lower levels of the operations of society, we recognize what it is for a man to act like "a cog in the machine." Cogs are replaceable; as long as there is some cog operating, we do not care too much about the identity of which cog is the one presently installed. Of course if the cog is a man, he cares.

The computer gives us a new metaphor. At the higher levels of society, an administrator may begin to feel that he is nothing but a logic circuit in the information processing system. A logic circuit is replaceable. Its function is of importance only in the operation of the system. Its function allows no importance to the logic circuit's identity. Our culture still has a strong inclination to measure the importance of identity—the degree to which someone is *some*body—by the importance to a system of the operations which someone is performing. As automation progresses, more and more of the systems in which men function and from which they seek importance will be seen to be automatic systems, allowing no importance to the individuality of their parts. Automation may well produce a revolution in our culture's ways of measuring importance of identity.

The truth is that a man who is not deluded undertakes a function in a system of preset meaning only out of necessity, because the system operates as an instrument to some purpose of importance. The functions in which a man is important for himself are the functions of living his own life and of creating conditions for truer understanding, fitter justice and fairer enjoyment.

It is doubtful that we shall see a Mr. John Henry bursting his poor brain trying to beat a computer at computing corporate decisions. A good executive, after all, knows how to delegate functions. What we are more likely to discover is that *we* have already delegated far too many of our functions as free men responsible for our own actions, far too many of our functions of real decision, to machines. The machines to which we have abdicated are not the electronic computers. They are the ancient machines of habit, hardened by cowardice into the mechanisms of institutions which have lost their functions as means to chosen ends, and whose operations go on for the debased purpose of giving their servants the illusion of being "somebody."

The electronic computer may prove to be a great purifier. Its operations will replace the operations of many people, but its functions will replace those only of the big mechanical frogs in the small ponds.

Part Three

IMPLICATIONS
FOR
INDUSTRY

■ 8 ■

The Promise of Automation*

by Peter F. Drucker

CHAIRMAN, DEPARTMENT OF MANAGEMENT

NEW YORK UNIVERSITY

GRADUATE SCHOOL OF BUSINESS ADMINISTRATION

Last December, in his presidential address to the annual convention of the CIO, Walter Reuther introduced an ungainly technical term into the headlines. He spoke of the coming "Automation Revolution." Automation, Reuther declared, is not in the future; it is already here.

Though the general public had not heard a great deal of automation before, Reuther of course was not the first to interest himself in either the word or the thing it stands for. The word was coined all of ten years ago—by Del Harder, Ford's manufacturing vice-president—and despite its ugliness is now firmly established in the business language. For the past three or four years, in fact, automation has become one of the most popular subjects of discussion

* Reprinted from the *Harper's Magazine* series, "America's Next Twenty Years, Part II," April, 1955, by permission of the Author and *Harper's Magazine*.

at management association meetings; whole three-day
sessions are sometimes devoted to this single topic. Two
flourishing technical magazines deal with nothing else, in
addition to a substantial number of books on "automation."

There can be no doubt that Reuther was entirely right
in his main assertion: Automation is not just in the future:
it is here. And there is just as little doubt that it represents
a major economic and technological change, a change as
great as Henry Ford ushered in with the first mass-
production plant fifty years ago. Automation is the technological revolution of the second half of the twentieth
century, just as mass production was of the first half. Its
impact may be equally great, and may come faster.

Examples of automation at work abound. A modern
oil refinery is a pretty good one; and so is the pipe-line system through which crude oil flows from Texas, guided by
electronic impulses sent out all over the country from one
control center. The way checks are cleared today in one
of the big New York banks is a good example, too;
and so is the system by which large insurance companies
send out premium notices to millions of policyholders. A
telephone dial exchange is another example; and so is
the machine that registers the time of a long-distance
call, computes the cost, and puts the amount on the customer's bill. Ford has an engine factory in Cleveland which
comes very close to automation; and the Sears Roebuck
mail-order plants, though there is very little machinery
in them, are organized on a system which remarkably resembles automation.

What do all these highly different applications have in
common? What makes them examples of automation?
How can the term be defined?

Automation can be defined simply though superficially
as the use of machines to run machines. We use machines
today primarily to *do* things to material; to cut it, to sew
it, to heat it or to cool it, to mix it or to separate it. But for
machines to be able to perform these functions four things
must be done to help them. First, material must be moved
—to the machine, in the machine, from the machine. Second, keeping the machine doing its job requires a lot of

routine judgments: Is the tool getting too hot? Is the speed right? Do the pieces come out the way they should? Third, the setting of the machine (and the tools in it) has to be changed every so often—in most production jobs, very often. Usually the machine has to be stopped to do this, has to be opened or partially dismantled and then put together again, all by hand. Fourth, and finally, we need a lot of information to keep the machines running—the number of pieces it turns out, what kind of pieces, how fast, how many of them are faulty and so forth. This information has to be gathered together somewhere, to be interpreted and to be passed on to other people.

On the whole, astonishingly little attention has been given by engineers and production men to these four jobs. Yet we have known for a long time that they cost more than the actual fabricating done by the machines. They take more people and more time; in a typical metal-working plant, for every hour the machine works, at least five, sometimes even ten, man hours have to be spent on them; and they account for practically all the employment on the production floor of a modern plant. Hence the importance of automation, for in essence it means that these four jobs of (1) materials handling, (2) routine judgment, (3) machine setting, and (4) data processing are done by machines—in a fraction of the time and at a very much lower cost.

As Mr. Reuther said, this is no longer in the future. For some time it has been possible to mechanize any *one* of these jobs. Mechanical machine setting, for instance, is as old as Jacquard's automatic loom, all of a hundred and fifty years. What has hitherto been lacking was primarily awareness of the size, cost and importance of running and controlling machines. Once these appeared—largely as a part of the World War II experience—automation was here, full-fledged. All that remained was the purely technical job of designing instruments, and that is being tackled with speed and energy.

So far this all sounds like a job largely for engineers and tool designers. That is the way it has often been tackled, the way Walter Reuther still sees it—a sort of push-button performance that puts men out of work. The automatic factory and an automated business are assumed to be almost the same thing.

But they are nothing of the kind. To try to build an "automatic factory" in a business that has not otherwise been automated is like trying to put a 1955 Turbojet aircraft engine into a 1913 Ford Model T. The business could not use the power that the automatic factory delivered; it would be impossible to connect one with the other; and, even if it weren't, the automatic factory would literally shake the business to pieces. To put automatic factories into a business that has not first been automated in other respects may well bankrupt it; at the very least, they will saddle it with risks and costs way beyond any benefit they can possibly produce.

The automatic factory is the end product rather than the beginning of automation. As we will see, automation properly does not start with production at all, but with an analysis of the business and its redesign on automation principles. The form that automatic production takes in the plant is determined by that analysis and redesign; and mechanization, the replacement of human labor by machines, is a detail of automation and not always the essential one. The reason for this, the reason why automation has to be business-focused rather than production-focused, is that it radically shifts the area of *business risk*.

In the traditional systems of production the major risk, that of economic fluctuation, is absorbed by production. Production is cut down when business falls off; it is stepped up when business improves. Our entire economic theory, as far as that goes, is based on this risk-absorbing function of production. Under automation, however, production can no longer absorb the risk of economic fluctuations, or only to a very limited degree.

Automation requires continuous production at a set level of output for a considerable period of time—three months, six months, maybe a year. This means that short-term adjustments cannot normally be taken care of by changing production schedules except at exorbitant cost. In fact, under automation it may no longer make much sense to speak of "cost per unit of production." A much more appropriate unit of cost may be "cost per time of production at a given capacity rate," which is the cost concept of our most nearly automated industry, petroleum.

One illustration of the marketing system developed, of necessity, by the petroleum industry is the old story of John D. Rockefeller's giving away kerosene lamps to the Chinese coolies, to establish an assured demand for his products.

For automation, as an absolute first condition, requires the establishment of a fairly predictable, stable and expanding market. For example, to apply automation to the manufacture of kitchen appliances such as ranges, dishwashers and automatic washing machines would require an organized market for secondhand appliances. It might even be necessary for the manufacturer to stop selling appliances entirely and instead sell the housewife a five-year service policy, with the appliances on loan or at a nominal rent. At the end of five years they would then be replaced by new appliances—thus making possible a predictable production schedule. Nor is this idea as outlandish as it sounds: a study made for one appliance company concluded that the service contract would work, if only a manufacturer existed who knew how to make good on it.

Automation requires that management find out the basic facts about its business, the market for its products, its demand expectations, the variations between different products and different product lines. It requires hard work on product planning, pricing, product design and product service. Indeed automation in many cases requires a complete "rethinking" of the product. It certainly requires deliberate planning for technological change—that is, directed efforts to make products systematically obsolete by bringing out better ones on a preset schedule. It requires new concepts and new methods of information and measurement. And it requires exceptionally clear thinking about the design and structure of the entire business—its goals, its environment, its resources and its organization.

There are three basic principles which make up the logic of automation. Wherever the three are actually used there is genuine automation even if there are no automatic machines, no electronic controls or computers, no mechanical brains. Unless they are understood and consciously applied, automation will not work.

The first of these is the principle of *economic activity as a process*. In early industry, as typified by the job shop, the integrating principle of work was skill. In Henry Ford's concept of mass production the organizing principle was the product. In automation, however, the entire activity of the business is a whole entity which must be harmoniously integrated to perform at all.

A process knows neither beginning nor end. It may have stages but it does not divide into parts as such. From the ultimate consumer back to the first supplier of raw materials it has to be seamless, so to speak, yet at the same time conform to the second principle: that of *pattern, order, or form* behind the seemingly random and unpredictable flux of economic phenomena. If a business is to be considered a continuous process instead of a series of disjointed stop-and-go events, then the economic universe in which a business operates—and all the major events within it—must have rhyme, rhythm or reason.

Without this underlying structure of forms in the economic universe, automation would be both inconceivable and incapable of achievement. Such patterns apply to events of all kinds. They might be found in the rate and distribution of incoming orders. They might have to do with the "mix" in the demand for different products at different times. They might concern the speed with which the market becomes ready for new products. They might relate to personnel problems such as absenteeism, sickness, turnover or employee performance. Even changes which appear unpredictable, such as changes in fashion, should be found to follow a clear (perhaps even a strict) pattern if properly analyzed.

Finally automation has a principle of *self-regulating control* which derives from its nature as process. As every true process must, it contains the means of its own regulation and correction. It must be able to maintain the equilibrium between ends and means, output and effort. And it must be able ahead of time to set standards of acceptable performance, which it then can use as pretests and as governors. In electronics this is called feedback—that is, a control in which the process, by its own product, regulates itself. The businessman has of course long been familiar with one such control: profit—the simple, though crude, device that uses the results of economic activity to control its future direction and the quantity of new resources devoted to it.

In these basic principles, automation is little more than a projection into the economic sphere of philosophical beliefs that have become dominant in the past fifty years. The idea is distinctly characteristic of the twentieth-century thought that a diversity of patterns, processes or forms—each capable of logical expression, logical analysis and systematic synthesis—underlies all phenomena. It is the common contribution of the founding fathers of modern scientific philosophy like Poincaré, Bohr and Planck; Willard Gibbs, Mendel, Hunt and Malinowski. It was clearly understood by Henry Adams. It might, with considerable oversimplification, be called an organic philosophy—if only to distinguish it from the strictly mechanistic approach on which Henry Ford's concept of mass production was based.

It is of course not necessary for a business manager to know anything about the philosophical foundations of automation, let alone to be a philosopher or scientist himself. It is not even necessary for the experts in automation within a business to know these things. But it is absolutely necessary for both the businessman and his automation specialists to understand clearly that automation is not a box of tricks or a bagful of gadgets. Automation is a methodology, with all the strengths and limitations that the term implies.

If automation were a simple matter of technology, or replacement of human labor by machines, its social impact would be precisely what Walter Reuther predicted: large-scale displacement of workers. It might still be arguable whether this displacement would result in mass unemployment, as Reuther says; the fact that during the next twenty years our working population will grow but slowly makes it implausible that there will be chronic unemployment, even if automation comes very fast. Still, as long as automation is seen as a mere matter of technology, displacement of workers would be the thing to worry about. But considered in its larger dimensions, as we have been considering it here, automation's most important impact will not be on employment but on the qualifications and functions of employees.

There may actually be no workers on the production floor of tomorrow's push-button factory. There are practically none today in a power-generating station or an oil refinery. But at the same time incredibly large numbers of men will be required behind the scenes in new, highly skilled jobs as machine builders, machine installers, repair men, controllers of the machinery and of its performance, and programmers to prepare information and feed it into the machine. In addition, large numbers of highly educated men will be needed in new jobs as designers of machinery, draftsmen, system engineers, mathematicians or logicians. Finally, large numbers will be needed for new managerial jobs requiring a high ability to think, to analyze, to make decisions and to assume risks. And this increase both in the numbers of managers and in the demands made on them may well be the largest of all the social impacts of automation.

Many people seem to fear that automation will downgrade the worker by making him a slave to a mechanical monster. "I have charge of one of the large electronic computers," a young engineer said to me a few months ago. "I am constantly appalled by the number of people who seem to think that the machine has charge of me."

One look at the industries that are virtually automated now, such as electric-power generation or oil refining, should show that they have plenty of employees, that they pay the highest wages and that there is little room in them for unskilled or untrained labor.

Mass production upgraded the unskilled laborer of yesterday into the semiskilled machine operator of today— and in the process multiplied both his productivity and his income. In just the same way, automation will upgrade the semiskilled machine operator of today into a highly skilled and knowledgeable technician—multiplying his income again. Norbert Wiener, MIT's distinguished mathematician, who did much of the conceptual thinking that underlies the new technology, has predicted that automation will lead to "the human use of human beings"—that is, to our using man's specifically human qualities, his ability to think, to analyze, balance and synthesize, to decide and to act purposefully—instead of using him, as we have done for millennia, to do all the dreary work machines can do better.

There are two reservations to the prediction that automation will not cause large-scale labor displacement. First, automation will mean a sharp cut in employment for routine office work. There machines will indeed replace men and women. But this, in total numbers, is not a major segment of the working population: it is largely composed of young, unmarried girls fresh out of school, who are in short supply today and will remain so for at least ten years. This has also been a labor force with a very high turnover where it will therefore be possible to introduce automation without laying off people—all that is needed is to replace at a progressively slower rate the employees who quit.

The second reservation is that automation will involve a considerable shifting of men to new jobs with new employers. For instance, there will be a tremendous demand for men to build machinery and equipment, but this demand may not arise for them in the same company that employs them now. Thus there may be considerable "dislocation unemployment" in a particular industry, and it may extend to a whole area that one industry dominates.

But the most important of these dislocations is likely to be a shift of employment opportunities to *smaller* business. In the first place, automation should strengthen the competitive position of the small company, if only because mechanical machine setting enables the small organization to offer a more complete and diversified range of products at a competitive cost. Secondly, automation will create opportunities for countless small businesses to specialize in servicing equipment. One indication of the growth we can expect is shown by the small but highly expert tool and die makers who serve the automotive industry; it is an open secret in Detroit that these small shops make a higher profit on their capital and enjoy greater stability than General Motors.

Socially, the shift in job opportunities therefore should be healthy. But it will still impose on management a responsibility to plan systematically for the retraining and placement of workers during the shift to automation. Union leaders, too, should similarly accept responsibility for the changes in their rules that will be necessary. Even such sacred cows as seniority or apprenticeship restrictions may have to be slaughtered. It is a good sign that some managements—notably General Electric—and some unions—notably Reuther's United Auto Workers—are already at work on these matters.

The really serious social problem is not employment but the need to upgrade whole segments of the population in very short time. Automation requires trained and educated people in unprecedented numbers. The quantitative need alone will be so great that the eight or ten million college students we can expect fifteen years hence will be barely sufficient. One large manufacturing company (now employing one hundred fifty thousand) figures that it will need *seven thousand* college graduates a year, once it is automated, just to keep going; today it hires three hundred annually.

But the need is above all qualitative—for *better-educated* people. The "trained barbarian," the man who has acquired high gadgeteering skill, will not do. Even in routine jobs, automation will require ability to think, a trained imagination and good judgment, plus some skill in logical methods, some mathematical understanding and some ability well above the elementary level to read and write—in a word, the normal equipment of educated people. Under automation, a school could do a student no greater disservice than to prepare him, as so many do today, for his first job. If there is one thing certain under automation it is that the job—even the bottom job—will change radically and often.

The greatest educational need may well be in management. Of course there will always be need for intuition, hunch, and experience in business enterprise, at least as long as we eschew state planning. But in an automated business the intuitive manager is obsolete; and experience under automation will not be a very reliable guide. To be a manager in an automated business, of course, a man need not have a formal education, let alone a degree; indeed it would be hard to find an institution of learning where he could acquire today the education he needs to be a manager tomorrow. But, in the sense of being able to handle systematic knowledge, he will have to be *highly* educated.

This educational job will have to be done, to a very large extent, in and by the business itself; and large companies in particular will have to become educational institutions—and interest themselves in formal education—even more than they do today. For the foreseeable future, there will simply not be enough new people with the new knowledge and skill required to fill the new jobs; and this will be true in all areas of the organization: rank and file, office work, technical and professional work, managerial work. On every level, adult education—largely on the job—will be needed.

In any case, whatever dislocation automation produces will take place in the period of transition from the old to the new, and it will be temporary. Permanently, automation should introduce a new stability into the economic society. For automation will have to stabilize the two factors which have hitherto both caused and suffered the greatest instability: capital investment and employment.

Piecemeal capital investment—to replace a machine here, to make an operation more efficient there—is simply not possible under automation. Nor is it possible to make capital expenditure entirely dependent on cash income and business conditions, lopping them off as soon as sales or prices fall and hectically pushing them up in good times. The whole plant, under automation, must be conceived as one integrated piece of machinery. No one part can be replaced, improved or changed without changing the entire plant and all its parts; and once a capital project has been started it has to be carried through, on a timetable pretty well fixed in advance. If the project is abandoned midway, the sums already invested may be lost entirely.

This obviously creates new and serious risks. Obviously it will raise still higher the demands on management's ability to make long-range decisions. But at the same time it also means that a sizable portion of our capital spending will increasingly be carried out independently of the business cycle, and this in turn will stabilize the cycle. It will hardly eliminate economic fluctuations altogether, but it should prevent the extremes of boom and bust.

Probably we are already feeling these effects. Both the inventory recession of 1951 and the recession of 1954 were expected by the great majority of businessmen to turn into long, hard downswings. Yet few businesses stopped their capital expenditures programs; few even cut them back. The reason they gave for this totally unprecedented behavior was that capital investment programs are integrated and long-term and can hardly be adapted, once they have been begun, even to major cyclical fluctuations. As a result, neither recession went very far.

Automation should bring even greater stability to employment. In this area lies one of its greatest opportunities, but also one of the hottest political issues of the coming years.

Management today still proceeds on the assumption that labor is a current expense which fluctuates, on the whole, with volume of production. Already this concept may be obsolete; in most large companies one-third or more of the employees are salaried; and of the hourly employees, a half or even two-thirds, in many industries, have to be kept on the job as long as the plant is open, regardless of output.

Under automation, however, the traditional concept will be untenable, if not dangerous. Labor under automation must be considered a capital resource, with wage costs being treated virtually as fixed costs. The essence of automation is its inability to adjust production to short-range economic fluctuations, except within narrow ranges. The number of people employed will therefore not fluctuate directly with volume, and the investment in the skill and training of workers will be much too great for the enterprise to disperse them, except in a situation of extreme peril.

Automation thus creates the opportunity for a high degree of employment stability—an opportunity that comes none too soon, since the social pressure for such stability has long been building up. This is partly a result of the American economy's success in making the worker "middle class"; the most potent emotional symbol of middle-class status has always been the salary in contrast to the wage. In part it is also the result of the disproportion between the rapid increase in total population and the slower increase in working population, and of the resulting labor pressure. But, in any case, the demands for stabilized employment and predictable income are certainly not inventions of the power-hungry union bosses. They are the most important goals of the American worker.

This is the background of Walter Reuther's demand for the Guaranteed Annual Wage, which seems likely to be the storm center of American labor relations in the years ahead. But the Guaranteed Annual Wage, in my opinion, will not do the job. Any such absolute guarantee of income for all, or most, of the men on pay roll could simply keep management from hiring new workers. It could actually create unemployment, and on a large scale.

The horrible example is Italy's experience with a state-imposed guaranteed annual wage. When the law was adopted in 1947 a virtual ban on laying off or dismissing any employee with more than a year's seniority was necessary; it probably prevented Italy from going Communist during those crucial days. Today the same law is the cause for a very large part—maybe a quarter, if not a third —of Italy's chronic unemployment, the worst in Europe. For very few employers will hire new workers. Even if he has to meet a tremendous demand for his product, an employer will prefer to pay ten hours' overtime each week at double and triple wages—as a manufacturer of Italy's ubiquitous motorscooters has done—rather than bring in new people; for, once hired, they stay on the pay roll forever, regardless of future business. Or the employer, like Italy's largest power company, will string out a five-year building program over ten or fifteen years rather than hire new crews, despite a crippling power shortage and constant "brownouts." In fact, no Italian employer could easily take on additional workers as long as his present employees do not want to share—and inevitably dilute—their own security. Everybody in Italy, the unions included, knows perfectly well that the guaranteed annual wage has become a deadly disease. Yet no one, not even the secretary of the Manufacturers Association, dares criticize it in public; for, being "security," it has become untouchable.

Yet, in most industries here, there is a way to give a high degree of employment stability—amounting to an all but absolute guarantee for the bulk of the employees. That is to guarantee a carefully worked out employment prediction for the twelve months ahead, based on the worst experience of the past. With the stability in production which automation requires, this prediction would be increasingly reliable for workers in the majority of manufacturing and service industries. It should enable most of them to budget on an insurable promise of at least two-thirds of a full year's income for the year ahead.

To work out such a predictable income and employment plan—or at least to find out whether it is possible—ought to be a major management task even if automation had never been heard of. Failing in it, management will have no defense against the demands for a guaranteed annual wage; it will not even have the facts to rebut the union's argument. Certainly any promise of employment stability should at first be modest, but the aim should be to improve as experience is gained. Management should hold itself committed to this goal—and primarily because the business demands it, not just because the union demands it. Above all, it is the American public that should demand that both management and union leadership seize automation's opportunity for making income predictable and for stabilizing mass purchasing power.

The Automation Revolution is here, and it is proceeding at high speed. But it will be many years before it permeates the entire economy. Most businesses will not convert to automation overnight but will go at it piecemeal, which will not be easy. It will require more capital than whole-sale automation, and it will entail greater risks. But the mental strain will be less. Fewer people will have to re-learn fewer things; and they will have more time to do it in. While it is a major revolution, automation is therefore not likely to be dramatic; there will be no point when one can say: "This is the year when the American economy went into automation."

But only the speed of automation is uncertain. There can be little doubt that the direction of our progress is to-ward it. There can be little doubt that it means a tremen-dous upgrading of the labor force in terms of skill, employ-ment security, standard of living and opportunity. Above all, there can be little doubt that automation is not tech-nocracy under another name and that the push-button fac-tory is not its symbol. Automation is not gadgeteering, it is not even engineering; it is a concept of the structure and order of economic life, the design of its basic patterns integrated into a harmonious, balanced and organic whole.

· 9 ·

The Corporation:
Will It Be Managed by Machines?*[1]

by Herbert A. Simon

I don't know whether the title assigned to me was meant seriously or humorously. I shall take it seriously. During the past five years, I have been too close to machines— the kinds of machines known as computers, that is—to treat the question lightly. Perhaps I have lost my sense of humor and perspective about them.

My work on this paper has been somewhat impeded, in recent days, by a fascinating spectacle just outside my office window. Men and machines have been constructing the foundations of a small building. After some preliminary skirmishing by men equipped with surveying instru-

* Reprinted by permission from *Management and Corporation: 1985*, edited by Anshen & Bach, Copyright ©, 1961, McGraw-Hill Book Company, Inc. Originally prepared for a Symposium at the Graduate School of Industrial Administration, Carnegie Institute of Technology, Pittsburgh, Pennsylvania. Reprinted with the permission of the Author and the Graduate School of Industrial Administration, Carnegie Institute of Technology.

ments and sledges for driving pegs, most of the work has been done by various species of mechanical elephant and their mahouts. Two kinds of elephants dug out the earth (one with its forelegs, the other with its trunk) and loaded it in trucks (pack elephants, I suppose). Then, after an interlude during which another group of men carefully fitted some boards into place as forms, a new kind of elephant appeared, its belly full of concrete which it disgorged into the forms. It was assisted by two men with wheelbarrows—plain old-fashioned man-handled wheelbarrows—and two or three other men who fussily tamped the poured concrete with metal rods. Twice during this whole period a shovel appeared—on one occasion it was used by a man to remove dirt that had been dropped on a sidewalk; on another occasion it was used to clean a trough down which the concrete slid.

Here, before me, was a sample of automated, or semi-automated, production. What did it show about the nature of present and future relations of man with machine in the production of goods and services? And what lessons that could be learned from the automation of manufacturing and construction could be transferred to the problems of managerial automation? I concluded that there were two good reasons for beginning my analysis with a careful look at factory and office automation. First, the business organization in 1985 will be a highly automated man-machine system, and the nature of management will surely be conditioned by the character of the system being managed. Second, perhaps there are greater similarities than appear at first blush among the several areas of potential automation—blue-collar, clerical and managerial. Perhaps the automated executive of the future has a great deal in common with the automated worker or clerk whom we can already observe in many situations today.

First, however, we must establish a framework and a point of view. Our task is to forecast the changes that will take place over the next generation in the job of the manager. It is fair to ask: Which manager? Not everyone nor every job will be affected in the same way; indeed, most persons who will be affected are not even managers at the present time. Moreover, we must distinguish the gross effects of a technological change, occurring at the point of impact of that change, from the net effects, the whole series of secondary ripples spreading from that point of initial impact.

Many of the initial effects are transitory—important enough to those directly involved at the time and place of change, but of no lasting significance to the society. Other effects are neither apparent nor anticipated when the initial change takes place but flow from it over a period of years through the succession of reactions it produces. Examples of both transient and indirect effects of change come to mind readily enough—e.g., the unemployment of blacksmiths and the appearance of suburbia, respectively, as effects of the automobile.

Since our task is to look ahead twenty-five years, I shall say little about the transient effects of the change in the job of the manager. I do not mean to discount the importance of these effects to the people they touch. In our time we are highly conscious of the transient effects, particularly the harmful ones, the displacements of skill and status. We say less of the benefit to those who acquire the new skills or of the exhilaration that many derive from erecting new structures.

Of course, the social management of change does not consist simply in balancing beneficial transient effects against harmful ones. The simplest moral reasoning leads to a general rule for the introduction of change: The general society which stands to benefit from the change should pay the major costs of introducing it and should compensate generously those who would otherwise be harmed by it. A discussion of the transient effects of change would have to center on ways of applying that rule. But that is not the problem we have to deal with here.

Our task is to forecast the long-run effects of change. First of all, we must predict what is likely to happen to the job of the individual manager, and to the activity of management in the individual organization. Changes in these patterns will have secondary effects on the occupational profile in the economy as a whole. Our task is to picture the society after it has made all these secondary adjustments and settled down to its new equilibrium.

Let me now indicate the general plan I shall follow in my analysis. In the first section, "Predicting Long-run Equilibrium," I shall identify the key factors—the causes and the conditions of change—that will mold the analysis. Then I shall show how a well-known tool of economic analysis—the doctrine of comparative advantage—permits us to draw valid inferences from these causes and conditions. In the second section, "The New Technology of Information Processing," I shall describe the technological innovations that have appeared and are about to appear in the areas of production and data processing, and I shall use this material to draw a picture of the business organization in 1985, with particular attention to the automation of blue-collar and clerical work. In the third section, "The Automation of Management," I shall consider more specifically the role of the manager in the future business organization. In the final section, "The Broader Significance of Automation," I shall try to identify some of the important implications of these developments for our society and for ourselves as members of it.

PREDICTING LONG-RUN EQUILIBRIUM

To predict long-run equilibrium, one must identify two major aspects of the total situation: (1) the variables that will change autonomously and inexorably—the "first causes," and (2) the constant, unchanging "givens" in the situation, to which the other variables must adjust themselves. These are the hammer and the anvil that beat out the shape of the future. The accuracy of our predictions will depend less upon forecasting exactly the course of change than upon assessing correctly which factors are the unmoved movers and which the equally unmoved invariants. My entire forecast rests on my identification of this hammer and this anvil.

THE CAUSES OF CHANGE

The growth in human knowledge is the primary factor that will give the system its direction—in particular, that will fix the boundaries of the technologically feasible.

The growth in real capital is the major secondary factor in change—within the realm of what is technologically feasible, it will determine what is economical.

The crucial area of expansion of knowledge is not hard to predict, for the basic innovations—or at least a large part of them—have already occurred and we are now rapidly exploiting them. The new knowledge consists in a fundamental understanding of the processes of thinking and learning or, to use a more neutral term, of complex information processing. We can now write programs for electronic computers that enable these devices to think and learn. This knowledge is having, and will have, practical impacts in two directions: (1) because we can now simulate in considerable detail an important and increasing part of the processes of the human mind, we have available a technique of tremendous power for psychological research; (2) because we can now write complex information-processing programs for computers, we are acquiring the technical capacity to replace humans with computers in a rapidly widening range of thinking and deciding tasks.

Closely allied to the development of complex information-processing techniques for general purpose computers is the rapid advance in the technique of automating all sorts of production and clerical tasks. Putting these two lines of development together, I am led to the following general predictions: Within the very near future—much less than twenty-five years—we shall have the *technical* capability of substituting machines for any and all human functions in organizations. Within the same period, we shall have acquired an extensive and empirically tested theory of human cognitive processes and their interaction with human emotions, attitudes and values.

To predict that we will have these technical capabilities says nothing of how we shall use them. Before we can forecast that, we must discuss the important invariants in the social system.

THE INVARIANTS

The changes that our new technical capability will bring about will be governed, particularly in the production sphere, by two major fixed factors in the society. Both of these have to do with the use of human resources for production.

1. Apart from transient effects of automation, the human resources of the society will be substantially fully employed. Full employment does not necessarily mean a forty-hour week, for the allocation of productive capacity between additional goods and services and additional leisure may continue to change as it has in the past. Full employment means that the opportunity to work will be available to virtually all adults in the society and that, through wages or other allocative devices, the product of the economy will be distributed widely among families.

2. The distribution of intelligence and ability in the society will be much as it is now, although a substantially larger percentage of adults (perhaps half or more) will have completed college educations.

These assumptions—of capability of automation, accompanied by full employment and constancy in the quality of the human resources—provide us with a basis for characterizing the change. We cannot talk about the technological unemployment it may create, for we have assumed that such unemployment is a transient phenomenon—that there will be none in the long run. But the pattern of occupations, the profile showing the relative distribution of employed persons among occupations, may be greatly changed. It is the change in this profile that will measure the organizational impact of the technological change.

The change in the occupational profile depends on a well-known economic principle, the doctrine of comparative advantage. It may seem paradoxical to think that we can increase the productivity of mechanized techniques in all processes without displacing men somewhere. Won't a point be reached where men are less productive than machines in *all* processes, hence economically unemployable? [2]

The paradox is dissolved by supplying a missing term. Whether man or machines will be employed in a particular process depends not simply on their relative productivity in physical terms but on their cost as well. And cost depends on price. Hence—so goes the traditional argument of economics—as technology changes and machines become more productive, the prices of labor and capital will so adjust themselves as to clear the market of both. As much of each will be employed as offers itself at the market price, and the market price will be proportional to the marginal productivity of that factor. By the operation of the market place, manpower will flow to those processes in which its productivity is comparatively high relative to the productivity of machines; it will leave those processes in which its productivity is comparatively low. The comparison is not with the productivities of the past, but among the productivities in different processes with the currently available technology.

I apologize for dwelling at length on a point that is clearly enough stated in the *Wealth of Nations*. My excuse is that contemporary discussion of technological change and automation still very often falls into error through not applying the doctrine of comparative advantage correctly and consistently.

We conclude that human employment will become smaller relative to the total labor force in those kinds of occupations and activities in which automatic devices have the greatest comparative advantage over humans; human employment will become relatively greater in those occupations and activities in which automatic devices have the least comparative advantage.[3]

Thus, if computers are a thousand times faster than bookkeepers in doing arithmetic, but only one hundred times faster than stenographers in taking dictation, we shall expect the number of bookkeepers per thousand employees to decrease but the number of stenographers to increase. Similarly, if computers are a hundred times faster than executives in making investment decisions, but only ten times faster in handling employee grievances (the quality of the decisions being held constant), then computers will be employed in making investment decisions, while executives will be employed in handling grievances.

THE NEW TECHNOLOGY
OF INFORMATION PROCESSING

The automation of manufacturing processes is a natural continuation and extension of the Industrial Revolution.

We have seen a steady increase in the amount of machinery employed per worker. In the earlier phases of mechanization, the primary function of machinery was to replace human energy with mechanical energy. To some extent in all phases, and to a growing extent in recent developments, another goal has been to substitute mechanical for human sensing and controlling activities. Those who distinguish the newer automation from the older mechanization stress our growing ability to replace with machines simple human perceiving, choosing and manipulating processes.

THE NEARLY AUTOMATIC FACTORY AND OFFICE

The genuinely automatic factory—the workerless factory that can produce output and perhaps also, within limits, maintain and repair itself—will be technically feasible long before our twenty-five years have elapsed. From very unsystematic observation of changes going on in factories today, one might surmise that the typical factory of 1985 will not, however, be fully automatic. More likely the typical factory will have reached, say, the level of automaticity that has been attained in 1960 by the most modern oil refineries or power generating stations.

The same kinds of technical developments that lead toward the automatic factory are bringing about an even more rapid revolution—and perhaps eventually a more complete one—in large-scale clerical operations. The very abstract nature of symbol manipulation facilitates the design of equipment to do it, and the further automation of clerical work is impeded by fewer technical barriers than the further automation of factory production. We can conjecture that by 1985 the departments of a company concerned with major clerical functions—accounting, processing of customers' orders, inventory and production control, purchasing and the like—will have reached an even higher level of automation than most factories.

Both the factory and the office, then, are rapidly becoming complex man-machine systems with a very large amount of production equipment, in the case of the factory, and computing equipment, in the case of the office, per employee. The clerical department and the factory will come more and more to resemble each other. The one will present the picture of a small group of employees operating (I am tempted to use the more accurate phrase "collaborating with") a large computing system; the other, the picture of a similar small group of employees operating a large production system. The interrelation of man with machine will become quite as important a design problem for such systems as the interrelation of man with man.

Now we must not commit the error I warned against in discussing the doctrine of comparative advantage. When we foresee fewer employees in factory and office, we mean fewer per unit of output and fewer per unit of capital equipment. It does not follow that there will be fewer in total. To predict the occupational profile that will result, we must look more closely at the prospective rates of automation in different occupations.

Before we turn to this task, however, it is worth reporting a couple of the lessons that are currently being learned in factory and clerical automation:

(1) Automation does not mean "dehumanizing" work. On the contrary, in most actual instances of recent automation jobs were made, on the whole, more pleasant and interesting, as judged by the employees themselves, than they had been before. In particular, automation may move more and more in the direction of eliminating the machine-paced assembly-line task and the repetitive clerical task. It appears generally to reduce the work-pushing, man-driving and expediting aspects of first-line supervision.

(2) Contemporary automation does not generally change to an important extent the profile of skill levels among the employees. It perhaps calls, on the average, for some upgrading of skills in the labor force, but conflicting trends are observable at different stages in automation.[4]

THE OCCUPATIONAL PROFILE

To predict the occupational distribution of the employed population in 1985, we would have to go down the list of occupations and assess, for each, the potentialities of automation. Even if we could do this, our inferences would not be quite direct. For we also have to take into account (1) income elasticity of demand—the fact that as productivity rises, the demands for some goods and services will rise more rapidly than the demands for others; (2) price elasticity of demand—the fact that the most rapidly automated activities will also show the greatest price reductions, so that the net reduction in employment in these activities will be substantially less than the gross reduction at a constant level of production.

As a fanciful example, let us consider the number of persons engaged in the practice of psychiatry. It is reasonable to assume that the demand for psychiatric services, at constant prices, will increase more than proportionately with an increase in income. Hence, the income effect of the general increase in a society's productivity will be to increase the proportion of psychiatrists in the employed population. Now, let us suppose that a specific technological development permits the automation of psychiatry itself, so that one psychiatrist can do the work formerly done by ten.[5] It is not at all clear whether a 90 per cent reduction in price of psychiatric services would increase the demand for those services by a factor of more or less than ten. But if the demand increased by a factor of more than ten, the proportion of persons employed in psychiatry would actually increase.

Thus prediction of the occupational profile depends on estimates of the income and price elasticity of demand for particular goods and services as well as estimates of relative rates of increase in productivity. This is not the only difficulty the forecaster faces. He must also be extremely cautious in his assumptions as to what is, and what is not, likely to be automated. In particular, automation is not the only way to reduce the cost of a process—a more effective way is to eliminate it. An expert in automation would tell you that the garbage collector's job is an extremely difficult one to automate (at any reasonable cost) in a straightforward way. It has, of course, simply been eliminated in many communities by grinding the garbage and transporting it in liquid through the sewerage system. Such Columbus-egg solutions of the production problem are not at all rare, and will be an important part of automation.[6]

ANOTHER APPROACH TO PREDICTION

With all these reservations and qualifications is any prediction possible? I think it is, but I think it requires us to go back to some fundamentals. The ordinary classification of occupations is basically an "end-use" classification—it indicates what social function is performed by each occupation. To understand automation, we must begin our classification of human activities at the other end—what basic capacities does the human organism bring to tasks, capacities that are used in different proportions for different tasks?

Viewed as a resource in production, a man is a pair of eyes and ears, a brain, a pair of hands, a pair of legs and some muscles for applying force. Automation proceeds in two ways: (1) by providing mechanized means for performing some of the functions formerly performed by a man, and (2) by eliminating some of these functions. Moreover, the mechanized means that replace the man can be of a general-purpose character (like the man) or highly specialized.

The steam engine and the electric motor are relatively general-purpose substitutes for muscles. A butter-wrapping machine is a special-purpose substitute for a pair of hands which eliminates some eye-brain activities the human butter wrapper would require. A feedback system for controlling the temperature of a chemical process is a special-purpose substitute for eyes, brain and hands. A digital computer employed in preparing a pay roll is a relatively general-purpose substitute for eyes, brain and hands. A modern multitool milling machine is a special-purpose device that eliminates many of the positioning (eye-brain-hand) processes that were formerly required in a sequence of machining operations.

The earlier history of mechanization was characterized by: (1) rapid substitution of mechanical energy for muscles; (2) partial and spotty introduction of special-purpose devices that performed simple, repetitive eye-brain-hand sequences; (3) elimination, by mechanizing transport and by coordinating sequences of operations on a special-purpose basis, of many human eye-brain-hand sequences that had previously been required.

Thus, man's comparative advantage in energy production has been greatly reduced in most situations—to the point where he is no longer a significant source of power in our economy. He has been supplanted also in performing many relatively simple and repetitive eye-brain-hand sequences. He has retained his greatest comparative advantage in (1) the use of his brain as a flexible general-purpose problem-solving device, (2) the flexible use of his sensory organs and hands, and (3) the use of his legs, on rough terrain as well as smooth, to make this general-purpose sensing-thinking-manipulating system available wherever it is needed.

This picture of man's functions in a man-machine system was vividly illustrated by the construction work going on outside my window. Most of the energy for earth digging was being supplied by the mechanical elephants, but each depended on its mahout for eyes and (if you don't object to my fancy) for eye-trunk coordination. The fact that the elephant was operating in rough, natural terrain made automation of the mahout a difficult, although by no means insoluble, technical problem. It would almost certainly not now be economical. But other men—the men with wheelbarrows particularly—were performing even more manual and primitive tasks. Again, the delivery of the concrete to the forms could have been much more fully automated but at a high cost. The men provided a flexible, if not very powerful, means for delivering small quantities of concrete to a number of different points over uneven terrain.

Flexibility and general-purpose applicability is the key to most spheres where the human has a comparative advantage over the machine. This raises two questions:

(1) What are the prospects for matching human flexibility in automatic devices?

(2) What are the prospects for matching humans in particular activities by reducing the need for flexibility?

The second question is a familiar one throughout the history of mechanization; the first alternative is more novel.

FLEXIBILITY IN AUTOMATA

We must consider separately the sensory organs, the manipulatory organs, the locomotive organs and the central nervous system. Duplicating the problem-solving and information-handling capabilities of the brain is not far off; it would be surprising if it were not accomplished within the next decade. But these capabilities are so much involved in management activity that we shall have to discuss them at length in a later section.

We are much further from replacing the eyes, the hands and the legs. From an economic as well as a technological standpoint, I would hazard the guess that automation of a flexible central nervous system will be feasible long before automation of a comparably flexible sensory, manipulative or locomotive system. I shall state later my reasons for thinking this.

If these conjectures are correct, we may expect (other things being equal) automation of thinking and symbol-manipulating functions to proceed more rapidly than the automation of the more complex eye-brain-hand sequences. But before we grasp this conclusion too firmly, we need to remove one assumption.

ENVIRONMENTAL CONTROL
A SUBSTITUTE FOR FLEXIBILITY

If we want an organism or mechanism to behave effectively in a complex and changing environment, we can design into it adaptive mechanisms that allow it to respond flexibility to the demands the environment places on it. Alternatively, we can try to simplify and stabilize the environment. We can adapt organism to environment or environment to organism.

Both processes have been significant in biological evolution. The development of the multicellular organism may be interpreted as simplifying and stabilizing the environment of the internal cells by insulating them from the complex and variable external environment in which the entire organism exists. This is the significance of homeostasis in evolution—that in a very real sense it adapts the environment to the organism (or the elementary parts of

the organism) and hence avoids the necessity of complicating the individual parts of the organism.

Homeostatic control of the environment (the environment, that is, of the individual worker or the individual
machine) has played a tremendous role in the history of
mechanization and in the history of occupational speciali-
zation as well. Let me cite some examples that show how
all-pervasive this principle is:

(1) The smooth road provides a constant environment
for the vehicle—eliminating the advantages of flexible
legs.

(2) The first step in every major manufacturing sequence (steel, textiles, wood products) reduces a highly
variable natural substance (metallic ore, fiber, trees) to
a far more homogeneous and constant material (pig iron,
thread, boards or pulp). All subsequent manufacturing
processes are thus insulated from the variability of the natural material. The application of the principle of inter-
changeable parts performs precisely the same function
for subsequent manufacturing steps.

(3) By means of transfer machines work in process in
modern automated lines is presented to successive machine tools in proper position to be grasped and worked,
eliminating the sensory and manipulative functions of
workers who formerly loaded such tools by hand.

We see that mechanization has more often proceeded
by eliminating the need for human flexibility—replacing
rough terrain with a smooth environment—than by imi-
tating it. Now homeostatic control of the environment
tends to be a cumulative process. When we have mechanized one part of a manufacturing sequence, the regu-
larity and predictiveness secured from this mechanization
generally facilitates the mechanization of the next stage.

Let us apply this idea to the newly mechanized data-
processing area. One of the functions that machines perform badly at present, humans rather well, is reading
printed text. Because of the variability of such text, it
would seem that the human eye is likely to retain for some
time a distinct comparative advantage in handling it. But
the wider the use of machines in data processing, the more
pains we will take to prepare the source data in a form

that can be read easily by a machine. Thus, if scientific journals are to be read mostly by machines, and only small segments of their scanning presented to the human researchers, we shall not bother to translate manuscripts into linotype molds, molds into slugs and slugs into patterns of ink on paper. We shall, in time, use the typewriter to prepare computer input—punched tape or cards, for example, and simply by-pass the printed volume.

Now these considerations do not alter our earlier conclusion that humans are likely to retain their comparative advantage in activities that require sensory, manipulative and motor flexibility (and, to a much lesser extent, problem-solving flexibility). They show, however, that we must be careful not to assume that the particular activities that now call for this flexibility will continue to do so. The stabilization of the environments for productive activity will reduce or eliminate the need for flexible response at many points in the productive process, continuing a trend that is as old as multicellular life. In particular, in the light of what has been said of the feasibility of automating problem solving, we should not make the simple assumption that the higher-status occupations, and those requiring most education, are going to be the least automated. There are perhaps as good prospects technically and economically for automating completely the job of a physician, a corporate vice-president or a college teacher, as for automating the job of the man who operates a piece of earth-moving equipment.

MAN AS MAN'S ENVIRONMENT

In most work situations, an important part of man's environment is man. This is, moreover, an exceedingly "rough" part of his environment. Interacting with his fellow man calls on his greatest flexibility both in sensory activity and response. He must read the nuances of expressions, postures, intonations; he must take into account in numerous ways the individuality of the person opposite him.

What do we mean by *automating* those activities in organizations that consist in responding to other men? I hardly know how to frame the question, much less to answer it. It is often asserted—even by people who are quite sophisticated on the general subject of automation—that personal services cannot be automated, that a machine cannot acquire a bedside manner or produce the positive effect that is produced by a courteous sales clerk.

Let me, at least for purposes of argument, accept that proposition. (It leaves me uneasy, for I am aware of how many people in our own culture have affective relations with such mechanisms as automobiles, rolling mills—and computers.) Accepting it does not settle the question of how much of man's environment in the highly automatized factory or office will be man. For much of the interpersonal activity called for in organizations results from the fact that the basic blue-collar and clerical work is done by humans, who need supervision and direction. Another large chunk of interpersonal activity is the buying and selling activity—the work of the salesman and the buyer.

As far as supervisory work is concerned, we might suppose that it would decrease in the same proportion as the total number of employees; hence that automation would not affect the occupational profile in this respect at least. This may be true in first approximation, but it needs qualification. The amounts and types of supervision required by a work force depend on many things, including the extent to which the work pace is determined by the men or by machines and the extent to which the work is prescheduled. Supervision of a machine-paced operation is a very different matter from supervision of an operation where the foreman is required to see that the workers maintain a normal pace—with or without incentive schemes. Similarly, a highly scheduled shop leaves room for much less expediting activity than one where scheduling is less formal and complete.

As a generalization, I would predict that work-pushing and expediting will make up a much smaller part of the supervisory job at lower and middle levels in highly automated operations than they generally do at present. Whether these activities will be replaced, in the total occupational profile, by other managerial activities we shall have to consider a little later.

What about the salesman? I have little basis for conjecture on this point. If we think that buying decisions are not going to be made much more objectively than they have in the past, then we might conclude the automation of the salesman's role will proceed less rapidly than the automation of many other jobs. If so, selling will account for a larger fraction of total employment.

SUMMARY: BLUE-COLLAR AND CLERICAL AUTOMATION

We can now summarize what we have said about the prospects of the automatic factory and office and about the general characteristics of the organization that the executive of 1985 will manage. Clearly, it will be an organization with a much higher ratio of machines to men than is characteristic of organizations today. The men in the system can be expected to play three kinds of roles:

(1) There will be a few vestigial workmen—probably a smaller part of the total labor force than today—who will be part of in-line production, primarily doing tasks requiring relatively flexible eye-brain-hand coordination (a few wheelbarrow pushers and a few mahouts).

(2) There will be a substantial number of men whose task is to keep the system operating by preventive and remedial maintenance. Machines will play an increasing role, of course, in maintenance functions, but machine powers will not likely develop as rapidly relatively to those of men in this area as in in-line activities. Moreover, the total amount of maintenance work—to be shared by men and machines—will increase. For the middle run, at least, I would expect this group to make up an increasing fraction of the total work force.

(3) There will be a substantial number of men at professional levels, responsible for the design of product, for the design of the productive process and for general management. We have still not faced the question of how far automation will go in these areas, and hence we cannot say very firmly whether such occupations will be a larger or smaller part of the whole. Anticipating our later analysis, I will conjecture that they will constitute about the same part as they do now of total factory and office employment.

A second important characteristic of future production

and data-processing organizations is that some of the kinds of interpersonal relations—in supervising and expediting —that at present are very stressful for most persons engaged in them will be substantially reduced in importance.

Finally, in the entire occupied population, a larger fraction of members than at present will be engaged in occupations where personal service involving face-to-face human interaction is an important part of the job. I am confident in stating this conclusion; far less confident in conjecturing what these occupations will be, for the reasons already set forth.

In some respects—especially in terms of what work means to those engaged in it—this picture of the automated world of the future does not look drastically different from the world of the present. Under the general assumptions we made—rapid automation, but under full employment and with a stable skill profile—it will be a happier or more relaxed place than it is now; perhaps more of us will be salesmen. As far as man's productive life is concerned, these do not appear to be earth-shaking changes. Moreover, our conclusions do not depend very sensitively on the exact degree of automation we predict: A little more or a little less would not change the occupational picture much.

THE AUTOMATION OF MANAGEMENT

I have several times sidestepped the question of how far and how fast we could expect management activities to be automated. I have said something about supervision, but little about the large miscellany of management activities involving decision making, problem solving and just plain "thinking."

In what follows I shall use the terms "decision making" and "problem solving" in a broad sense to refer interchangeably to this whole range of activities. Decision making in this sense involves much more than the final choice among possible courses of action. It involves, first of all, detecting the occasions for decision—the problems that have to be dealt with—and directing the organization's attention to them. It involves, second, developing possible problem solutions—courses of action—among which the final choice can be made. Discovering and defining problems, elaborating courses of action and making final choices are all stages in the decision-making process. When the term decision making is used, we generally think of the third stage, but the first two account for many more man hours of effort in organizations than the third. Much more management effort is allocated to attention-directing functions and to the investigation, fact gathering, design and problem solving involved in developing courses of action than to the process of selection. Decision making, defined in this broad way, constitutes the bulk of managerial activity.

The problems that managers at various levels in organizations face can be classified according to how well structured, how routine, how cut and dried they are when they arise. On the one end of the continuum are highly programmed decisions: routine procurement of office supplies or pricing standard products; on the other end of the continuum are unprogrammed decisions: basic, once-for-all decisions to make a new product line, or strategies for labor negotiations on a new contract or major styling decisions. Between these two extremes lie decisions with every possible mixture of programmed and nonprogrammed, well-structured and ill-structured, routine and nonroutine elements.

There is undoubtedly a rough, but far from perfect, correlation between a manager's organization level and the extent to which his decisions are programmed. We would expect the decisions that the president and vice-president face to be less programmed, on the average, than those faced by the factory department head or the factory manager.

We are now in the early stages of a technological revolution of the decision-making process. That revolution has two aspects, one considerably further advanced than the other. The first aspect, concerned largely with decisions close to the programmed end of the continuum, is the province of the new field called *operations research* or *management science*. The second aspect, concerned with unprogrammed as well as programmed decisions, is the province of a set of techniques that are coming to be known as *heuristic programming*.

OPERATIONS RESEARCH

I will not recount the history of operations research. It is largely the product of efforts that began on a large scale during World War II. Nor will I essay a careful definition, for operations research is as much a social movement—a migration of natural scientists, econometricians and mathematicians into the area of business decision making—as it is a definable body of knowledge.

Operations research attempts to apply mathematics and the capabilities of modern electronic computers to business decision making. By now it is clear that the attempt is going to be highly successful. Important areas of business and engineering decision making have yielded to these techniques, and the area of possible and actual application continues to grow.

Let me be more concrete and show how operations research is affecting management and how it will affect it. I shall ignore business data processing—the automation of clerical activities—and look exclusively at management activities. I can describe the situation by examples, for we are interested in the technical and economic potential of these techniques, not the present extent of their use.

(1) Managers make a whole series of decisions to control inventory and production: purchasing decisions, setting the production rate and product mix, ordering stock for warehouses, shipping decisions and the like. Several alternative mathematical techniques are now available for making such decisions; these techniques have been more or less extensively tested in practical situations, and they are being used in day-to-day decision making in a number of companies. The evidence seems to me convincing that decisions of these kinds can now be made, in most situations, with the aid of operations research techniques and with the virtual elimination of managerial judgment, far better than such decisions have been made in the past. Moreover, in most tests that have been made, even at this early stage in the development and application of such techniques, they have shown that they can

justify themselves economically. There is little or no excuse for purchasing agents, production control managers,
factory managers or warehouse managers intervening in
such decisions any more. (I hasten to add that, as with
any new technique, a company that wishes to make use of
it must be willing to incur some development and training
expense.)

(2) The injection of the mathematical techniques just
mentioned into the clerical processes involved in procurement, factory production control and filling customers'
orders can permit the virtually complete automation of
this flow in many situations, with the removal of both
clerical and low-level management participation from the
day-to-day activity. Customers' orders can be received and
filled, the customer invoiced, orders placed on the factory
and raw-material stocks replenished—all untouched by
human hands and unthought of by human decision
makers.

(3) Mathematical techniques for detailed scheduling of
factory production, while less far advanced than the techniques just described, will almost certainly have reached
within five or ten years the point where scheduling can
also be completely automated, both in its clerical and in
its decision-making aspects.

(4) In the early years of the computer, one of its main
applications was to relieve engineering organizations of
the bulk of routine calculations in design. The computer
initially was a clerical aid to analysis. Within the past three
or four years, we have discovered how the computer can
also take over the design-synthesis job in many relatively
simple situations. (Though these situations are "simple,"
they were complex enough to require the services of college-trained engineers.) To put it simply, computers can
now take customers' orders for many types of electric
motors, generators and transformers, synthesize devices
that meet the design specifications, and send the manufacturing specifications to the factory floor—again untouched by human hands. Where these techniques are
now used, it is reported that they yield improved designs
at about the same cost as the human design process they
replace.

(5) Computers, programmed to carry out linear programming calculations, are now widely used to determine product mix for oil refineries and to determine formulas for commercial feed mixes. The Iowa farmer who tunes in to the morning radio reports of hog prices now learns from the commercial that XYZ feed gives him the best nutrition at the lowest cost because it is blended by electronic computers using modern mathematical techniques.

(6) A large commercial air line has used computers to simulate major parts of its flight and terminal operation and has used the simulation to decide how many reserve aircraft it needed—an investment decision of great magnitude.

The plain fact is that a great many middle-management decisions that have always been supposed to call for the experienced human judgment of managers and professional engineers can now be made at least as well by computers as by managers. Moreover, a large part of the total middle-management job consists of decisions of the same general character as those that have already yielded to automation. The decisions are repetitive and require little of the kinds of flexibility that constitute man's principal comparative advantage over machines. We can predict with some confidence, I think, that persons making such decisions will constitute a much smaller fraction of the total occupied group within a few years than they do now.

HEURISTIC PROGRAMMING[7]

The mathematical and computing techniques for making programmed decisions replace man but they do not generally simulate him. That is to say, a computer scheduling a refinery does not make the same calculations as would be made by an experienced refinery scheduler —even if it comes out with a very similar solution.[8]

This fact has led to some misconceptions about the nature of computers and about their potentialities. "Computers are just very speedy morons for carrying out arithmetic calculations," it is often said. "They only do what you program them to do." These statements belong to that class of half-truths that are important just because their implications are so misleading. I shall have to pause long enough to make some categorical statements about computers. I do not have space here to develop them at length.

(1) Computers are very general devices capable of manipulating all kinds of symbols—words as readily as numbers. The fact that computers generally do arithmetic is an historical accident. If a particular decision-making situation is not quantitative we cannot handle it with traditional mathematical techniques. This constitutes no essential barrier to computerization. Much successful research has been carried out in the past five years on the use of computers for processing nonnumerical information.

(2) Computers behave like morons only because we are just beginning to learn how to communicate with them in something better than moronic language. There now exist so-called compiling techniques (e.g., FORTRAN) that instruct computers in general language very similar to the ordinary language of mathematics. With these compilers, we now can program a computer to evaluate a formula by writing down little more than the formula itself comparable power have been developed for nonnumerical computing. They have not reached the point where they permit the programmer to communicate with the computer in idiomatic English, but only in a kind of simple pidgin English.

(3) Computers do only what you program them to do, but (1) you can program them to behave adaptively, and (2) you can program them to improve their own programs on the basis of their experiences—that is, to learn. Hence, the more accurate statement is: Computers do only what you program them to do in exactly the same sense that humans do only what their genes and their cumulative experiences program them to do. This assertion leaves little room for free will in either computer or human, but it leaves a great deal of room in both for flexible, adaptative, complex, intelligent behavior.

(4) It has now been demonstrated, by doing it, that computers can be programmed to solve relatively ill-structured problems by using methods very similar to those

used by humans in the same problem-solving situations: that is, by highly selective trial-and-error search using all sorts of rules of thumb to guide the selection; by abstracting from the given problem and solving first the abstracted problem; by using analogy; by reasoning in terms of means and ends, goals and subgoals; by adjusting aspirations to the attainable. There is no longer reason to regard phenomena like judgment and insight as either unanalyzable or unanalyzed, for, in some forms at least, these phenomena have been simulated—computers have exercised judgment and exhibited insight. The range of capabilities of computer programs of this sort is still extremely narrow, but the significant point is that some such programs have been written, tested and even compared in their behavior with the behavior of human laboratory subjects performing the same tasks.

Computer programs that handle nonnumerical tasks, use humanoid problem-solving techniques (instead of the systematic algorithmic techniques of classical mathematics) and sometimes include learning processes, are called *heuristic programs*. They incorporate, in their processes, one or more aspects of what has been called the art of plausible reasoning, an art that guides us through the numerous, diverse, ill-structured decisions of everyday life.

The engineering design programs I mentioned earlier are really heuristic programs, for they involve inductive reasoning. Heuristic programs have now been written for such tasks as playing checkers, playing chess, finding proofs for geometry theorems and for theorems in elementary symbolic logic, solving trigonometric and algebraic identities, balancing a factory assembly line, composing music (the ILLIAC Suite) and memorizing nonsense syllables. One program, the General Problem Solver, while not as general as its name may suggest, is entirely free from reference to any particular subject matter and is, in fact, a quite flexible scheme for reasoning in terms of goals and subgoals about any subject.[9]

Let me make my point perfectly clear. Heuristic programs do not merely substitute machine brute force for human cunning. Increasingly, they imitate—and in some

cases improve upon—human cunning. I can illustrate this
by describing briefly the three existing computer programs for playing chess.[10] One of these, the Los Alamos
program, depends heavily on machine speed. The program examines, at each move, almost one million alternative possibilities, evaluating them on the basis of simple,
crude criteria and selecting the one that appears best.
Clearly it is doing something quite different from the human chess player—the human neither could nor would
select moves in this way. The second program, Bernstein's
program, is much more selective. It examines about 2,500
alternatives, chosen on the basis of rules of thumb a chess
player would use and evaluates them in a slightly more
complicated way than does the Los Alamos program. The
third program, the RAND-Carnegie program, is still more
selective. It seldom examines as many as fifty alternatives
but selects those to be examined and evaluates them in a
rather involved way. All three programs, at present, play
about the same level of chess—a very low level, it should
be said. But they achieve this result in quite different
ways. The Los Alamos program, though it embodies certain heuristic ideas, calls for machine speed rather than
machine intelligence. The RAND-Carnegie program begins to approach, in the rules of thumb it embodies, the
processes a human uses in choosing a chess move. Bernstein's program lies midway between the other two. Thus,
in talking about our increasing capacity to write heuristic
programs that simulate human problem solving, I am
speaking of programs that lie toward the RAND-Carnegie
end of this continuum rather than the Los Alamos end. I
am speaking of programs that reason, think and learn.

The microcosm of chess may still appear to you far more
structured and programmed than the macrocosm of the
everyday world. Perhaps it is, although the point could
be argued. However that may be, the microcosm of chess
is sufficiently complex, sufficiently rich in alternatives,
sufficiently irregular in structure that it poses to the problem-solving organism or mechanism the same *kinds* of
difficulties and requirements that are posed—perhaps in
higher degree—by ill-structured problems in general.
Hence, the fact that chess programs, theorem-proving

programs, music-composing programs and a factory-scheduling program now exist indicates that the conceptual mountains have been crossed that barred us from understanding how the human mind grapples with everyday affairs. It is my conviction that no major new ideas will have to be discovered to enable us to extend these early results to the whole of human thinking, problem-solving, decision-making activity. We have every reason to believe that within a very short time—I am even willing to say ten years or less—we will be able technically to produce computers that can grapple with and solve at least the range of problems that humans are able to grapple with and solve—those that are ill-structured as well as those that are well-structured.

If the technical prediction is correct, what about the economics of the matter? Again, we must apply the doctrine of comparative advantage. To what extent, in 1985, will managers and other humans be occupied in thinking about and solving ill-structured problems, as distinct from doing other things? On this point the image in my crystal ball is very dim. I will nevertheless hazard some guesses. My first guess is that man will retain a greater comparative advantage in handling ill-structured problems than in handling well-structured problems. My second guess is that he will retain a greater advantage in tasks involving sensory-manipulative coordination—"physical flexibility" —than in ill-structured problem-solving tasks—"mental flexibility." If this is true, a larger part of the working population will be mahouts and wheelbarrow pushers and a smaller part will be scientists and executives—particularly of the staff variety. The amount of shift in this direction will be somewhat diminished by the fact that as income and general productivity rise, the demand for work involving ill-structured problem solving will probably increase more than the demand for work involving flexible manipulation of the physical environment. The demand for psychiatric work will increase more rapidly than the demand for surgical work—but the rate of automation of the former will be much greater than the rate of automation of the latter.

A SUMMARY: THE AUTOMATION
OF MANAGEMENT

Our analysis rests on the assumption that managers are largely concerned with supervising, with solving well-structured problems and with solving ill-structured problems. We have predicted that the automation of the second of these activities—solving well-structured problems—will proceed extremely rapidly; the automation of the third—solving ill-structured problems, moderately rapidly; and the automation of supervision more slowly. However, we have also concluded that, as less and less work becomes man paced and more and more of it machine paced, the nature of supervision will undergo change. There is no obvious way to assess quantitatively all these cross currents and conflicting trends. We might even conclude that management and other professional activities, taken collectively, may constitute about the same part of the total spectrum of occupations a generation hence as they do now. But there is reason to believe that the kinds of activities that now characterize middle management will be more completely automated than the others and hence will come to have a smaller part in the whole management picture.

SOME OTHER DIMENSIONS
OF CHANGE IN MANAGEMENT

There are other dimensions for differentiating management and professional tasks, of course, besides the one we have been using. It is possible that if we described the situation in terms of these other dimensions, the change would appear larger. Let me explore this possibility just a little bit further.

First, I think we can predict that in future years the manager's time perspective will be lengthened. As automated subsystems take over the minute-by-minute and day-by-day operation of the factory and office, the humans in the system will become increasingly occupied with preventive maintenance, with system breakdowns and malfunctions, and—perhaps most important of all—with the design and modification of systems. The automatic

factory will pretty much—and subject to all of the qualifications I have introduced—run itself; the company
executives will be much more concerned with tomorrow's
automatic factory. Executives will have less excuse than
they now have to let the emergencies of today steal the
time that was allocated to planning for the future. I don't
think planning is going to be a machineless function—it
also will be carried out by man-machine systems, but with
perhaps a larger man component and a smaller machine
component than day-to-day operations.

Does this mean that executives will need a high level
of technical competence in the engineering of automated
factories or data-processing systems? Probably not. Most
automation calls for increased technical skills for maintenance in the early stages; but the farther automation proceeds, the less those who govern the automated system
need to know about the details of its mechanism. The
driver of a 1960 automobile needs to know less about what
is under the hood than the driver of a 1910 automobile.
The user of a 1960 computer needs to know less about
computer design and operation than the user of a 1950
computer. The manager of a highly automated 1985 factory will need to know less about how things are actually
produced, physically, in that factory than the manager
of a 1960 factory.

Similarly, we can dismiss the notion that computer programmers will become a powerful elite in the automated
corporation. It is far more likely that the programming
occupation will become extinct (through the further development of self-programming techniques) than that it
will become all-powerful. More and more, computers will
program themselves; and direction will be given to computers through the mediation of compiling systems that
will be completely neutral so far as content of the decision
rules is concerned. Moreover, the task of communicating
with computers will become less and less technical as
computers come—by means of compiling techniques—
closer and closer to handling the irregularities of natural
language.[11]

I suppose that managers will be called on, as automation proceeds, for more of what might be described as

systems thinking. They will need, to work effectively, to understand their organizations as large and complex dynamic systems involving various sorts of man-machine and machine-machine interactions. For this reason, persons trained in fields like servomechanism engineering or mathematical economics, accustomed to dynamic systems of these kinds, and possessing conceptual tools for understanding them, may have some advantage, at least initially, in operating in the new world. Since no coherent science of complex systems exists today, universities and engineering schools are understandably perplexed as to what kinds of training will prepare their present students for this world.

THE BROADER SIGNIFICANCE OF AUTOMATION

I have tried to present my reasons for making two predictions that appear, superficially, to be contradictory: that we will have the technical capability, by 1985, to manage corporations by machine; but that humans, in 1985, will probably be engaged in roughly the same array of occupations as they are now. I find both of these predictions reassuring.

Acquiring the technical capacity to automate production as fully as we wish, or as we find economical, means that our per capita capacity to produce will continue to increase far beyond the point where any lurking justification will remain for poverty or deprivation. We will have the means to rule out scarcity as mankind's first problem and to attend to other problems that are more serious.[12]

Since, in spite of this increased productivity, the occupations that humans will find in the corporation of 1985 will be familiar ones, we can dismiss two fears: first, the fear of technological unemployment, second, the "R.U.R. fear" —the fear that many people feel at the prospect of fraternizing with robots in an automated world. Fraternize we shall, but in the friendly, familiar way that we now fraternize with our automobiles and our power shovels.

Having dismissed, or dealt with, these two issues, we shall be better prepared to face the more fundamental problems of that automated world. These are not new problems, nor are they less important than the problems of scarcity and peace. But they are long-range rather than short-range problems, and hence seldom rise to the head of the agenda as long as there are more pressing issues still around. Three of them in particular, I think, are going to receive a great deal of attention as automation proceeds: developing a science of man, finding alternatives for work and production as basic goals for society and reformulating man's view of his place in the universe.

A SCIENCE OF MAN

I have stressed the potentialities of the computer and of heuristic programming as substitutes for human work. The research now going on in this area is equally important for understanding how humans perform information-processing tasks—how they think. That research has already made major progress toward a psychology of cognitive processes, and there are no reasons to hope that the potential of the new tools is not limited to cognition but may extend to the affective aspects of behavior as well.

We can predict that in the world of 1985 we shall have psychological theories that are as successful as the theories we have in chemistry and biology today. We shall have a pretty good understanding of how the human mind works. If that prediction is correct, it has obvious and fundamental consequences for both pedagogy and psychiatry. We may expect very rapid advances in the effectiveness and efficiency of our techniques of teaching and our techniques for dealing with human maladjustment.

SOCIAL GOALS

The continuing rise in productivity may produce profound changes, in addition to those already caused by the Industrial Revolution, in the role that work plays in man's life and among man's goals. It is hard to believe—although this may just exhibit the weakness of my imagination—that man's appetite for gadgets can continue to expand at the rate required to keep work and production in central roles in the society. Even Galbraith's proposal for diverting expenditures from gadgets to social services can only be a temporary expedient. We shall have to, finally, come to grips with the problem of leisure.

In today's society, the corporation satisfies important social and psychological needs in addition to the needs for goods and services. For those who do well in managerial careers, it satisfies needs for success and status. For some of these men and for others, it is one of the important outlets for creativity. In a society where scarcity of goods and services is of little importance, those institutions, including the corporation, whose main function is to deal with scarcity, will occupy a less central position than they have in the past. Success in management will carry smaller rewards in prestige and status than it now does. Moreover, as the decision-making function becomes more highly automated, corporate decision making will perhaps provide fewer outlets for creative drives than it now does. Alternative outlets will have to be supplied.

MAN IN THE UNIVERSE

It is only one step from the problem of goals to what psychiatrists now refer to as the identity crisis, and what used to be called cosmology. The developing capacity of computers to simulate man—and thus both to serve as his substitute and to provide a theory of human mental functions—will change man's conception of his own identity as a species.

The definition of man's uniqueness has always formed the kernel of his cosmological and ethical systems. With Copernicus and Galileo, he ceased to be the species located at the center of the universe, attended by sun and stars. With Darwin, he ceased to be the species created and specially endowed by God with soul and reason. With Freud, he ceased to be the species whose behavior was—potentially—governable by rational mind. As we begin to produce mechanisms that think and learn, he has ceased to be the species uniquely capable of complex, intelligent manipulation of his environment.

I am confident that man will, as he has in the past, find a new way of describing his place in the universe—a way that will satisfy his needs for dignity and for purpose. But it will be a way as different from the present one as was the Copernican from the Ptolemaic.

FOOTNOTES

1. In preparing this paper, I have drawn heavily on two previous essays written in collaboration with Allen Newell: "Heuristic Problem Solving: the Next Advance in Operations Research," *Operations Research,* Vol. 6 (Jan.-Feb., 1958), 1-10; and "What Have Computers to Do with Management?" in G. P. Shultz and T. L. Whisler, eds., *Proceedings of the McKinsey Seminar* (1959).

2. The difficulty that laymen find with this point underlies the consistent failure of economists to win wide general support for the free trade argument. The central idea—that comparative advantage, not absolute advantage, counts—is exactly the same in the two cases.

3. I am oversimplifying, for there is another term in this equation. With a general rise in productivity and with shifts in relative prices due to uneven technological progress in different spheres, the demands for some kinds of goods and services will rise more rapidly than the demands for others. Hence, other things being equal, the total demand will rise in those occupations (of men and machines) that are largely concerned with producing the former, more rapidly than in occupations concerned largely with producing the latter. I have shown elsewhere how all these mechanisms can be handled formally in analyzing technological change.

See "Productivity and the Urban-Rural Population Balance," in *Models of Man* (New York: John Wiley & Sons, Inc., 1957), Chap. 12; and "Effects of Technological Change in a Linear Model," in T. Koopmans, ed., *Activity Analysis of Production and Allocation* (New York: John Wiley & Sons, Inc., 1951), Chap. 15.

4. I think I have fairly summarized the conclusions reached by those few observers who have looked in detail at actual cases of recent automation. Two excellent references are James R. Bright, *Automation and Management* (Boston: Harvard University Graduate School of Business Administration, 1958); and S. Lilley, *Automation and Social Progress* (New York: International Publishers Co., Inc., 1957).

5. This example will seem entirely fanciful only to persons not aware of some of the research now going on into the possible automation of psychiatric processes.

6. I advise the reader, before he makes up his mind as to what is feasible and infeasible, likely and unlikely, to try out his imagination on a sample of occupations, e.g., dentist, waitress, bond salesman, chemist, carpenter, college teacher.

7. The ideas in this section grew out of work in a joint Carnegie Tech-RAND Corporation research project, and I am deeply indebted to Allen Newell, J. C. Shaw, and other colleagues in that project for this common product.

8. On the other hand, the computer programs for synthesizing motor, transformer, and generator design do mimic rather closely the processes previously used by engineers. These programs stand on the border line between the operations research techniques discussed in the previous section and the heuristic techniques discussed in this section.

9. See A. Newell, J. C. Shaw and H. A. Simon, "Report on a General Problem-solving Program," reprinted in *Computers and Automation,* Vol. 8 (July, 1959), 10-17.

10. See A. Newell, J. C. Shaw and H. A. Simon, "Chess-playing Programs and the Problem of Complexity," *IBM Research and Development Journal,* Vol. 2 (Oct., 1958), 320-35.

11. We can dismiss in the same way the fears that some have expressed that only mathematicians will be able to cope with a computerized world.

12. In saying this, I am not unaware of the apparent instability of wants. We can, however, make moral distinctions between the neediness of an Indian peasant and the neediness of an American middle-class one-car family.

Part Four

IMPLICATIONS
FOR
LABOR

· 10 ·

Congressional Testimony*

by Walter P. Reuther

PRESIDENT, UNITED AUTOMOBILE, AIRCRAFT &
AGRICULTURAL IMPLEMENT WORKERS OF AMERICA

Almost five years have passed since the Subcommittee on
Economic Stabilization of the Joint Economic Committee,
also under the chairmanship of Congressman Wright Patman, commenced its investigations into the impact of automation on the economy of the United States.

In those five years, considerable advances have been
made in the techniques of automation—much greater, unfortunately, than the advances that have been made in
the development of programs to deal with the problems
it creates.

In this testimony I intend to use the term "automation"
in the same general sense as the subcommittee accepted
it five years ago. The subcommittee's report stated:

* Reprinted from Testimony Submitted to the Sub-Committee
on Automation and Energy Resources, 86th Congress, Second
Session. Reprinted by permission of the Joint Economic
Committee.

The subcommittee has . . . used the term broadly. It has been used to include all various new automatic and electronic processes, along with rapid technological advance and improved know-how generally.

In what follows it should be understood that the term automation is intended to cover the same broad ground.

At the 1955 hearings I discussed some of the problems that were already apparent in connection with automation. Most of what was said at that time could be said again today, often with increased emphasis, and some of those problems will be referred to again below. However, I do not want at this time merely to repeat what I said in 1955.

Today, we can see much more clearly the impact of automation of our economy as a whole, and I want to commence by looking at this broader aspect—the state of our economy today, the possibilities for future growth which automation now more clearly opens up to us, and the very real problems of large-scale job displacement it has also created.

In its day-to-day activities the UAW has had to face up to these questions of job displacement, not as academic issues, but as stern realities which vitally affect the lives of hundreds of thousands of its members. I should like to say something of what the union has done at the collective bargaining table and in the plants to help solve these problems, of further steps that have been planned for the future and of those areas in which legislative action also is required.

One of the major problems closely related to automation and technological change is the increase in areas of chronic distress in our country—whole communities that have had their economies virtually destroyed by shifts of industry. These are the areas in which there has been the most serious failure to meet the problems or seize the opportunities created by automation, but as I shall endeavor to show, throughout our whole economy we have failed to use the potential benefits of automation as we could have done, to solve many of the problems which are piling up on us today. Finally, I will discuss specifically some of the policies that the UAW believes our country should adopt to meet the challenge of automation in the future.

UNSOLVED ECONOMIC PROBLEMS

Since the subcommittee's hearing in 1955 the scientists and technicians have been providing us with continuing technological advances, while those already developed have been continually spreading throughout industry and business. Unfortunately, solutions to the problems of production have not been accompanied by equally effective solutions to the problems of distribution. For most of the past five years our economy has failed to generate the purchasing power necessary to absorb the volume of goods and services which we have the technologies and the physical and human resources to produce. As a result, we have not even come close to realizing our full potentialities for economic growth. We have not developed as we could the material basis for elimination of poverty among our own people, for the meeting of our social needs along with an adequate program of national defense, or for the provision of sufficiently generous assistance to those of other nations who are still struggling with the absolutes of national hunger and economic hardship, and with the obstacles to democratic progress which those evils create.

Instead, we have suffered our third postwar recession, sharper and more severe than either of the two which preceded it, and economists are almost unanimous in their prophecies of still a fourth decline, differing only as to whether it is likely to begin this year or next.

Even in so-called good times, the tide of unemployment washes higher and higher. When I testified on automation in October, 1955, unemployment, after adjustment for seasonal factors, represented 4.4 per cent of the labor force. That in itself was a substantially higher figure than is commensurate with our national goal of full employment. But for almost three years now the rate of unemployment has been continuously higher than it was at that time. Not in any month since August, 1957, have we seen an unemployment figure below that for October, 1955—

which, incidentally, was the highest month in the last half
of that year.

Side by side with human unemployment we face the
waste of unused physical productive capacity. This year,
although we already have gloomy forebodings of troubled
times to come, we are supposedly still in the upward-mov-
ing phase of the business cycle. Yet, as this is written,
steel production for the week beginning July 10, 1960, is
scheduled at 53.1 per cent of capacity. In the automobile industry actual current capacity is difficult to measure
because it is so long since the industry has produced at
anything like its peak. On the basis of earlier years, however, it would seem conservative to estimate that the industry has a capacity of at least ten million passenger cars
per year. On that basis, the industry for the first six months
of this year operated at only 76 per cent of capacity, and
for the full year will probably average about 65 to 70 per
cent.

For manufacturing industry as a whole, production in
May, 1960, was less than 1 per cent higher than at the end
of 1959, when we were utilizing only 85 per cent of our
available manufacturing capacity, and there has been some
expansion of capacity in the intervening five months.

The significance of these figures to the study of automation is, we hope, readily apparent. The ability of our
economy to meet the needs of the men and women who
make it up is to be measured primarily not by the degree
of its technological progress—the variety of new and awe-
inspiring machines it can produce to take over human
functions. The major measure of an economy's success
must be the extent to which it utilizes the productive resources available to it, both physical and human, to meet
human needs and to fulfill human aspirations. No amount
of advanced technological equipment serves its purpose
if it is not used—or if its use means only that men and
women are left without the employment they want and
need.

The greatest tragedy of our failure to make full use of
the productive resources available to us is that so many
of the needs of our people are still unmet. Millions of
families still live in conditions of economic need. Accord-

ing to the Census Bureau, in 1959 there were still 22.7 per cent of American families (not counting single persons living alone) with incomes below three thousand dollars. In the fields of education, of health, of housing, in our lack of adequate programs for urban redevelopment, for the recovery of distressed areas, for highways, for conservation of land and water resources and for numerous community facilities, we have achieved far less than our needs dictate. And the help we have extended to other peoples far less fortunate than we has been but a pittance in comparison with their tremendously greater needs.

ACCELERATION OF PRODUCTIVITY

Automation and technological progress generally provide the physical and technical means by which these needs can and should be met. These means to progress are increasing, not at a linear rate of advance, but at an accelerating rate.

In my testimony before the subcommittee in 1955 I indicated our conviction, supported by statements from numerous leaders of industry, that such acceleration was taking place. I said:

> This great expansion of industrial research, and the flood of routine technological innovations it produces, have been sufficient, alone, in recent years to boost the rate of rising productivity to the extent that past notions of what were normal productivity increases are already obsolete. Technological improvements of this sort, and on an increasing scale, can be expected to continue. By themselves, they would pose serious problems of adjusting our economy so as to provide sufficient purchasing power to absorb the steadily accelerating flow of goods which can be produced with every man hour of labor.

> Beyond these routine technological improvements, however, we are now confronted with the potentially explosive impact of automation, and we can be sure that this new technology, too, will grow by leaps and bounds.

Since that time, further investigation and analysis have strikingly confirmed the fact of acceleration in the trend of productivity advance. In November, 1955, Professor Sumner H. Slichter of Harvard indicated that in the following ten years—

. . . we can look forward with considerable confidence to a more rapid growth in productivity mainly because of the increasing scale of industrial research and the prospective improvement in the art of management.

In 1956 John Kendrick of the National Bureau of Economic Research, a pioneer in the field of productivity measurement, wrote:

. . . one striking fact stands out: there has been a significant acceleration of productivity advance since the end of World War I as compared with the prior two decades.

Even more specific evidence of a continuing trend to acceleration was provided by Solomon Fabricant, research director of the National Bureau of Economic Research. In the Bureau's 1959 annual report he wrote:

Also—a fact of great importance—the long-term pace of advance in output per man-hour has been speeded up. It was 22 per cent per decade during the quarter century preceding World War I. It has averaged 29 per cent since. During the most recent period—after World War II—national product per man-hour has been rising at an even greater rate, 35 to 40 per cent per decade. This means, in absolute terms, that a 10-year period sees added to the output of each man-hour of American labor an amount well in excess of the *total* output obtained from an hour of work in most parts of the earth. [Emphasis in original.]

In 1958, in connection with automobile industry negotiations of that year, UAW technicians made a careful statistical analysis of changes in the rate of productivity advance over the past fifty years in the United States private economy. The analysis showed a definite, strong trend toward acceleration which had speeded up the trend of productivity advance from 0.9 per cent per year as of 1910 to 3.9 per cent per year as of 1956, the last year covered by the analysis. A continuation of the trend would produce a current figure well above 4 per cent.

Last year the Bureau of Labor Statistics published an analysis entitled "Trends in Output per Man-Hour in the Private Economy, 1909-58," and although the presentation was such as to obscure the significance of the findings, the Commissioner of Labor Statistics later stated that in his opinion it did show the presence of acceleration. The study produced a trend curve similar to that developed by the UAW, using data on man hours worked, which showed a derived trend rate of productivity advance for the year 1958 of 3.9 per cent. A continuation of the trend would put the figure currently at 4 per cent.

Figures for 1959 which have just been released show that the actual rate of productivity increase for that year was 4.2 per cent. What is more significant, in spite of the lagging advance in recent years of economic stagnation, the total productivity advance since the 1947-49 base period has been only 2 per cent less than that indicated by the BLS acceleration curve.

What do these figures mean? They certainly do not provide a guarantee that in any given year the rate of productivity advance will be 4 per cent or more. In 1958, for example, as a direct consequence of the recession, the rate of productivity advance was less than 1 per cent. What the figures mean is simply that on the basis of past experience our economy possesses the capacity to achieve productivity advances at an accelerating rate, and that if the economic policies we adopt are such as to permit full production, we should be able to anticipate a 4 per cent rate of productivity advance now, accelerating to still higher levels in the years ahead.

In addition to advances in the rate of production per man hour, of course, we have a sustained growth in the labor force. This is particularly marked at present as the sharp rise in the birth rate which took place in the 1940's is now beginning to be reflected in a rise in the number of young people reaching working age. The labor force in the past twelve years has increased at a rate well in advance of 1 per cent a year, and the demographers tell us we may expect a rate of about 1.7 per cent during the coming decade.

These two factors together—a rate of productivity advance accelerating upward from 4 per cent a year, and a rate of labor force growth of 1.7 per cent a year—mean that in the next decade we have only to order our economic affairs sensibly to achieve an annual growth rate of 5 per cent or more in our total production, and still have an ample margin for increased leisure.

This is the picture of what automation and other forms of technological advance can mean for us and our economy.

It opens up wide new possibilities for human and social betterment.

A 5 per cent annual growth rate in our national product means that the total volume of all the goods and services we produce can be doubled in just over fourteen years. By 1975 we could have a total production of goods and services in the United States worth a trillion dollars—one thousand billion dollars—at today's prices. Taking population growth into account, this would make possible a personal income after taxes which would average almost three thousand dollars per year for every man, woman and child in America or twelve thousand dollars for an average family of four.

It could mean the absolute elimination of poverty in our land.

It could mean greatly improved standards of living, including increased leisure, for every family.

It could mean rapid progress in providing the fullest educational opportunity to every child, based on adequate facilities and a sufficient number of well-trained and well-paid teachers.

It could provide the means to make the best of health care available to all.

It could mean the elimination of slums, the regeneration of depressed areas and the redevelopment of neglected areas in our cities.

It could give us the means to provide effective assistance to other countries which need help in building up their economies—help which may make the difference between survival or failure of freedom in those lands.

Automation and technological advance have put all these highly desirable goals within our reach. They have done something more. They have made it not merely desirable, but absolutely essential that we reach them.

A 5 per cent growth rate or better can be achieved simply by generating sufficient demand to make full use of our productive resources and provide employ ent for those who are able and willing to work. T is is a major responsibility of government. Alvin Ha en, professor of political economy at Harvard University, wrote in 1943:

> Private business can and will do the job of production. It is the responsibility of government to do its part to insure a sustained demand. We know from past experience that private enterprise has done this for limited periods only. It has not been able to insure a continuous and sustained demand. The ever-increasing gigantic powers of production of the modern industrial system, far exceeding those of any earlier experience in history, mean that an enormous output has to be reached before full employment is approached. Private industry and government together must act to maintain and increase output and income sufficiently to provide substantially full employment.

If we fail to create the necessary demand, we fail to solve the unemployment problem.

That is a very real threat, which automation greatly intensifies.

Automation makes possible a 5 per cent growth rate, provided we develop economic policies which will generate sufficient private and public demand to make use of an additional 5 per cent of goods and services each year.

If we fail to do so, automation will not mean growing

prosperity, but growing unemployment—as it has done, for the most part, during the past seven years.

This is the problem we must solve.

Our enemies believe we cannot solve it. When Premier Khrushchev says, "We will bury you," he means simply that he believes our economic system will fail to solve the problem of distribution. He believes that we will continue to fail, as we have in the past seven years, to match or approach the rate of growth achieved in the Soviet Union. He believes it is only a matter of time until Soviet production surpasses ours, and the Communists are able to take world leadership away from us, not by military might but by economic power alone.

If we fail to make proper use of the opportunities which automation offers us, Premier Khrushchev's prophecy could very well come true.

It is our task to prove him wrong.

FAULTY ECONOMIC POLICIES
AND AUTOMATION PROBLEMS

In referring to the economic troubles which have beset our country in the past seven years, I do not want to suggest that automation can be held responsible for them. The cause of our troubles has been that those who had been placed in positions of responsibility have been trying to live and to force our country to live by the economic theories of the nineteenth century. They have been obsessed with the idea that a balanced budget is more important than a balanced economy. They have clung stubbornly to the belief that the general prosperity can best be served by a system of incentives to the wealthy, by helping the rich to grow still richer so that some of their surplus riches may trickle down to those below. They have rejected entirely the alternative view of modern economists that the only way to assure a prosperous industry is to insure that the demand for goods and services keeps pace with industry's growing ability to produce. They have failed to recognize the true cause of inflation in today's economy, the abuse of the power which is held by a relatively small group of corporations to administer prices without effective competitive checks, and in consequence they have persisted in applying monetary policies which have not stopped inflation but have very seriously checked our economic growth and have been among the major causes of our economic difficulties.

It is perfectly true that automation has helped to accelerate the rate of productivity advance, and to that extent has made it more necessary than ever before that we adopt vigorous and imaginative policies designed to insure the full utilization of our growing productive capacity. But for the most part it is our failure to adopt economic policies suited to our needs that has aggravated the problems caused by automation, rather than automation's having been responsible for our economic difficulties.

The danger that by allowing ourselves to fall into economic troubles we would multiply the problems arising out of automation was foreseen by the subcommittee five years ago. One of its findings stated:

> The shift to automation and the accelerated pace of technological change is taking place today against the background of relatively high employment levels and of a prosperous economic situation. Under such conditions, dislocations and adjustments tend to be less painful. Any significant recession in levels of employment and economic activity might very well create new problems and greatly magnify the adjustment pains growing out of increased mechanization. After all, the challenge to the economy in the maintenance of reasonably full employment involves a great deal more than simply finding new positions for those displaced, whether by automation or other cause. Without giving any regard to changing rates of individual participation in the labor force, our work force is increasing at the rate of more than three-quarter million workers each year. If it should become apparent that automation is, on balance, lessening the job chances of these new entrants into the labor force, the appraisal of its significance would have to be greatly revised.

It requires only the most cursory comparison of today's

levels of unemployment with those which existed when that finding was written to realize that something is lessening the job chances of men and women in our labor force. In my opinion, as I have said, automation is not the primary cause, but there can be no doubt that the generally higher level of unemployment has made tremendously more difficult the problems of those who are displaced by automation.

FORESEEING AUTOMATION PROBLEMS

In my testimony in 1955 I pointed out that we were fortunate in being able to foresee some of the human and economic problems which automation was certain to create. I felt then, as I still feel today, that far too little was and is known as to what we can expect in the way of new problems created by automation. Our government, which under the Employment Act of 1946 has a major responsibility for maintenance of employment opportunities, still knows far too little about what is planned by business and industry in the way of technological innovations, or even the planned application of known technologies, to be able to foresee the impact that such developments will have on employment.

We still know too little about what the consequences of automation have been, to what extent workers have been directly or indirectly displaced, what problems they have had in finding new employment, or what special help in the way of retraining or other assistance would have enabled them to find jobs more quickly. It is quite true that the Department of Labor has done a few studies of the impact of automation in specific instances, but the employers who have been willing to cooperate in making such studies possible appear to be those for whom automation has presented no serious problems of worker displacement.

It is quite true also that such groups as the Special Senate Committee on Unemployment Problems, under the chairmanship of Senator Eugene McCarthy, have taken a long and serious look at the very grave problems which have resulted when whole communities have been left without economic roots because of technological change, and have come up with excellent reports on their findings. But here again there is not, as there should be, any official body whose primary and continuing function it would be not only to analyze such situations and recommend continuing programs to remedy them, but to obtain the information as to business plans which would enable it to foresee such situations and prevent them from developing into local or regional disasters.

Nevertheless, even though we did not know in detail in 1955 what future developments in automation were going to take place, it was possible to foresee in general terms some of the kinds of problems that it was bound to create, and some of them were referred to in my testimony at that time. We knew, for example, that development of new machines and new processes was going to result in the direct displacement of many workers, and that frequently their problems would be more difficult than simply finding the same kind of work somewhere else. We knew that there would be a decreasing demand for the services of the unskilled or semiskilled worker, and that such a worker, once displaced, might find it most difficult to obtain a new job unless he were given the opportunity to learn some useful skill. We knew that there would be problems for skilled workers whose particular skills were taken over or made obsolescent by the new machines. We knew that there would be special problems for older workers, too old to learn new skills, often too old to find suitable employment on any terms. We knew that there would be distress in store for whole communities as automation and other technological changes caused industries to shift their locations.

Some appreciation of the large numbers of workers who have been displaced from their jobs through automation and other technological change in the past 5 years can be obtained from overall statistics of industry. When I testified in 1955 I reported that there had already been a decline of 600,000 wage and salary jobs in manufacturing in the previous 2 years. That decline has continued. In 1955 there were 16,563,000 wage and salary workers in manufacturing industries. By 1959, this had fallen by 400,-000 to 16,156,000—a decline of 2.4 per cent. The index of manufacturing production, incidentally, rose from an average of 145 in 1955 to 158 in 1959. Thus there was a decline of 2.4 per cent in employment while production rose 9 per cent.

Combined wage and salary figures give a picture of the total number of jobs available in manufacturing industries, but this does not tell the whole story of workers displacement. In addition to the overall decline in jobs, there has been a sharper decline in production workers while white-collar jobs have increased. But relatively few factory production workers have either the training or the opportunity to move to a white-collar job. Thus, it is important in terms of worker displacement to note that between 1955 and 1959 production worker employment in manufacturing declined by 837,000—from 13,061,000 to 12,224,000. The fact that about 430,000 other workers had gained office employment in the industry during the same period was of no great help to those who lost their production jobs.

The same facts can be shown for many individual industries. The automobile industry, for example, in the first quarter of 1960 manufactured 2,382,000 cars and trucks, only 0.4 per cent fewer than in the first quarter of 1955. Yet average production worker employment fell from 735,900 to 661,600, a decline of 10.1 per cent. Average weekly hours fell from 43.7 to 42. Total wage and salary employment fell from 888,100 to 827,100, a decline of 6.9 per cent, representing a loss of 61,000 jobs.

Let me make our position clear. We welcome automation as a major force for growth in our economy, holding forth the promise of increasing abundance for all if we use it wisely and well. But it is necessary to look facts in the face if we ever hope to enjoy the benefits of automation without the cost of unnecessary hardship for those whose lives it dislocates. And when the combination of national policies which hamper economic growth and new technologies which accelerate man-hour productivity results in employment declines and displacement of hundreds of thousands of workers in major industries, it is clear that there is going to be hardship and suffering unless active measures are taken to prevent it. In fact, during the past five years there has been a tremendous amount of hardship and suffering affecting millions of American families which could have been prevented and was not because necessary measures were not taken.

In this regard I feel it necessary to answer some of the superficial propaganda and public relations material which major employers in the automobile industry have seen fit to place before other congressional bodies investigating unemployment and associated problems, and which they may well place before this subcommittee, also. Last year, for example, representatives of General Motors and Ford appeared before the Senate Special Committee on Unemployment Problems, under the chairmanship of Senator Eugene McCarthy. They cited the increase in the number of their employees over the previous decade or so as evidence to imply that technological change was not really a problem at all and that it was only necessary to give these big corporations a free hand to carry on their business in their own way and temporary problems of unemployment would disappear.

Even as statistics concerning their own companies, the figures they presented told only half the truth. The representative of General Motors Corporation, for example, cited an increase of 100,000 in General Motors's total United States employment between 1948 and the first 9 months of 1959. He conveniently neglected to say that between 1955 and 1958, largely as a result of General Motors's price and profit policies, United States production worker employment in his corporation had declined by 128,000 (we do not have equivalent figures for total United States employment) and for 1959 was still almost 100,000 below 1955.

This decline was primarily due, of course, to the drop in purchases of motor vehicles, which was in turn related to the 1958 economic recession. But a major cause of that recession was the imbalance in the economy caused by high-price, low-volume policies of corporations like General Motors. A corporation as large as General Motors, with sales totaling close to ten billion dollars even in a bad year, cannot pretend that its price and profit policies do not have a significant effect on the health of the economy as a whole.

An even more significant fact, however, which the corporation spokesmen also neglected to mention, was that the expansion of employment in their plants was in fact more than counterbalanced by displacement of the employees of other employers in the industry. We do not have total United States employment figures for General Motors for the whole of 1959, but it is safe to assume that it would not be too far off the figure quoted for the first 9 months, 100,000 above the employment level for 1948. The annual reports of the other 2 major automakers show that Ford's total United States employment in 1959 was almost 28,000 higher than in 1948, and Chrysler's United States employment was about 15,000 higher. Thus, the Big Three together in 1959 had about 143,000 more wage and salary employees in the United States than in 1948. Yet the motor vehicle industry as a whole had 61,000 fewer wage and salary employees in 1959 than in 1948. Thus, if there were 143,000 more job opportunities with the Big Three, there were over 200,000 fewer job opportunities with other employers in the industry, with all that that implies in terms of worker displacement and individual hardship. And as we shall show, loss of a job with one motor industry employer gives no assurance of finding a job with another.

This change has come about primarily through two developments, both of which are closely related to automation. The first is the increasing concentration of motorcar manufacture among the Big Three. The number of car producers of any significance shrank from 10 in 1948 to 5 in 1959, and the Big Three's share of new car production increased from 80.4 per cent in 1948 to 90.1 per cent in 1959. Automation greatly increases the economies of scale and has undoubtedly raised substantially the minimum volume below which a manufacturer can scarcely hope to produce competitively. At the same time, the increasing frequently of extensive model change and the vast sums spent on advertising and publicity by the major manufacturers make it still more impossible for the small companies to keep up.

The second development has been the increasing integration of parts and accessory manufacture into the operations of the motorcar makers, and the consequent disappearance from the industry of many long-established supplier firms. This, too, has resulted in part from the economies of scale which automation makes possible to the manufacturer who can make the necessary capital investment. Such investment is much more feasible for the motorcar companies, both because of their larger resources and because a car manufacturer can establish a parts plant with a long-range plan of production in mind, whereas the parts supplier is always subject to the buying decisions of the few firms on which he depends.

The Ford department of the UAW has listed some of the major Ford parts which Ford purchased from supplier companies prior to 1948 and which Ford now produces for the most part in its own plants.

Bodies and stampings were formerly purchased from three companies. Now all but one body is made by Ford, and that one will be taken into a Ford plant with the 1961 model.

The six-cylinder engine block used to be cast by a supplier. Ford now casts it at a Ford plant.

Automatic transmissions, formerly purchased, are now made in Ford facilities.

Ford used to purchase approximately half its gears. Now, we understand, all of them will be produced in a new Ford plant.

One firm used to supply Ford with 80 per cent of its wheels. Ford now makes its own wheels.

Prior to 1950, nearly all Ford's die casting was done by various supplier firms. Now it is done by Ford.

Smaller parts such as carburetor, shock absorbers, heater shells and motors, windshield wiper motors and instrument panels used to be purchased for the most part from suppliers. Now they are made in Ford facilities.

Similar lists could undoubtedly be prepared for other manufacturers.

We make no objections to these instances of dynamic change in the automobile industry. We have never supported the view that firms which cannot meet fair competition should somehow be kept in business anyway. To do so would be to subsidize inefficiency. It would raise costs to consumers, and in our experience it almost inevitably means that the workers in such failing plants are expected to provide a major portion of the required subsidy by accepting lower wages and less favorable working conditions than the employees of more efficient producers. Our union has on many occasions made substantial concessions to assist employers who were in temporary difficulties, but we do not accept the principle that workers should permanently subsidize management inefficiency.

On the contrary we have always maintained that managements have the responsibility, as one of the costs of doing business, to make provisions that will help to cushion the impact on their employees of technological change or other changes which may lead to unemployment.

The nature and extent of that impact in the extreme case of a complete plant shutdown was illustrated by a study prepared by Harold L. Sheppard, Louis A. Ferman and Seymour Faber of the Institute of Labor and Industrial Relations, University of Michigan and Wayne State University, and published by the Senate Special Committee on Unemployment Problems. The study was based on interviews in 1957 and 1958 with nearly 500 former employees of the Packard Motor Company, whose Detroit plant was permanently closed in 1956. These were mostly older workers, because the younger men had been laid off earlier as the company's business declined. Only about 14 per cent were under 40 and over 50 per cent were past the age of 55. When they were interviewed, 1 to 2 years later, 22 per cent had not been able to find any kind of job at all, and 51 per cent had been unemployed long enough to exhaust their unemployment compensation. Of those who did find jobs, a substantial proportion had to accept work at lower levels of skill and with lower rates of pay than they had formerly held. In general, the lower their skill and the greater their age, the longer they were unemployed.

Of particular significance as a measure of the occupational displacement which took place is the fact that out of 173 workers interviewed in 1957, only 46, or slightly more than 25 per cent, had been employed by any of the Big Three auto companies, and most of those were among the younger workers. Of the sample, those hired by the Big Three included 58 per cent of the men under 45 years of age, 30 per cent of those 45 to 54 years, 15 per cent of those 55 to 64 years and 5 per cent of those 65 and over. Thus, even at age 45, some 70 per cent of these experienced auto workers were unable to find jobs with the other auto makers.

This emphasizes the fact that increases in the number of workers employed by any one company, and even data about total employment in an industry, may give only a partial picture of the extent to which workers are displaced not only from their jobs but from the industry itself.

What can be done and what has been done to protect workers against either temporary or permanent severance from their jobs, or to cushion the impact of unemployment when it does occur? As I said above, our union has long maintained the principle that protection of workers against such catastrophes should be considered one of the costs of doing business. Industry as a whole profits from technological advance and from the general dynamism of our economy, and one of the first charges against those profits should be the cost of reasonable protection for those workers to whom the change brings only loss of a job.

This is not merely a principle which we in the UAW hold; it is one which as far as possible we have put into practice through the provisions of our collective bargaining agreements. We have not yet achieved all that we would like or all that our members need, but we have made progress.

In the hearings of the Senate Committee on Unemployment Problems, referred to above, representatives of all the Big Three made a major point of the steps they have taken to prevent avoidable unemployment in their plants, to provide new job opportunities to workers displaced by automation and to provide financial assistance to those laid off. In some cases they did not attempt to disguise the fact that these measures had been negotiated with the UAW, since they are written right into our bargaining agreements. However, one employer (Ford) attempted to take full credit even for SUB, and none gave any indication of the hard battles, in many cases extending over years, which they had put up in opposition to these provisions before they were finally written into the agreements. No mention was made of the fact that many of them were won only after the union had been forced to resort to strike action.

One of the major forms of protection which was pioneered by the UAW, not only against the opposition of the auto manufacturers but against all the propaganda weapons of the NAM and the United States Chamber of Commerce, is the supplemental unemployment benefit plan. This plan, as amended in 1958, provides our members with amounts which, when added to unemployment compensation, assure most laid-off workers of income equal to 65 per cent of their take-home pay for periods up to 39 weeks. From the time benefits under these plans first became payable in June, 1956, through the end of 1959, over $86,000,000 had been paid out of SUB trust funds to UAW members laid off from Big Three auto plants alone. Tens of millions more have been paid under SUB plans negotiated with other employers. Not only have these payments averted much hardship for UAW members and their families, but by helping to maintain their buying power during the recession the payments also made a significant contribution to preventing the decline from going farther than it did, and toward speeding recovery. Similar protection is provided to workers in the steel, rubber, aluminum and many other industries through plans of the same nature.

Perhaps the greatest benefit derived by workers from SUB plans, however, especially in the auto industry, is their effect in stimulating management to provide increased stability of employment by making unemployment costly to the employer. For many years one of the bugbears of work in the auto industry has been its uncertainty. Workers laid off for model changes might be unemployed for a few weeks or for months. There were sharp alternations between full employment and overtime in one month and reduced work weeks and layoffs in another. The danger that whole plants might be closed as a consequence of modernization programs added to the instability. That instability has by no means disappeared, but we believe it has to some extent been curbed. A statement made by a Ford vice president before the Senate Committee on Unemployment Problems is, I think, significant. He said:

> In the course of this experience [the expansion and substantial automation of its plant between 1951 and 1957] Ford Motor Co. developed and pursued policies designed to minimize layoffs in connection with the movement of operations, and particularly the difficulties that might confront older workers seeking jobs elsewhere. *These policies had to be developed and carried out, of course, within limitations dictated by the company's need to achieve and maintain competitive costs.* [Emphasis mine.]

Later the same speaker referred to improved planning designed to reduce the amount of unemployment at model change-over time.

The particular significance of the above statement, in my opinion, is the importance placed on costs, because the UAW SUB plans have stimulated company efforts to prevent avoidable unemployment, by reflecting unemployment as a cost on the companies' books. Every company policymaker knows that decisions which result in layoffs of employees will result in payments from SUB funds which must subsequently be replaced at a rate of 5 cents per man hour in added labor costs. In companies where funds have been built up to the neighborhood of 100 per cent of maximum funding requirements, this effect can be felt very rapidly, but in all cases company planners know that layoffs mean pay-outs of funds which will sooner or later be reflected in higher costs.

This was one of the major principles incorporated in the guaranteed employment plan which the UAW proposed in 1955 auto industry negotiations, and was carried through into the supplemental unemployment benefits plans which came out of those negotiations. A corporation's plans, such as the automation programs in the auto industry, are based for the most part on calculations of what will in the long run produce the greatest profit. If those plans also involve, as they frequently must, decisions which can mean unemployment for some of the company's workers, the social cost of that unemployment ought to be considered one of the costs of the program adopted, just as much as the cost, for example, of discarding usable machinery. Only then can we be sure that avoidable unemployment will in fact be avoided. Only then can we be sure that decisions will be influenced by at least a part of the social costs which they involve. And by such means we can best insure also that corporations make an adequate contribution toward the protection of those whose employment is sacrificed for the sake of technological progress.

Over the years we have been able to negotiate numerous provisions in our collective bargaining agreements which protect our members against dismissal in the event of job displacement. These provisions are the worker's frontline of defense against the threat which automation poses to him as an individual. Even the employers who fought most stubbornly against them when we first proposed them now point with pride to the measures they have taken under these provisions as evidence of their concern to cushion the impact of automation on their employees.

For the most part now employees who are permanently displaced from their jobs can exercise plant-wide seniority in transferring to other jobs they can do. This eliminates the evil of older workers being dismissed because job requirements in one department of a plant have changed, while another department might be hiring new men off the street.

In areas such as Detroit, where one company may have several plants, our major agreements now provide that a plant which is hiring must give preference to seniority employees of the company laid off from other plants. These employees can now carry with them to the new job the rights to such benefits as insurance, pensions and supplemental unemployment benefits which they may have built up at another plant.

When jobs are transferred to a new plant, many of our agreements protect the right of workers to transfer with the job if they wish, carrying with them their seniority rights. In addition, some agreements provide that when a new plant is hiring it will give preference to laid-off employees from any other of the company's plants.

Willingness of employers to make such arrangements has been affected by the negotiation in 1958 of amendments to our SUB plans which provide for separation payments, graduated in accordance with length of service up to thirty weeks' full pay, to workers who are permanently displaced from their jobs. Once again, by making loss of employment a cost item on the employer's books, we have been able to increase greatly the employer's concern to maintain employment.

In a period of rapidly advancing technology many problems revolve around the acquisition or updating of workers' skills. Our major agreements have been broadened to help workers meet these problems. Apprenticeship programs, for example, have traditionally provided an upper age limit, typically in the mid twenties, after which an applicant would not be accepted for skilled trades training. We have been able to negotiate the elimination or very substantial raising of this age limit for employees already on company pay rolls, so that workers beyond the normal apprenticeable age have an opportunity of training themselves in new skills.

An important protection for the older worker who may find it impossible to adjust to the demands imposed by automation has been the negotiation of flexible pension programs permitting retirement before the normal age. Typical provisions permit workers to retire of their own volition at any time after age sixty with a pension which is actuarially reduced in accordance with the added years of payment, or to retire at company request or by mutual agreement with a pension which until age sixty-five is double the normal amount, to compensate for the fact that the retiree is not yet eligible for OASI. The latter provision, for retirement by mutual agreement, is commonly applied to meet the problems of workers over sixty in such situations as plant closing or large-scale job displacement due to automation.

In addition, the vesting of pension rights, although not yet complete, affords workers who are displaced with substantial protection of the pension rights they may have earned through many years of service.

The substantial progress we have made in negotiating the protection workers need in the age of automation has not blinded us to the fact that many improvements in the present programs are still required. We anticipate that such improvements will be opposed by employers just as the present programs were when we first proposed them. We anticipate also that their opposition will be overcome, and that in future hearings management representatives will be claiming full credit for the advances they now oppose, just as they now claim credit for those they opposed in the past.

Among those features of our proposed collective bargaining program which relate closely to the needs created by automation, strengthening and extension of workers' transfer rights when jobs or plants are moved rank high. Workers displaced by a change in plant location should have the right to transfer to the new location whether or not the same job as they have been doing will be available, provided there is work at the new plant which they can do or can learn to do. This is now the practice under some of our agreements, but should be extended to many more.

Workers transferring to new locations because a company decision has displaced them from former jobs should be reimbursed by the employer for the costs involved in effecting such transfer, including allowances to defray the workers' unusual expenses connected with the move. Many corporations already recognize this principle as it applies to their executives. The principle behind this demand is the familiar one that the company will not make such a move unless it expects to profit by it, that the worker's moving and relocation costs are in fact part of the total cost of the company's decision, that the worker should not have to make a financial sacrifice in consequence of a decision from which his employer will profit, and that by reflecting such costs on the company's books, moves which in fact are not economically sound will be discouraged.

Workers who elect not to transfer should receive adequate separation pay without loss of seniority status. Under present agreements, a worker has to choose between forfeiting all future rights to be rehired if suitable work should become available, or forfeiting his claim to separation pay. We have proposed to the major corporations a formula by which the employee could receive separation pay and still retain his seniority status, while at the same time protecting the employer by provision for reduction of future separation payments by any amounts previously received.

In multiplant corporations, we have made a start at broadening area-wide preferential hiring agreements into area-wide seniority agreements. Broadening of many seniority agreements within plants is also progressing.

Area-wide preferential hiring agreements should also be broadened to cover not merely plants of the same corporation, but other companies in the same industry and area. This would mean, for example, that when a plant is closed because one company cannot withstand competition, or even more importantly when a plant is closed or workers laid off because the major manufacturers have withdrawn contracts from a supplier firm, the employees in those plants would be given preference by other companies in the industry in that area when they are hiring new employees. Such agreements, generally applied, would be of benefit to employers as well as their workers, since by reducing periods of unemployment they would also reduce the drain on SUB funds.

The age of automation requires the establishment of programs under joint union-management control and direction, to train or retrain workers without loss of wages for jobs which will enable them to meet the requirements of technological change. Agreements should also protect against threatened dilution of skills and encroachments on standards of workmanship.

Other unions are also facing and meeting the problems

created by automation. Thus, for example, the recent steel
settlement provided for establishment of a joint labor-management committee to work out such problems. Recent agreements in the meat-packing industry provide for
the setting up of joint union-management committees,
financed by company contributions of one cent for each
one hundred pounds of meat shipped. From the funds so
established the committees will institute—

> a program of training qualified employees in the
> knowledge and skill required to perform new and
> changed jobs so that the present employees may be
> utilized for this purpose to the greatest extent possi-
> ble.

The committees will also study other programs, such as
extension of transfer rights from plant to plant, and—

> any other methods that might be employed to pro-
> mote continued employment opportunities for those
> affected.

While collective bargaining has an essential role to
play in meeting the problems raised by automation, it
cannot provide all the answers. Negotiated programs must
function side by side with public programs. Negotiated retraining programs, for example, cannot meet the needs of
all workers who require retraining, nor can negotiated relocation programs help the employees of a firm which has
gone out of business. In addition, programs similar to
those negotiated through collective bargaining will have
to be provided for the millions of workers still unorganized. Such programs should include vocational training
and retraining for workers in need of new skills; adequate
unemployment compensation benefits extended over a
sufficient time to enable displaced workers to prepare for
and find suitable work without hardship to their families;
travel and relocation allowances for those forced to move
to new communities; pensions at a reduced age for displaced older workers who are unable to find suitable

new jobs; and industrial development and rehabilitation of communities left stranded by the moving of plants.

DISTRESSED AREAS AS SPECIAL PROBLEM

One of the most distressing features of the advance of automation is the spread of areas of chronic unemployment, where industries have either moved out or have sharply declined as a result of technological change. Communities can become blighted for reasons not closely related to technological change, and the distinction matters little if their problems are the same, but in a high proportion of cases the advance of technology can be accorded a large measure of responsibility—whether it be an automobile center such as Detroit, a Pennsylvania railroad town hit by the replacement of steam by Diesel locomotives, a West Virginia mining community affected by technological advances in mining plus the change from coal to other power sources, or a New England textile town abandoned by runaway employers when the need to modernize plants gave them the excuse to relocate elsewhere.

Although the number of distressed areas is somewhat less today than it was during the recession, it is still substantially above the prerecession level. When the subcommittee was first considering problems of automation in November, 1955, for example, a Bureau of Employment Security survey showed 19 major areas and 74 smaller areas which were classified as areas of substantial labor surplus. As of May, 1960, there were 35 major areas and 113 smaller areas listed as areas of substantial labor surplus.

In May, 1960, the bureau made a further classification, within this group, of "areas of substantial and persistent labor surplus," consisting of those areas with 6 per cent or more unemployment whose average annual unemployment rate had been at least 50 per cent above the national average for 3 of the past 4 years, or at least 75 per cent above the national average for 2 of the past 3 years, or at least 100 per cent above the national average for 1 of the past 2 years.

The survey showed that in May, 1960, there were 20 major labor surplus areas and 71 smaller labor surplus areas which met these criteria and in which, as the bureau reported, "high unemployment has been a relatively persistent problem over most of the past few years." Thus, the number of areas with a persistent labor surplus problem today is almost the same as the number with any labor surplus problem in 1955. In fact, 14 of the major areas and 43 of the smaller areas with persistent labor surplus problems today were among the labor surplus areas listed in 1955.

The continuing plight of our distressed areas is a particular responsibility of the Republican administration. One congressional committee after another has investigated the problem, and has reported on the need for assistance. Congress has harkened to those reports, and has voted measures which would have afforded substantial assistance. But congressional action has been repeatedly nullified by the Presidential veto, exercised under the persuasive pressure of those who insist that it would be unAmerican and subversive to use Federal funds to find solutions to local problems.

The problems of the distressed areas, however, are not just local problems. These pockets of concentrated human misery are the by-products of a technological advance from which the whole of society has profited. When the economy of a local community is disrupted and destroyed by that advance, the price of such progress should be shared by the whole of society. It should not be concentrated, as it has been through the administration's refusal to act, among the very communities and families hardest hit and therefore least able to defray the cost of recovery measures.

We are quick enough to apply the principle of mutual assistance against overwhelming misfortunes in the case of natural disasters such as tornado and flood. There was no unseemly delay in our dispatch of field hospitals and supplies to Chile in the wake of recent earthquakes and tidal waves.

The communities in our own country devastated by the decline of the industries on which they were based have waited years, however, for the American conscience to respond to their plight.

The special misfortune of the distressed areas has been that they fell victim to a man-made calamity. For according to the peculiar logic of the conservatism which rules administration economic attitudes, natural calamities are met with a vigorous human response, while the adversity caused by human failures must wait for natural remedies.

This logic flies in the face of the actual experience of the distressed areas, which have continued to be plagued by abnormally high unemployment and its bitter consequences long after the "natural" forces of recovery pulled the rest of the country out of recession.

The testimony of witnesses before the Senate Committee on Unemployment Problems and other congressional panels is replete with evidence of the human cost which technological progress can impose through prolonged unemployment.

There has been so much study and so little remedial action that the patient endurance of the human victims of delay almost surpasses understanding. Congressional inquiry, if it seems at times to be a mere succession of echoes in the void created by the administration's negativism and immobility, at least can serve the function of reiterating the simple facts of human suffering until the national conscience demands an adequate Federal response.

Wherever the committees travel, human suffering lies just under the statistical surface: stagnant communities, broken families, undernourished children, breadwinners whose humanity is daily diminished by a sense of uselessness and futility.

School principals in West Virginia told the Senate committee how unemployment in that state meant hunger, sickness, educational loss for children. Some reports were:

This has been our worst year as far as children not having clothes and school supplies.

We are unable to operate our lunch program because of the few pupils who can buy lunches. Many of our children are not able to buy the school supplies they need.

Many children have been absent until such time as

the parent was able to purchase needed clothing or
shoes.

Many students seem to feel a sense of insecurity
and the general morale of the school has been lowered. Teachers report that they can sense the feeling
of unrest and unhappiness.

In one school, 120 out of 290 children came from homes
in which no wage earner was employed. The principal reported:

> Quite often children come to school without break-
> fast because there is no food in the house. Whenever
> we discover a condition like this we manage to feed
> them. Lack of food and respectable clothing causes a
> bad psychological reaction among the children. Much
> of the teachers' time is spent in trying to supply the
> children with necessities.

In Raleigh County, West Virginia, 17 per cent of the
employed heads of families were reported to have had to
accept jobs which required them to live away from home.
A survey made in 11 schools of the county found that 39
per cent of all heads of families were unemployed. Juvenile delinquency was on the increase. A principal reported:

> Children receive little or no medical service, have
> frequent colds, are poorly clothed, and many are es-
> pecially in need of shoes.
> Our lunch program is not adequate to supply a free
> or reduced-price lunch for all the pupils who do not
> have lunches or who have substandard lunches.

In 11 typical schools surveyed, 239 children were getting free lunches, but 433 others, who wanted and were
entitled to them, could not be fed without overburdening
the program to the point of complete breakdown.

> It is heartbreaking when children we are unable to
> carry on the program rush home for lunch and return

before the lunch period is over at the school and ask
the cook if she has any leftovers. . . .

In most needy cases we provide a sandwich and
milk in the morning, since many children come to
school without breakfast.

In many areas of West Virginia, where mines had
closed, company doctors were no longer employed and
medical service was no longer available in the vicinity:

Therefore, illnesses sometimes thought to be minor
are treated at home without medical advice, and in
many cases this has resulted in more serious conditions. An example of this is the rise in the number of
rheumatic fever cases reported. A large percentage of
these give a history of strep throat treated at home
without a doctor. . . .

These have been some of the consequences of attempting to treat West Virginia unemployment at home, without the help of a Federal program for area redevelopment.

An unparalleled local and state effort at industrial
redevelopment in eastern Pennsylvania has not been sufficient to compensate for job losses due to technological
changes in our demand for fuel. The Senate Special Committee on Unemployment Problems found that 54 per cent
of the unemployed in that area were skilled or semiskilled.

A district representative of the ILGWU read into the
record of the committee the letters of men and women
seeking work in that area; she implored the senators to
get behind the statistics and do something about the children, the women and the men in the homes.

Here we have strong men proud of their families,
proud of their abilities to support their families,
thrown out of work. A man looks for a job and finds
none. His unemployment compensation expires. His
wife goes to work, and he stays home and looks after
the children.

What happens to that man? What happens to that home? In many cases, he loses self-respect. He becomes demoralized, and the family is broken up. . . .

Must a body of men who paid with their labor, many of them with their health, and too, too many of them with their lives for the industrial development of America also pay with their homes, and their self-respect, and their hopes for the industrial changes which have thrown them out of work?

Chronic unemployment undermines family human relations. The director of the Welfare Department of St. Louis County in Minnesota told the Senate committee:

In all too many families the stress of unemployment tends to separate rather than to mold the family into a smoother functioning unit. . . . The most important reaction is that there seems to be an increase in the hostile reaction toward one another and also toward society . . . the wife blames the husband for being out of work. . . . In many instances the roles become reversed. In many of these situations, the family is never able fully to recover, to the detriment of themselves and the community.

One of the most shameful consequences of our national apathy toward the distressed areas is that even little children are made victims of our unwillingness to share the price of progress. The Senate committee reported:

Children in one school were weighed in November and again at the start of their Christmas vacation to measure the effect of the school's hot lunch program. the net gain of between 3 and 5 pounds per pupil was completely wiped out during the Christmas vacation when the children had to eat at home.

In that Christmas story, the whole nation is weighed and found wanting.

The suffering and deprivation experienced by communities and families which have experienced concentrated chronic unemployment is perhaps the most moving impressive evidence that for tens of thousands of families automation has meant something very far from the abundance it promises. We have failed to meet even their basic needs. But failure to meet our national needs can be observed in every community.

It can be seen in the teeming slums of every large city and in pitiful areas of rural slums as well, where millions of children have never known what it means to grow up in a good home in a good neighborhood—while residential construction slumps disastrously for lack of customers who can afford the homes they need.

It can be seen in the continuing shortage of school buildings which condemns children in almost every community to the deficiencies and dangers of crowded classrooms in obsolescent buildings, many of them hazardous firetraps. The Department of Health, Education, and Welfare has revealed that it would require a building program of at least six hundred thousand new classrooms in the next ten years to clean up the backlog and meet the needs of our growing population; but no program of such magnitude is in sight.

Our failure can be seen in the growing backlog of needed hospital beds. In 1955, when the subcommittee first looked into the problems and promises of automation, the Department of Health, Education, and Welfare revealed that we had a shortage of well over eight hundred thousand hospital beds. Since that time, according to data published in the 1960 Economic Report of the President, we have added only sixty-seven thousand beds, not even enough to match the rate of population growth.

We have not met our national needs for safe highways, for modern airports, for programs to conserve our land and water resources.

Most of our cities could add to the list of our needs their requirements for modern public buildings, for recreation facilities, improved police and fire protection, civil defense, adequate roads and parking facilities, water supplies and sewer systems.

As noted earlier, some 23 per cent of American families which in 1959 had incomes below three thousand dollars certainly lack the means to meet their individual needs.

Yet we live in a world where most of the population have far greater unmet needs than ours. We have a moral responsibility, even out of our present wealth and far more so out of our potential abundance, to give them the help which will enable them to build up their own economies to satisfactory levels.

Where are we to find the means to meet these needs?

A more realistic question would be: Why has the wealthiest country in the world failed to meet them with the means already to hand?

The wealth to do so could have been ours if we had simply used our available resources to create it.

As I have indicated above, the accelerating pace of automation and other technological advance and the steady increase in our population have made it perfectly feasible for us to increase our national production of goods and services by at least 5 per cent per year.

Since 1953, our actual rate of increase has been at less than half that rate, a bare 2.3 per cent per year.

This is the price we have paid for policies which led to rising unemployment and recurrent recession, rather than full employment, full production and economic stability.

If we had achieved a growth rate of 5 per cent per year from 1953 through the end of 1959, our total gross national product for those 6 years, expressed in dollars of 1959 buying power, would have been $292,000,000,000 greater than it actually was.

For the year 1959 alone our total production would have been $80,000,000,000 greater, $559,000,000,000 instead of the $479,000,000,000 we actually achieved.

If this extra wealth had been created it would have meant that in 1959 we could have had $63,000,000,000 more in personal income before taxes—an average of $356 more per person, or $1,424 more for an average family of four. This would have made possible about $4,000,000,000 more in personal savings.

Corporate and personal savings combined would have made available about $12,000,000,000 more for private investment to provide the basis for continuing growth.

With a broader tax base, and without any change in tax rates, the Federal Government would probably have received about $16,000,000,000 more in revenues, which could have been used to strengthen our national defense, to meet more civilian needs, to increase generously our assistance to other countries—and to balance the budget.

One of the ominous signs for the future is that business itself is looking at automation, not primarily as a road to growth, but as a road to cutting labor costs and so cutting employment for a given volume of production. The annual McGraw-Hill report on planned capital outlays, published in *Business Week* of April 30, 1960, shows that the share of business expenditures planned for modernization is increasing in proportion to the share planned for expansion of production facilities. Normally this development occurs during recessions, but not in periods of upswing.

It is expected that 65 per cent—a record high—of all plant and equipment expenditures in 1960 will be for modernization.

After adjustment for price changes, 1960 outlays for expansion of manufacturing facilities will be approximately 40 per cent less than in 1957, while spending on automation and other modernization will be about 25 per cent greater than in 1957.

Increased emphasis on automation accompanied by a declining interest in expansion means that business has attuned its investment programs to the inevitable consequence of the present administration's economic policies—continued stagnation rather than adequate growth in levels of production, and a continuing rise in levels of unemployment.

How could we have realized our potential 5 per cent growth rate?

Chiefly by recognizing in our public and private economic policies one basic fact: that the major problem in our economy in peacetime is not how to achieve production, but how to obtain markets—in other words, how to achieve a level of effective demand for goods and services

which will insure that our productive resources are used
to optimum capacity, and that business is stimulated to
invest in further growth.

Thus, for example, if workers during the past seven
years had obtained real wage increases sufficient to restore
the imbalance of purchasing power and to match the potentialities of our economy to advance its productivity at
full production levels, their increased buying power
would have been a major factor in stimulating demand to
full production levels.

If the policies of our administration had been directed
more toward meeting the needs of our nation and less toward efforts—which proved in vain—to balance the
budget, production of the goods and services required to
meet those needs would have been stimulated. For example, more adequate levels of old-age pensions would
have meant measured spending by senior citizens—and
better markets for the producers of the consumer goods
they need. An adequate unemployment compensation
system would have helped the unemployed and their
families to maintain their buying power, and, in conjunction with other measures, might well have meant that less
had to be paid out in total unemployment benefits. An effective program to maintain farm income would have
helped prevent unemployment in the farm implement
industry and others that serve the farmers, while higher
living standards for all would have helped to absorb farm
surpluses and maintain farm income. More money made
available for housing programs, for hospitals, for schools
and other needed facilities would also have meant more
workers employed to build them and to produce and
transport the building materials.

If such policies had been followed we could have
achieved full production, a 5 per cent rate of growth, and
the balanced, prosperous economy which is the one sure
means of providing a strong tax base for a balanced
budget.

POLICIES FOR THE AGE OF AUTOMATION

What policies will best help us to meet the challenge
of the age of automation, not merely to deal with the

problems it creates, but through positive, constructive action to derive the maximum of individual and social benefit from the great possibilities which it opens out to us?

One of our primary needs, as I have suggested above, is to be much better informed on a current, continuing basis as to the developments taking place every day which may open up new vistas and create new problems. Many congressional committees do an excellent job of obtaining information from time to time on matters of public concern, and the Joint Economic Committee and its various subcommittees are to be congratulated on their outstanding record of thorough, pertinent investigations and imaginative, forward-looking recommendations. However, it would be completely unrealistic to ask a committee or subcommittee to maintain a constant survey of a field so broad and complex as that of technological change. What is needed for that task is a permanent commission on technological change, with the resources and staff required to carry such a heavy responsibility.

Because technological change will continue to have a revolutionary impact on almost every sector of our economy, such a commission should be as broadly based as possible. Its membership should include representatives of government, labor and management. The commission would have the duty and be given the authority to gather information on, and to keep under constant security, developments in such areas of technological advance as automation, major new developments in production processes and equipment, development of atomic and solar energy for industrial use, development of important new materials, and similar innovations, and to make appropriate recommendations to Congress and the President in order to insure that the social gains and the social costs of technological progress are fairly shared, and full employment achieved and maintained.

To function effectively, the commission should be instructed and given the necessary authority to discover, for example, the present and planned extent of automation and the effect it has had and is having and may be expected to have on displacement of workers. Its field of investigation should cover not only direct displacement in plants where automated equipment has been introduced, but the equally important indirect displacement which may have occurred in consequence in competing firms or even in competing industries.

It must study the extent to which workers' skills have been made obsolete by introduction of automatic equipment, and what, if anything, has been done to enable them to learn new skills.

It should study the special problems of older workers who may find themselves prematurely relegated to the economic scrap heap.

It should find out whether sufficient new job opportunities are being created to provide jobs for the millions of young people who enter the labor market without displacing older workers.

The commission should obtain from employers the fullest information as to their plans for technological innovations which will increase productivity, and the anticipated effect of such changes on employment, as well as any plans for moving or closing plants, and should study the probable effect of such plans on the communities affected, and the necessity for programs to counteract such effects.

It should look into the price and profit policies of industry to determine whether consumers and workers are sharing in the cost savings brought about by technological progress.

There are numerous measures which are so obviously required that they need not wait upon further investigation. Especially at a time when our economy stands perilously close to the brink of another recession, significant additions to consumer purchasing power are essential if unsold goods are not to commence piling up on the merchants' shelves and in the warehouses. About 70 per cent of all consumer purchasing power is distributed through wages and salaries. For the most part, wage and salary adjustments are matters to be determined by free collective bargaining between unions and management. There is one area, however, in which only Congress can act to improve the living standards of several million Americans and their families whose need, among all workers, is greatest. That area is the determination of minimum wage standards, which apply almost entirely to workers who are unable to form effective union organizations. The responsibility of Congress is all the greater in view of legislation now on the books which places serious obstacles in the way of organization among the weak and unorganized.

As this is prepared, final action has not yet been taken on amendments proposed to the Fair Labor Standards Act. Before Congress recessed it appeared probable that · once again, as in the past, minimum wage levels would be raised too slowly and coverage would remain grossly insufficient. It should be a primary objective of Congress when it returns to raise the minimum wage level immediately to at least $1.25 per hour, and to extend its provisions to the millions of workers, unable to speak or act effectively for themselves, who require its protection.

The Fair Labor Standards Act should also be amended to provide for appropriate reduction of the standard working week as technological advance permits us to take some of its benefits in the form of increased leisure. The previous subcommittee, recognizing the validity of this principle, had some questions as to how soon such action should be taken. It reported:

> For the most part, the industrial witnesses who appeared before the subcommittee were of the view that new and better products would so intrigue the consumer demand that we would see little near-term shortening of the workweek. Some, indeed, foresee a distinct shortage of labor supply as likely if the expected demands for new goods are to be fulfilled. Representatives of labor, on the other hand, while recognizing that such a choice may have to be made, were rather more inclined to the view that a continued and marked shortening of the workweek is in prospect.

In the five years that have passed since those hearings, events have confirmed that the representatives of labor were right and those of industry were mistaken. Not only has there been a rising number of men and women with no employment at all, but for those with jobs the actual amount of work available in a week has declined. By 1958, average hours of work in manufacturing industry were one and one-half hours less than in 1955, and even in 1960, for the first five months, they have averaged almost an hour less than in 1955.

Unfortunately, these shortened work weeks have not meant increased leisure to enjoy the good things of life, but merely a decreasing opportunity to earn them, and in consequence a decrease in the potential market for industry.

A reduction in the standard work week without reduction in weekly pay would have meant an increase in genuine leisure along with maintenance of earning power.

It may be argued that the evidence of all our unmet needs refutes the argument for a shorter standard work week. Historically, however, we have always taken part of the benefits of advancing technology in the form of increased leisure, yet at the same time we have been able to make dramatic increases in our production of goods and services. Professor William Haber of the department of economics, University of Michigan, has estimated that "in the past, about 60 per cent of the increase in productivity has gone into higher real wages and about 40 per cent into more leisure."

Certainly, it is impossible to argue that our economy cannot afford a shorter work week when there are still 5 per cent of the labor force for whom no jobs are available at all.

If we had re-established, or were even moving toward a full employment, full production economy, then it would be realistic to say that we must choose between more goods and services or more leisure, although the abundance of goods that we could produce at full production would make it obvious that we could afford more leisure. In our circumstances today it is not really a matter of making that choice. A shortened standard work week without reduction in weekly pay would increase employment, increase the total income of workers, increase purchasing power and so stimulate an actual increase in production.

With the presidential veto twice applied to measures

for assistance to distressed communities, it becomes painfully apparent that this issue can be satisfactorily determined only by another Congress and a new and different administration. But the absolute necessity for such legislation should be taken before the forum of the whole American people and there made plain. Ample reports have been made to convince any reasonable person that there is no possible answer to the plight of these sick and wasting communities but generous Federal assistance. With the shriveling away of their economic roots, most of them have lost the means of restoring economic health by their own efforts. In large part the most distressed areas are found concentrated in states whose total economies have been so undermined that adequate aid from the state level is no longer possible. No source of help is left except the Federal Government.

Morally and economically these communities are the responsibility of all of us. Whether their decline results directly from technological causes, or from other forms of that dynamic change which is an essential feature of our free economy, it is a consequence of the forces which lead ultimately to economic advance and improved living standards for the people as a whole. We cannot turn our backs on the victims of those forces from which we ourselves benefit.

Legislation is necessary which will provide practical assistance, in adequate amounts, to help rehabilitate idle plants and facilities, or to create new productive facilities where necessary, to purchase machinery, to provide loans and grants for needed facilities of a community nature, and to provide for the retraining of workers and proper maintenance for themselves and their families while they are in training.

As a further measure, policies for the placing of defense and other government contracts and for the location of defense plants financed in whole or part by government funds should be directed, wherever feasible, toward assisting areas suffering from chronic unemployment. As evidence given before the Senate Committee on Unemployment Problems made very clear, only an infinitesimal fraction—less than one-half of 1 per cent in fiscal 1958—

of defense procurement contracts have been placed under
the policy of aiding distressed areas. In fact, it was revealed
that a provision of the Defense Appropriation Act actually
prohibits the payment of any price differential on such
contracts for the purposes of relieving economic
dislocations. The fact that total gains to the national economy and even to the Federal budget resulting from the
relief of economic dislocations might far outweigh the cost
of such a price differential is given no weight whatever.
In that regard I would repeat to this subcommittee the
recommendation that I made to the Committee on Unemployment Problems:

> I would urge your committee to consider seriously
> a recommendation for amendment of the Defense Ap-
> propriation Act to provide that within a strictly lim-
> ited margin, and with ample safeguards against profit-
> eering by any contractor, the Defense Department be
> permitted to pay a reasonable differential in price
> specifically for the purpose of placing contracts in
> areas where they will help to relieve economic dislo-
> cations.

In the same way, where a contract is such as to require the building of a new plant, procurement policies
should provide that if an area of continued heavy unemployment is otherwise suitable, it should be given first
choice as a location for such plant.

One of the problems arising out of automation is that
industrial sites which were formerly satisfactory may no
longer meet the needs of more modern industries. For example, automated plants very frequently function most
efficiently when built on a single level, and therefore require a much greater area of land than the old-style mul-
tistory plant. In consequence, a firm which has decided to
automate may change location and leave behind it a site
which no longer meets present industrial requirements
even with the old buildings removed, and an area of industrial blight is created in what may be an otherwise
healthy community. Loans and grants to such communities which would enable them to put together such areas

in parcels of useful size and otherwise develop them for modern industrial use would be well repaid in the economic benefits thus created.

Even if we solve problems of chronic unemployment in our economy, technological change is always going to mean that some workers will be displaced from their jobs for a shorter or longer time and will require unemployment insurance protection. To the extent that we fail to solve our chronic unemployment problems, that need is so much the greater. Here again, we believe that the overriding principle should be that unemployed men and women are the innocent victims of a process from which most of us benefit, and that we have no moral right to turn our backs upon them. The experience of the last recession proved the gross deficiencies of many of our existing state unemployment compensation systems as to duration of benefits, amount of benefits, eligibility requirements, and disqualification provisions. A particularly vicious form of interstate competition to keep unemployment insurance costs down, regardless of the inadequacy of the laws, is fostered by large sections of industry. In consequence, only one of the states has established a program which meets even the inadequate criteria that have for many years now been urged upon them all by the administration.

We call once more, therefore, for the enactment of additional Federal standards which will extend duration, raise benefit levels to an adequate proportion of earnings, and remove present restrictive eligibility requirements and harsh disqualification provisions.

Even in an economy of general full employment, automation will frequently involve large-scale displacement of workers from their jobs. In order to reduce both the loss to the individual and the loss to the economy of any unnecessary prolongation of his unemployment, our employment services should be strengthened in every way possible.

One of the obstacles to an adequate employment service program is the antisocial employer who refuses to cooperate with the state employment service by listing with the service job vacancies he may have. Public employ-

ment services have been organized as a means of bringing order and efficiency into the labor market, by matching
available workers to suitable vacant jobs and thus minimizing their periods of unemployment. The effect of refusal by employers to list job openings with the employment service, coupled with requirements under state
unemployment insurance laws that workers must be "actively seeking work," means that workers are put to unnecessary sacrifice of time and money visiting plants
where there may be no openings, that their periods of
unemployment are unnecessarily prolonged, that the employment service is hindered in placing applicants, and so
the cost of unemployment compensation to all employers
is increased. A suitable method of discouraging such practices would be an amendment to the existing Federal law
which would require every employer to list job openings
with the public employment service or else pay the full
amount of unemployment compensation tax provided for
in the Federal law, without any so-called merit rating tax
reduction to which he would otherwise be entitled.

Because of changes in the kinds and levels of skill that
it requires, automation frequently presents special problems for the worker who is displaced from his job and
finds that no other employer requires his particular abilities. To help meet these problems and avoid the waste
of idleness, we recommend Federal assistance for programs of vocational training and rehabilitation, including
adequate payments for support of workers and their families during training. Where displaced workers are too old
to learn new jobs or to find suitable employment, early
retirement should be possible. The Social Security Act
should be amended so as to provide, with suitable safeguards, for early retirement of workers for whom there is
clearly no opportunity of further employment on account
of their age. Such amendment might provide, for example,
that after a given age any person who has been unemployed and registered for employment for a given period
of time, and who is certified by the state employment
service as unlikely to be re-employed because of age,

would be permitted to retire with full pension rights payable immediately. It would not be unduly costly. In most cases it would probably relieve some other agency of the cost of maintenance, and it would give such older workers a measure of economic security to which they are morally entitled.

Where local job opportunities are insufficient, especially in chronically distressed areas, assistance in relocation should be provided for workers and their families. In many cases assistance of this kind would be most helpful, both to the workers affected and as a partial solution to a local problem.

I would warn, however, that it must be handled with the greatest of care, to avoid even the appearance of any undue persuasion. For many workers, moving is no solution at all. It is no easy matter to sever family ties and roots in the community formed over long years of residence and participation in community and church activities. Those who own their own homes will be forced to sell those homes in a depressed market, and if they are moving to an expanding community will probably have to buy in an inflated market. If they have children of school age, those children face additional problems of adjustment.

In most cases, any attempt at wholesale removal of workers and their families from a community would also involve a tragic waste of community investment in public facilities of all kinds. It could involve creation of new serious economic problems for local retail and service business and professional men and women if the local population is drastically reduced.

For many workers, however, particularly younger persons who have not yet struck deep roots in the community, moving to an area of greater opportunity may represent the easiest and most satisfactory solution to their individual problems, while at the same time it relieves some of the pressure on the local labor market. I would urge, however, that any program of financial assistance to those who wish to move must contain adequate safeguards to insure that no worker is induced to move against his will and, where alternatives are feasible, that no community is endangered by the loss of an undue proportion of its working force.

As has been indicated above, effective trade unions have been able to work out solutions to many of the problems of automation at the collective bargaining table, and we shall continue to do so. We believe in the principle of settling questions of this kind at the bargaining table whenever possible.

Trade unionism is an essential element and instrument of democracy. It carries the democratic process into the workshop, and insures that when problems arise both management and workers will have a voice in finding the answer to them.

However, if trade unions are to play a fully effective role in helping to work out democratic solutions to the problems raised by automation, it is time for Congress to take another look at some of the labor legislation it has enacted. The right of workers to organize and to bargain collectively through representatives of their own choosing is now greatly hampered, and too often effectively nullified.

We must return to the basic principles originally embodied in the Wagner Act, which recognized the role of trade unions as part of the essential machinery of a democratic society, to be actively encouraged, rather than as an annoyance to employers, to be merely tolerated, grudgingly conceded or effectively frustrated.

Congress must be alert to resist further encroachments on collective bargaining rights which would restrict the right of unions to bargain on some of the most important questions raised by automation. Senator Dirksen has introduced a bill, for example, which would remove from the area of required collective bargaining "the creation or discontinuance of positions." Its passage would deny to unions the right to bargain on practically all the vital issues raised by adjustment to automation.

The spread of automation underlines the need for improvement of our educational facilities, both through school construction and through grants to help raise teachers' salaries to levels consonant with the skills and responsibilities demanded of them, and for extension of educational opportunity through a Federal scholarship program.

One of the effects of automation is to eliminate many of the unskilled jobs for which no extensive educational background was required, and to increase demand for both blue-collar and white-collar skills. Beyond that, reduced manpower requirements for production of goods should give us the opportunity to educate more students to provide the professional and technical services of which there is an undoubted shortage in many fields.

Nor should our educational program stop short at consideration of practical needs. The age of automation will be an age of increasing leisure, and it should be an age of increasing cultural opportunity. Facilities for increased study of the humanities should be considered just as important as facilities for technical, vocational and scientific education.

Increased facilities for the constructive use of leisure time will also need to be provided or expanded. Facilities for adult education, for study groups, hobby classes, art and music appreciation, improved libraries, as well as more national parks and other facilities for relaxation will help many men and women to live fuller and richer lives in the age of automation.

Meeting these needs will require more schools, more and better paid teachers, and more financial aid to young people whose own families do not have the resources to finance extended education. In devising programs to provide these necessities, one factor which should be taken into account is the special need of some minority groups in our country, and particularly the Negroes. Not only in the South but in many parts of the North also, large numbers of colored children are crowded into obsolescent, understaffed schools where in practice the educational opportunities offered them are far inferior to those available to other parts of the community. At the same time, a high proportion of them come from families whose low income makes any thought of higher education virtually impossible. It is high time we recognize the disadvantages to which a large proportion of Americans are subjected, and developed programs specifically devised to assure them full equality of educational opportunity.

The above recommendations are intended for the most part to deal with the immediate problems arising out of automation. But if we are to meet its real challenge we must adopt policies which will make full use of the possibilities of automation to achieve an optimum rate of economic growth under conditions of full production and full employment.

The essential quality of such policies is that they must be designed to meet the needs which are still unmet today. In meeting those needs we shall make demands upon our productive capacity which will provide jobs for the unemployed and stimulate new investment. Programs to raise the incomes and protect the health of our senior citizens, to increase educational opportunities for our young people, to clear away the slums and build the decent homes we need, to build more schools and more hospitals, to improve our highway system, to conserve our natural resources, and to meet more fully our responsibilities abroad, all can contribute to economic growth while at the same time helping to meet needs that should be met.

Automation intensifies the need for such programs, because the same machines which hold within themselves the possibilities of creating abundance if we plan wisely how to use abundance, can also create increasing unemployment if we plan badly or fail to plan our course at all.

The American economy has always been a dynamic one, constantly changing. In economic life those who have been able to foresee the trends of the future and change their thinking with changing times have been those who have become leaders. In the areas of public responsibility we require today more than ever the same flexibility, the same vision, the same imagination. The challenge of automation cannot be faced by looking to the past.

The passage of events makes it increasingly clear that automation will present us with increasing problems. The solutions to those problems will not always be easy to find. They will require courage, determination and above all a willingness to blaze new trails where the old roads have led us to obvious dead ends. These are the qualities we have a right to expect in our leaders. These are the qualities we must find if we are to meet the challenge, if automation is not to become an unguided monster leaving hardship and suffering where it passes by, but a tool which we can use to create abundance for all.

▪ *11* ▪

Labor Relations
and Employment Aspects
After Ten Years [1962]

by Everett M. Kassalow

RESEARCH DIRECTOR,

INDUSTRIAL UNION DEPARTMENT,

CIO-AFL

It is only about ten years since the term "automation" was coined for popular usage to describe the third phase of the Industrial Revolution which first struck the United States (and other western industrial nations) about two hundred years ago. In spite of its rather short life, automation has already triggered an enormous volume of literature, ranging from at least three separate congressional inquiries to almost daily editorials in one newspaper or another.

This extraordinary volume of discussion speaks well of the nation's determination to avoid the great social upheaval and misery which accompanied the earlier technological revolutions. Indeed, while there continue to be many important differences of opinion between groups about the gravity of the social impact of automation as well as the programs needed to control and harness it, there is nevertheless an important growing area of agreement on some of these programs. It is doubtful that even this area of agreement would have emerged in the absence of the many discussions, conferences and committees which have tried to come to grips with automation in the past half dozen years. The recent report of the President's Labor-Management Policy Committee on automation is a good example of the spreading area of consensus as well as some of the differences that still exist in the social evaluation of automation.[1]

Certainly in the course of just half a dozen years the relative optimism about automation which seemed to characterize most of the first 1955 Congressional inquiry into the subject has given way to much greater concern and anxiety about the impact of this latest revolution in technology. Concluding the 1955 inquiry, the subcommittee of the Joint Economic Committee, which was chaired by Wright Patman and contained a firm three to two liberal Democratic majority, was quite optimistic and almost on the *laisser-faire* side (*laisser-faire* at least in the sense that although some mitigating programs were discussed in the final report these were not pressed with any urgency). In the wake of automation it expected that "whole new industries . . . may be expected to arise . . . goods and services not previously available or possible are made possible by the introduction of automatic processes . . . [the subcommittee stressed] the employment possibilities arising out of the service industries associated with many of these new products. . . ." The subcommittee did note that automation, in 1955, was going forward "against the background of relatively high employment levels and of a prosperous economic situation." It added that if this background changed, the impact of automation could be less favorable on employment.

On the social side, "the most disturbing thing which came to the subcommittee's attention was the nearly unanimous conclusion of the witnesses that the nation is faced with a threatened shortage of scientists, technicians, and skilled labor. . . ." In the light of this, the subcommittee stressed the necessity for improved education and training programs to meet these needs. It called for an improved employment service as well as other devices to improve labor mobility. It enjoined industry and management to ease and share the human costs of displacement and re-training "as charges against the savings from the intro-duction of automation." [2]

Only a little more than six years later a nearly unanimous labor-management-public committee studying automation seemed to be much less certain about its im-pact, at least in the present era. Its report noted that "the current rate of technological advance has created social problems . . . it is clear that unemployment has resulted from displacement due to automation and technological change. . . ." While continuing to support automation as a force which could strengthen the United States economy, this new committee proceeded to lay out a fairly extensive program to mitigate some of its unfavorable by-products, including Federal action on public works, retraining, re-location allowances (costs to be shared with industry), an overhaul of the Unemployment Compensation system, as well as the public employment service. While refraining from endorsing any reduction in regular work time, it did note "a reduction in the basic work period has, however, historically been one means of sharing the fruits of tech-nological progress and there may well develop in the fu-ture the necessity and the desirability of shortening the work period either through collective bargaining or by law, or by both methods." [3]

Without doubt, the single most powerful influence in pro-ducing this shift from a near *laisser-faire* attitude to a growing concern about social disruption incident to tech-nological change has been the persistence of a nagging, chronic level of unemployment in the 1957-61 period, in contrast to the five years immediately preceding the Joint Committee's report.

In the years 1951-55 unemployment averaged some 3.8 per cent of the labor force. In the 1957-61 period unemployment averaged 5.8 per cent of the labor force. Indeed, during the four years since the onset of the recession of 1957 the seasonally adjusted unemployment rate has gone below 5 per cent of the labor force in only three months, despite the "recoveries" of 1959. At that, unemployment barely got down to 4.8 and 4.9 per cent at the most favorable moments of the '59 recovery, and it hasn't seriously approached 5 per cent in any month of the '61-'62 recovery. This is a far cry from the no more than 3 per cent unemployment level set for the economy by the late Sumner Slichter, a level generally accepted by economists in the American labor movement. It is well above even the more modest 4 per cent target rate of the new Kennedy Administration.[4]

FULL EMPLOYMENT: PRECONDITION
FOR ADJUSTMENTS TO AUTOMATION

American union leaders and economists have repeatedly emphasized that the precondition for satisfactory adjustment to the spread and development of automation is a strong full employment economy. This necessity has been underscored by the experience of the past few years.

Two meat-packing unions and the Armour Meat Packing Company made a rather heroic effort to deal with the human problems of technological change and displacement in the plants of this company between August, 1959, and the summer of 1961. In 1959 the company and the two unions set up a special joint committee which also included two distinguished academic economists, whose objective was to try to find solutions for the problems of automation. At the end of two years of hard work, some experimentation and reflection, this committee concluded:

Collective bargaining by itself cannot solve these problems. Most important of all is the rate of economic growth which depends on a combination of private initiative and public policy. This growth must be fast enough to absorb the currently excessive unemployment, the rapid additions to the labor force, the workers displaced by modernization in an increasing number of industries, and the increasing productivity of workers not displaced. Growth adequate to meet these needs is the essential prerequisite to the orderly social development of the nation.[5]

The relocation of workers to new jobs and new cities or the retraining of workers for different jobs, either in Armour plants or plants of other companies, these and other key programs to deal with the displacement effects of automation the Armour committee found to be virtually unmanageable in the absence of a vigorous, expanding economy. At one point, for example, the company offered to transfer workers (and their families) displaced in Oklahoma City to a Kansas City plant—with the company paying up to $325 for moving expenses. Half of the individuals who were offered this opportunity responded favorably, but just as the plan was to be activated the employment situation worsened and there were layoffs in Kansas City. Limited company assistance to workers who would undertake retraining in entirely new occupations in Oklahoma City was also offered. The results have been quite disappointing due largely to the weak employment situation in Oklahoma City.

LAW OF MORE MACHINES, MORE JOBS, IN DANGER OF REPEAL

We have already indicated that the optimism which seemed to characterize much of the 1955 Congressional inquiry into automation has largely disappeared. Some of the major myths which ran through those hearings have also been pretty much shattered or seriously questioned. So often in the 1955 hearings, for example, ran the theme that technological innovation created new opportunities and new markets and, hence, new employment opportunities. Experience in the past six years, as one writer has put it, rather seems to suggest that the old law of "more machines, more jobs" has been repealed. Aside from the old problem of the long- and short-run effects of technological innovation and how many workers may be economically dead in the short run, the 1955 optimism in this respect rested on the belief that major technological change would "naturally" occur in expanding industries and the growing markets would, of course, offset any possible employment displacement due to gains in productivity. This theme is appealing; it would be nice if it were true. Take, however, two key industries, automobile and basic steel, major forces in the economy and major employers—their entire performance since 1955 argues the contrary of the theme. Output in both of these industries has been down since that year and present prospects are that it will be at least several years before they reach even their 1955 levels of production.

Yet in spite of this adverse production trend, investment has proceeded at a vigorous rate in these industries. Actually the steel industry, with 1.6 billion dollars of new investment, maintained its rank as the number two new investor in new plant and equipment, among all industries even in 1960 after four "disappointing" production years compared to 1955. The automobile industry fell somewhat, but in 1960 it still expended some $900,000,000 on new plant and equipment. The combination of continued heavy investment leading to even higher man-hour productivity on the one hand and declining markets, on the other hand, have sharply reduced employment and especially blue-collar worker employment in these industries. Despite the fact that total industrial production in the nation was 12 per cent higher in 1960 than in 1955, employment in the automobile industry was down 163,000 or 18 per cent; steel employment was off 8 per cent, 54,000 jobs in 1960 as compared to five years earlier. For blue-collar workers the impact was even more severe, amounting to 21 per cent in autos and 12 per cent in steel. These latter figures reflected the changing labor force and technological "mix" of these industries, as well as the stagnation and decline in their markets.[6]

The notion that heavy investment and automation would proceed in industries where markets are not expanding seems to have been left out of most calculations in 1955. Moreover, there are no offsetting trends in related industries (related, that is, in some production and employment sense to autos and steel) of the type which seemed to preoccupy the 1955 automation congressional subcommittee.

Eventually the continued growth of the economy, even at the rather low rate of recent years, would probably restore auto and steel markets to their 1955 levels and eventually surpass these. This is not what anyone seems to have had in mind, however, during the early discussion of automation in the United States. In any event, by the time the 1955 production levels are restored in these industries, the continuing heavy level of investment in them will leave their levels of employment well below the 1955 point, even when the production records of that year are surpassed.

As previously suggested, the 1955 congressional inquiry stressed the probable shortage of skills among the work force in the future. By the same token, one finds a consistent theme running through most of the "early" automation literature,[7] to the effect that come what may the spread of automation would bring about an upgrading of the labor force. Even in particular plants where the work force might be reduced, those who were left would be more highly skilled and presumably better paid. This was, I would judge, a theme widely accepted by labor unions as well as by management and public officials.

AUTOMATION AND SKILL REQUIREMENTS

With the hindsight of just five years, there now appears to be good reason to question this second major social myth about automation. Professor James Bright, of Harvard, one of the most reflective and generally accepted experts in the automation field, categorically rejects the conclusion that automation leads to an upgrading of skill. He does agree that automation "results in more complex machinery." The next logical conclusion, however, namely, that as a consequence of this more complex machinery, "skill demands on the work force are going up," may be logical but he claims it "simply is not true." After studying fifteen highly automatic factories, he found that contrary to popular belief management moved into automation generally "to overcome the lack of skills" and that "skill requirements declined" after automation took over. Bright adds that if one stops to think about it, this is logical and in keeping with the main sweep of industrial evolution. The riots against machines in the earlier Industrial Revolution were not due to the fact that new machines were "beyond the people; it was the fact that they undermined" and rendered obsolete existing skills. After all, a prime incentive to mechanize and automate is to reduce and simplify the labor cost factor in production. One should not expect any other result than a decline in skill requirements. Bright argues.[8]

A congressional subcommittee report in 1961 on the employment aspects of automation concluded that ". . . Newly automated plants frequently hire inexperienced workers and give them only limited training. Some case studies show that former machine operators tend, after automation, to become only machine monitors. They rarely have to actually do anything but they must be constantly alert. Other evidence points to job enlargement but this is often in the form of a requirement that the operator be responsible for more complicated machinery or for a greater variety of machinery rather than requiring more intensive knowledge of the workers."[9]

A study conducted by a large aircraft manufacturing company to determine the abilities required of operators of electronic computing equipment concluded that there was a need for "a paradoxical combination of high technical competence and low mental capacity—the employee should have a B.S. degree in engineering and an I.Q. of 81!" [10]

The evidence to date is not really conclusive but it, at least, raises grave doubt about the likelihood that automation will bring about any significant upgrading of the jobs left in its wake.

AUTOMATION AND WHITE-COLLAR WORK

What about some of the new industries? What about white-collar work which many have confidently expected will provide employment outlets for workers displaced by technological change elsewhere in the economy? Will there be a rising level of skill requirements among white-collar workers? It is still too early to predict with certainty where industrial evolution is heading in this part of the economy, but if there is to be any job growth here it will certainly not be due to the direct influence of automation. The expanding sections of the economy tend to be primarily in the government and service areas. One could hardly attribute this expansion to the impact of automation.

Indeed, so far as white-collar work goes generally, the impact of automation may well be to cut back job opportunities and job skills. The interesting study of Mrs. Ida Hoos on the impact of electronic machines upon office work concludes that most workers believe their jobs are less interesting after automation than before. Indeed, "not only was there more intrinsic interest [before automation] since the employees might have been filing, checking, posting, or typing, but the former occupations involved a certain amount of moving about the office and contact with other employees or customers. The workers now complain of 'being chained to the machine.' " [11] Mrs. Hoos did find that there were some new highly skilled jobs created with the introduction of office automation, namely, the positions of programmers and analysts, but these were relatively few.

As for numbers of jobs, Mrs. Hoos finds that in the automated offices she has studied "for every five office jobs eliminated, only one is created by automation." Studies of the Bureau of Labor Statistics in automated offices are not quite so bleak but they do reveal that due to office automation hirings were curtailed and natural attrition served as a means for adjusting the size of the office labor force. As Mrs. Hoos comments, the Bureau of Labor Statistics failed to give adequate recognition to the fact that this process was foreclosing new opportunities for aspirants to office jobs in these companies. The experience to date in automating offices offers no comfort for those who are looking for new job opportunities for displaced factory workers.[12]

In some ways the re-employment problems of displaced office workers are even more severe than those of blue-collar workers. Office work is often, especially in the pre-automation period, very much geared to the routines and practices of a particular office or firm. Office workers who are displaced by automation under these circumstances

have little in the way of marketable skills to offer new
employers.

This process of accelerated skill obsolescence and displacement is apt to be even more destructive and socially
dislocating in its impact on professional and managerial
employees. As truly advanced automation takes over with
"computing: continuous decision-making control," Neil
Chamberlain suggests that the ranks of the displaced "will
include numbers of individuals occupying once highly
regarded supervisory and managerial positions, whose role
and status the new technology will make obsolete." Chamberlain adds that some of these may be provided with
make-work jobs but "like any manual workers whom
technological change has out-dated, they will be downgraded. At such time they will have to re-read, for their
own comfort, the strictures which they once read to the
employees under them about the long-term benefits of
technological improvements." [13]

AUTOMATION: THE LONG TERM
EFFECTS ON TRADE UNIONISM

One of the far-reaching effects of automation which
was scarcely foreseen ten or even five years ago is its impact, current and potential, upon trade unionism as a social
and political institution in the United States. For the
American labor movement probably the most significant
effect of these great changes in industry—the wider application of electronics, the shift to more integrated
processes and automatic equipment—has been its by-
product effect on the labor force. This shift in technology
has caused a radical shift in the demand for labor. Even
where firms and plants continue in business after automating, the nature of the labor force which is left in them is
being sharply transformed. The new flows and processes
require more engineers, technicians and computer clerks,
and fewer and fewer production and maintenance workers.

In just the five years from 1955-60 the proportion of
production and maintenance workers in manufacturing—
roughly what we call blue-collar workers—declined from
83.9 per cent to 75.1 per cent. For the entire economy
the proportion of manual workers fell nearly 4 per cent in

the 1950-60 decade while white-collar workers were increasing about 5½ per cent.

Against this changing labor force background you must set the fact that the American trade union movement has always been by tradition and by numbers primarily a manual workers' organization. In 1960 it is estimated that only about 12 per cent of United States union membership was from the white-collar ranks and this proportion has not grown in recent years despite the fact that in this decade the number of white-collar workers has actually come to surpass the blue-collar force. When you add to these trends the fact that nearly half of organized labor's total membership in the past two decades has been concentrated among blue-collar workers in manufacturing where the move toward white-collar work is even more rapid, you have the makings of a major organizational crisis for the unions in the years to come.

The United States Department of Labor has already stated that in spite of the great increase in the United States labor force between 1955 and 1960 of nearly five million people, the American labor movement actually declined in absolute numbers. This was in sharp contrast with the preceding two decades of steady and often spectacular growth. As a proportion of nonagricultural employment American union membership declined from 35.1 per cent in 1954 to 32.1 per cent in 1960—a drop of one-half per cent per year.[15]

A continuation of this trend would, eventually, seriously challenge the representative character of the United States labor movement. Unless it breaks out of its blue-collar shell, labor's social and political role in the broad stream of American society will inevitably undergo a change. Indeed, the very nature of the American economic and political system will be affected by these developments in one way or another.[16]

The problem posed for union organizers in the face of these and related trends lies outside of this paper. It is also true, however, that the unions' ability to find answers for the problems of displacement, relocation, retraining, which automation is raising, will be affected by the strength of the labor movement in the industrial as well as the political fields—which strength goes very much to the question of numbers.

AUTOMATION: "SOLUTIONS"
IN LIGHT OF RECENT EXPERIENCE

We have already indicated that a full employment economy is an absolute precondition for successfully handling automation—at least on the employment side. We shall not deal here with the general economic programs and policies which seem most essential if the stagnation and unemployment of the past four or five years are to be overcome. These should, however, be constantly kept in mind as we turn to survey the direct effects of labor and management in collective bargaining as well as related government programs to deal with the effects of automation.[17]

Experience in recent years suggests that if labor and management are to use collective bargaining to work out solutions to some of the problems attendant to the impact of automation, they must increasingly rely upon new concepts and techniques. William Gomberg has suggested, for example, that for the successful handling of automation and related problems there must be increasing acceptance in collective bargaining of the concept that workers have a property right in their jobs. With this in mind "the cost of obsolete workers should be viewed as a charge on industry just as rational as the cost" of machinery.[18]

In the light of this principle employers would approach the employment impact of automation with great care. They would concentrate attention on the possibilities of transferring and retraining workers for the new jobs that followed in the wake of automation. In the absence of the successful transfer or retraining of workers, a system of payments to compensate workers for their loss of jobs would have to be developed. While this basic approach has not as yet been fully and widely accepted, some parts of it have been incorporated in many collective bargaining settlements in recent years and in a few instances the principle itself has in fact, if not in explicit terms, been made operational. An agreement, for example, negotiated between the Chesapeake & Ohio Railroad and the Brotherhood of Railway Clerks to deal with the impact of the introduction of a computer system in a large railway office provides that new jobs that result from the introduction of the computer are to be filled from the ranks of older employees. These older employees are to be retrained for the new jobs at the expense of the employers. Rates of pay on the new jobs are also to be negotiated in such a way as not to disadvantage employees' existing rates. Where permanent displacement cannot be avoided, an elaborate system of compensation to help the employees affected is put into operation.

THE WEST COAST LONGSHORE AUTOMATION AGREEMENT

The application of a worker's inherent property right in his job has been practiced on an even wider scale in the West Coast longshore labor-management agreement which was signed in October, 1960. The longshore union and the employers some three or four years earlier had set out to develop an agreement which would provide for a formula whereby the fruits of automation on the West Coast docks could be shared between labor and the companies. An impartial United States Government economist labored with them for over a year in an effort to find such a formula.

In the end, the search for a precise formula was abandoned after employers came to adopt the position of "How much will it cost us to get a free hand in introducing new labor-saving machinery?" The parties then reached an agreement which granted broad freedom to management to introduce labor-saving machinery and work out new crew arrangements. In return for this, the employers agreed to pay into a jointly managed fund some $5.5 million a year for five and one-half years (after which there would be new negotiations)—which fund would be used to compensate the employees for the "rights" they were abandoning in the form of the old manning practices and work rules. In Gomberg's phrase, the union "was capitalizing the worth of the job in exchange for the workers' title to it."

This agreement provided that the fund would insure the regularly registered longshore force a minimum wage guarantee of at least thirty-five hours a week as a protection against any losses resulting from the new cargo handling methods. In addition, early (at age sixty-two, in contrast to the normal Social Security age of sixty-five), and, in some cases, mandatory retirement at generous retirement benefits would also be financed through the new fund as a further means of cushioning the job impact on the work force.

This agreement marks a significant departure in extending basic protection to workers whose job opportunities are reduced in the wake of automation or major technological change. It is not a perfect substitute for what most workers seem to want, job continuity itself as opposed to mere income continuity, but it does represent a serious effort to find some workable alternatives.

Despite its outstanding features, however, this agreement points up some inherent limitations of dealing with the displacement effects of automation on a single industry-union basis. Actually the agreement only applies to the "permanent" or registered workers in the industries. There is a large group of more casual workers in West Coast longshore work who, although they are occupationally attached to it, have never attained fully registered status. It would appear that these workers will not enjoy the benefits of the fund and many, if not most, of them may well be permanently displaced from the industry in the next few years.[19]

SPECIAL LABOR-MANAGEMENT
MACHINERY NEEDED TO DEAL WITH AUTOMATION

The advances made under the longshore agreement as well as the beginning efforts represented by the Armour Company and the meat-packing unions point up the value of, indeed the necessity for, the establishment of special committees where labor and management are sincerely anxious to come to grips with the knotty problems of automation. These problems are usually so complex, with such far-reaching implications, that efforts to deal with them fully in the ordinary collective bargaining channels are apt to prove frustrating.

In the usual course of events unions and managements

have two or perhaps three months to work out the details of a new collective bargaining agreement. Under these circumstances it is too much to expect the parties to make any more than a surface approach to the human problems of technological change and job displacement in any large company or industry. At the least, there are involved the problems of the shifting of operations from one plant to another in a different community, the introduction of new equipment with displacement effects on old jobs and new and different skill requirements for the new jobs, the impact on existing wage structures, and so forth. These are problems which require cool, detailed study, and are not best handled against a deadline of contract expiration.

With the likelihood that the handling of technological change will be the single most important subject area for collective bargaining in the decade of the sixties one would expect the further development of special joint labor-management study groups designed to deal with the impact of automation in different firms and industries. Professor George W. Taylor also looks for the increasing use of outside experts in the role of private mediators and fact finders to assist such efforts.[20]

Finally on the collective bargaining program side it should be noted that the examples of the longshore industry, the Armour Company, and even such smaller efforts as that represented by the Railway Clerks in the C & O office units, are still the exceptions insofar as they represent very broad and comprehensive efforts. On the other hand, in specific areas and industries there has been considerable, partial progress in devising programs to mitigate the impact of automation in industry. Many unions have negotiated severance pay plans to compensate employees who are permanently displaced from their regular jobs, elaborate systems of supplementary unemployment pay which in effect guarantee workers something close to a full year of income have been negotiated in the automobile industry and to some extent in steel, meat packing, rubber and other industries. Special relocation allowances under which the company pays at least part of the costs of moving a worker and his family when he transfers to a new plant to find a job in the company have also been established in some important industries.[21]

Most of these programs are still limited to a relatively small number of industries and companies, however, and even these steps were only accomplished with great difficulty, often after strikes, in the past five or six years.

One is, however, struck by the fact that although these programs provoked almost unanimous and sharp employer resistance in the very recent past, they now appear to be winning much wider acceptance. The recent report of the President's Labor-Management Committee on the Benefits and Problems of Automation, for example, has recommended serious consideration for such things as ". . . employer supplementation of public unemployment compensation should be accomplished through severance pay, supplemental employment benefits and similar measures . . . provide for early retirement . . . financial aid and the transfer of employees to other plants in a multi-plant system and protection of existing rights for individuals so transferred . . . the recognition by unions, individual employees and employers of the necessity of adopting seniority and other rules in order to facilitate mobility of workers while providing protection for the equities of employees. . . ." The same report also advocated advance consultation between management and unions where major technological change was pending, retraining of workers, protection of pensions when job movement becomes necessary and other related measures.

The members of the committee noted that "a reduction in the basic work period has . . . historically been one means of sharing the fruits of technological progress," but they held off endorsing any such reduction for the present. This is, however, likely to be one of the most important collective bargaining items for labor and management in the sixties.

To those who have not followed collective bargaining negotiations in recent years it may be difficult to realize how far a cry this is from 1955 and even later as concerns the traditional opposition of most employers to the acceptance of guide lines like these. Assuming that these ideas will gain wider and wider acceptance in the years ahead, it is fair to say that we shall be moving from an era in which industry normally unloaded most of the human costs of technological change onto workers and the communities in which they lived, to an era in which there will be a genuine effort to better distribute the fruits as well as the costs of automation.

PUBLIC PROGRAMS TO DEAL WITH
THE DIRECT EFFECTS OF AUTOMATION

A somewhat similar line can be traced in the development of public programs and the increased acceptance of public responsibility for mitigating the impact of automation. The Senate, for example, in 1961 passed the Manpower Development Act which for the first time would put the United States Government seriously into the business of retraining workers in the face of the changing American economy. Under this program, too, special provisions would be made to pay unemployment benefits to workers who undergo such retraining. The eventual passage of this bill by both houses of Congress seems likely in 1962 or shortly thereafter.

Experiences like that at Armour, where so many workers seemed almost "untrainable" and those who were retrained had so much difficulty in finding jobs in a slack economy, may have the effect of minimizing interest in training and retraining. This would be taking too short-run a view of our needs. Unless we are overtaken by a full-scale depression in the coming years, there will be millions of new and changing jobs created by the new technology.

Neil Chamberlain has argued that as the pace of technological advance intensifies our problems will be compounded by "the rapidly changing skill needs of our technology confronting the unchanged or slowly-changing skill composition of our people. . . . The knowledge we need is a constantly swelling stream while the knowledge we have remains an unchanging pool." Chamberlain argues that "the only way this kind of a problem can be adequately met is by a constant and continuing *up*grading of our people over their lifetimes. . . ." [22]

This concept goes beyond current views on training and

retraining but it suggests we cannot afford to delay even so modest a beginning as is contemplated in present legislative proposals.

Another example of the growing acceptance of public responsibility to meet the dislocation of technological change was the establishment by legislation in 1961 of the Area Redevelopment Agency which will provide assistance to communities and individuals suffering the adverse effects of industrial change. As yet this agency lacks sufficient resources to meet the near Herculean task of redeveloping whole areas in the United States, but even this beginning is important.

These are but examples of the kinds of programs which are required if we are to construct a social framework adequate to meet the problems of an automating society.

While the problem of achieving and maintaining a full employment economy is still with us as we move into the sixties, it is fair to say that on the labor-management front, on the individual firm and plant front, the parties with the help of government have learned enough to mitigate some of the worst effects of automation. What they can do, of course, is no substitute for a full-scale attack on the basic problems of economic stagnation and unemployment. On the other hand, the failure to implement and carry through what can be done even on these more limited fronts will subject millions of workers to needless hardship and dislocation in the sixties.

The task for the sixties will be to hurdle or push aside the social and political barriers which in the past have prevented American society from progressing on the social plane at a rate commensurate with its technical progress. Certainly the knowledge and experience to do this is at hand if the social and political will are forthcoming.

FOOTNOTES

1. The President's Advisory Committee on Labor-Management Policy, January 11, 1962, *The Benefits and Problems Incident to Automation and Other Technological Advances*. This report received the endorsement of all but one of the five public members of the committee, six of the seven industry members and all seven unions members. Six of the union members did call for more immediate consideration of shortening the work week.

2. *Automation and Technological Change*, Report of the Subcommittee on Economic Stabilization to the Joint Committee on Economic Report (84th Congress of the US, First Session [Washington, D. C.: US Government Printing Office, 1955]).

3. *Ibid.*

4. From its various public pronouncements the Kennedy Administration sets the 4 per cent standard as its first goal and, once having reached that, it would presumably come forth with additional programs to reduce unemployment below that figure.

5. *Progress Report Automation Committee*, Armour & Company and United Packinghouse and Allied Food Workers and Amalgamated Meat Cutters and Butcher Workmen, AFL-CIO, 1961, pp. 10-11.

6. I have avoided comparisons with 1961 which was a general recession year. The economics of concentration and pricing policies which continue to provide even

declining industries with great profits and liquidity, thereby insuring high investment, lie outside the compass of this article.

7. It is sometimes hard to believe that the first book on automation was published just ten years ago!

8. Bright has made this point in several of his books and articles. These quotes are drawn from "Does Automation Raise Skill Requirements?," *Governor's Conference on Automation* (The Commonwealth of Massachusetts [June 2-3, 1960]), pp. 10-13.

9. *Impact of Automation on Employment,* Report of the Subcommittee on Unemployment and the Impact of Automation of the Committee on Education and Labor (House of Representatives) (87th Congress of the US, First Session [June, 1961]).

10. Walter Buckingham, *Automation* (New York: Harper & Bros., 1961), p. 99.

11. Ida R. Hoos, "When the Computer Takes Over the Office," *Harvard Business Review* (July-Aug., 1960), 102-12. This complaint about the "machine" sounds surprisingly like the first reactions of a steel mill hand to the introduction of an automated steel pipe-making line: "I like the jobs on the old mill better than the jobs on the new because you're in control. What you do determines how the pipe goes and what the machines do. You're on top of the machines. In the new mill the machines are on top of you." In this particular factory, however, Charles R. Walker found that after a fairly long break-in period most workers came to prefer work in the new process. *Toward the Automatic Factory* (New Haven: Yale University Press, 1957).

12. Ida R. Hoos, *Automation in the Office* (Washington, D. C.: Public Affairs Press, 1961), pp. 5-6.

13. Neil Chamberlain, "Automation and Labor Relations," paper prepared for the 59th Anniversary Celebration of Reed College, Nov. 16, 1961.

14. For purposes of rough calculation, I am here equating blue-collar and manual workers. Other groups in the labor force, aside from blue-collar and white-collar workers are those employed in farm work and the services. See Everett M. Kassalow, "New Union Frontier: White Collar Workers," *Harvard Business Review* (Jan.-Feb., 1962).

15. Harry P. Cohany, "Membership of American Unions, 1960," *Monthly Labor Review* (Dec., 1961).

16. See Everett M. Kassalow, "Automation: Challenge to the American Labor Movement," *Dissent* (Autumn, 1959).

17. See article above by Walter P. Reuther, "Congressional Testimony," for statements of labor's views on the general economic measures needed to restore and maintain full employment.

18. William Gomberg, "The Work Rules and Work Practices Problem," *Labor Law Journal* (July, 1961).

19. See Harvey Swados, "West Coast Water Front—The End of an Era," *Dissent* (Autumn, 1961). Swados also makes the point that much of the attractive rough and ready nature of dock work will be transformed by the new automated pocesses. I have not attempted in this brief article to deal with the changing nature of work itself under the impact of automation.

20. George W. Taylor, "Recent Collective Bargaining Developments in the United States," *Trade Union Information, Bulletin of the Trade Union Section of the European Productivity Agency,* No. 34, 1961.

21. See the statements of Walter P. Reuther in this volume, "Congressional Testimony," for more details on some of the collective bargaining provisions that have been negotiated to deal with automation.

22. Chamberlain, *op. cit.* On the other side of the training problem are those thousands of workers displaced in mining, meat packing, steel, auto and other industries who are not "retrainable" in the usual sense. In many instances these workers never even had elementary school training or are so long past elementary school that they really have to begin with basic literacy training if they are to be adapted to new job opportunities.

Part Five

IMPLICATIONS
FOR THE
SOCIAL SCIENCES

■ *12* ■

Computer Simulation: New Laboratory for the Social Sciences

by Diana Crane

A PRESIDENT'S FELLOW IN THE GRADUATE FACULTY
OF POLITICAL SCIENCE, COLUMBIA UNIVERSITY

The advent of the electronic computer has created important new possibilities for social science research. This machine makes feasible the secondary analysis of vast quantities of survey data that have been accumulating over the past three decades. The findings of dozens of researchers can now be pooled to yield comprehensive information about American society. Even more impressive, the machine can be used to simulate the behavior of large groups of individuals. Simulation involves constructing a theory or a model of a system's processes. The conclusions are derived by allowing the computer to carry out the processes postulated in the theory, thus generating a hypothetical stream of behavior that can be compared with the behavior of the original system. Computer programs can thus be considered a new language in which the assumptions of a theory can be expressed and its conclusions derived. By this novel technique, we can extend our understanding of events, past, present and hypothetical, and increase our ability to predict the future. So far, computer techniques have been applied by sociologists only to a few areas of social research. Potentialities of these techniques, however, are enormous.

Presidential elections illustrate one type of problem for which the computer is a valuable tool for the sociologist. Numerous studies of the voting behavior of samples of the American electorate have revealed that a wide range of factors, such as age, sex, religion, social class and ethnic background, are related to individual voting preferences. However, each presidential election is different from every other. The influence of economic or ethnic variables depends upon the nature of the campaign, the characteristics of the candidates, and current problems, domestic and international. Since the election process is crucial to a study of the requirements for maintaining a democratic society, simulation can permit sociologists to study not only what happened in previous elections but what might conceivably happen in future elections by testing the influence of each of the variables known to effect voter decisions in a series of simulated, hypothetical election campaigns. Under what conditions, for example, does the election process reinforce the democratic bases of our society and under what conditions does it undermine them by bringing about a monopoly of electoral victories for a single political party?

So far, the most elaborate simulation of voting behavior has been applied to a purely practical problem, that of assisting a political party in planning its campaign strategy in the 1960 election. This project provided a rare test of the ingenuity and imagination of a team of social scientists. What they attempted to estimate for the Democratic presidential candidate was the number of voters who would vote Democratic if certain issues dominated the campaign. For example, if the religious issue was widely discussed, what would be the effect at the polls? The information required to answer the question was available to them from polls made during the four national elections which took place in the nineteen fifties. The problem was to organize the information so that it would be pertinent to the issue. Here sociological theory developed from previous studies made it possible to devise 480 types of voters based on demographic characteristics. In addition, certain assumptions were required if the data was to be used to make contingent predictions. One such assumption was that the voter types did not differ geographically. In other words, "upper income Protestant Republican rural white males" were similar no matter what state they resided in. This made possible the construction of a synthetic electorate. By an elaborate analysis of census, poll and voting data, they developed a set of estimates of the number of persons of each voter type in each state.

Similarly, to estimate the effect of the religious issue on each of the voter types, a combination of sociological theory and assumptions based on substantive knowledge of voting behavior was required. Previous research on voting permits the sociologist to estimate an individual's vote from certain demographic characteristics but cross-pressures resulting from multiple-group affiliations or loyalties can interfere with such predictions. Consequently, a good deal of effort has been expended by sociologists in trying to determine how voters behave under such cross-pressures. To choose illustrations from the 1960 election, in which the candidates were a Catholic Democrat and a Protestant Republican, Protestant Democrats and Catholic Republicans could be expected to experience conflicting loyalties. To cope with these and other groups under cross-pressure, a set of equations was devised, representing the probability of voting for each candidate for each group. Assumptions had to be made by the investigators as to which previous elections should be used as indicators of the groups' future political behavior and what proportion of the Catholic group in each party would vote for Kennedy. Using the appropriate set of equations, the computer made separate calculations for each voter type, putting into the equations values for turnout record, 1958 vote intention, 1956 vote intention and anti-Catholicism derived from poll information about each particular voter type. The result was a 1960 vote estimate for each voter type for a hypothetical presidential campaign in which religion was a major issue.

Not only did the vote estimate conform closely to the actual November outcome but it provided a basis for decision making within the Democratic party during the period when campaign strategy was being developed. For example, the results of the hypothetical election involving the religious issue were interpreted by the investigators as follows:

It is in Kennedy's hands to handle the religious issue during the campaign in a way that maximizes religious prejudice and minimizes further defections. On balance, he would not lose further from forthright and persistent attention to the religious issue, and could again. The simulation shows that there has already been a serious defection from Kennedy by Protestant voters. Under these circumstances, it makes no sense to brush the religious issue under the rug. Kennedy has already suffered the disadvantages of the issue even though it is not embittered now— and without receiving compensating advantages from it.[1]

The relevance of this technique for the theoretical study of voting behavior is emphasized by the fact that this simulation of the 1960 electorate was based entirely upon poll data from previous elections. One sociologist who has applied computer techniques to voting behavior, but for research not practical purposes, is William N. McPhee. The purpose of his simulation is to produce a "completely observable system" in which the processes determining voting choices can be studied as well as the outcome of any simulated election. The model incorporates two problems which are basic to research on voting behavior: the processes, such as learning and social influence, which lead to particular voting choices in the individual; and the effects upon the individual of varying stimuli, represented by the problems stressed and promises made by the political candidates. For example, we all know who did win the 1960 election, but under what circumstances might other candidates have secured the nomination or won the election? The best place to study this question is, of course, in the primaries. Assuming that voters have a strong or weak disposition to vote for a particular party, their actual vote will depend upon the strength of the appeals made by the candidate. A strong appeal will overcome a weak disposition to vote, while a weak appeal will be all that is required to induce those with strong dispositions to vote for the candidate anyway. Using Humphrey's strongest appeal, the farm issue, and studying its effects upon groups of voters the strength of whose dispositions to vote for him varied from strong to weak, McPhee was able to analyze his chances of winning against Kennedy in the Wisconsin primary where Nixon's appeal was at its weakest (since he did not campaign there). With Nixon's appeal low, those with weak dispositions to vote for him moved toward Kennedy, not Humphrey, since they tended to be Catholic, while those with strong dispositions to vote for him remained in his camp, being mainly Protestant. Thus no matter how strong an appeal Humphrey made to the voters he could not win the voters away from Kennedy and Nixon in that situation.[2]

Sociologists have also begun to apply computer technology to the prediction of small-group behavior. Eventually, they would like to develop their knowledge of interpersonal relations to the point where they could change motivation and behavior through person-to-person communication—to be able, for example, to develop appropriate and binding group decisions, to lead training groups in human relations or to foster cooperation and morale in work groups. As Robert F. Bales has stated:

> . . . what the therapist, leader or any other interested participant wants to be able to do is to read the signs that appear in the behavior—to diagnose accurately what is going on, predict where it is going, and

how it will change if he takes a given action—all of this soon enough for him to intervene and try to change the course of events if he deems it desirable.[3]

The problem, however, is to calculate the weights of various factors relative to one another under given conditions. He and his associates now believe that the ideal method of representing the kind of theory they require is computer simulation. For years, Bales and others at Harvard have been observing discussion groups, mapping the behavior of the participants in terms of twelve categories which summarize and quantify its direction and its emotional and task content. Their goal is to simulate the behavior of a discussion group. Given the personality characteristics of the group members and the topic for discussion, computer simulation could predict the actual content and process of the discussion that would be likely to ensue. The output of the computer would be a series of statements each indicating who is speaking, to whom he is making his comment, and the task and social-emotional content of the comment.

Steps in this direction have already been taken by A. P. Hare. His problem was to find out if a properly programmed computer could do as well as a group of five students in predicting the responses of someone they did not know to a series of statements designed to reveal his basic values (given samples of his previous responses in advance). The simplest aspect of the problem and the logical starting point was to figure out how a single subject reaches a decision. Hare hypothesized that the subject identifies a statement as belonging to one of several categories and then predicts that the unknown respondent would answer the new item as he had answered similar items on the average in the past. He was able to write a program illustrating this hypothesis. The next step was to simulate the way in which the five-man group reached its decision. Using the five individual predictions as inputs, the program assumed that the group members would reach a decision that represented an average of the individual members' judgments. Comparing the predictions generated by the machine with the actual predictions of individuals and decisions of groups, Hare found that the computer's predictions were somewhat better than those of the average subject, but that it was not as successful in predicting the responses of a group of subjects. Evidently what needed revision was the hypothesis that the decision reached by members of a group represents an average of individual members' judgments. Hare suggests that such groups may have leaders who influence group opinion. If such men could be identified before the experiment, prediction by computer could be improved.

Hare has also been trying to simulate the social-emotional side of interaction—how a statement is said, not just what is said. So far, his attempts to simulate "the initial perceptual part of the social act as the new group member looks around at the other members and decides on the basis of his past experience how he will act toward each one" have not been successful. However, he is convinced that in time simulation will make it possible "to make real predictions in real time about social interaction in small groups." [4]

Economists also have been using computer simulation to further their understanding of economic behavior. G. P. Clarkson has simulated the actual processes of an individual making investment decisions. The purpose of the simulation is to increase our understanding of human problem-solving behavior under uncertainty and to predict aggregate trust investment behavior. Built by observing the decision processes of individual trust investors, the model attempts to explain the content of individual decisions as well as the order in which they take place. For example, a hypothesis basic to the model asserts that investors develop expectations of what will happen in the stock market as a result of recognizing patterns in previous events.

Clarkson makes use of a technique for storing information in the machine that is analogous to the way in which human beings store many types of information and which could therefore be applied to a wide range of psychological problems. Information is stored in the computer's memory in the form of lists which contain closely associated pieces of information. In this case, there is a list of companies representing possible investment choices in each industry and for each company a list of attributes that contain relevant financial information. The model continually processes new information to form new lists that summarize basic data and provide the material for making decisions.

Another aspect of the process is the fact that investors associate different industries with different investment goals. In the model, scanner-selector mechanisms search the summarized lists and match their values against sets of desired criteria. Since new information on the economy, industries and companies is fed into the computer regularly, the scanner-selector mechanisms allow the model to adapt both the criteria by which it selects and the portfolio selections it makes to current economic and market conditions.

Clarkson believes that his model represents the structure of the investment decision process that is common to all investors. He views the program as a theory of the "representative investor." From this model, aggregate trust behavior could be predicted. So far, the validity of the model has been tested by comparing the model's selection of portfolios for a set of actual accounts with selections made by investment officers of several national banks.[5]

Even more ambitious is a simulation of the household sector of the American economy recently completed by Guy H. Orcutt.[6] His model contains a stratified sample of households classified in terms of twenty-three variables, such as race, age, sex, education, income, debt, and so on. The individual households have alternative types of behavior available. With each alternative, there is associated a probability, empirically determined. The simulated households form, grow, diminish, split and disappear according to statistics that fit the past, present and expectations for the immediate future. The model produces estimates which forecast population changes, purchases of durable and nondurable goods, demand for services and the need for housing among other items.

Orcutt's ultimate goal is to simulate the total economy of the United States. He sees his model as an instrument for "consolidating past, present and future research efforts of many individuals in varied areas of economics and sociology into one effective and meaningful model; an instrument for combining survey and theoretical results obtained on the micro-level into an all-embracing system useful for prediction, control, experimentation, and analysis on the aggregate level." [7]

Other economists have been studying the ways in which companies react to external change, for example, an increase in demand. One has simulated a perfectly competitive industry and another has a model of the shoe, leather and hide industries which incorporates some of the mechanisms determining behavior of producers and consumers in that area of the economy.

What, then, are the implications of this new technique? Undoubtedly, it will permit the social scientists of the future to map more precisely the complex interrelationships of variables affecting human behavior. Simulation may help to explain processes that can be studied in no other way, by making it feasible to handle systematically far more variables and relationships than an individual could hope to handle in a short period of time. Processes that social scientists have so far been unable to translate into mathematical terms can be studied directly by writing a program that manipulates symbols in the same way that the human being manipulates them. Not the least of its advantages is that it forces the social scientist to be accurate and precise about the variables in interpersonal behavior and the exact relations between them. The computer is a hard task master. It also permits the direct confrontation of theory with concrete behavior. By comparing the output of a computer model with empirical observations, the postulates about processes that have been incorporated in computer models can be tested and refined.

A typical criticism of computer simulation from those who have not used the technique is that the computer can only reproduce what is fed into it in the first place. What such critics overlook is the fact that the computer puts out the data in a new form, one which involves so many calculations that a human being would take years to perform them. Only when the relationships between variables are complex and the outcome unpredictable in advance is a process worth simulating.

A more significant criticism that has been suggested is the following: If the computer simulates behavior, does it necessarily mean that this is exactly how the person behaves? As one expert in the field has put it: "It may be that [computer] languages, in addition to the computer's logical operations and controlling functions, force us into describing behavior in an artificial manner. Thus, though the computer forces us to be precise, the manner and not the extent to which it does this may be inappropriate or not necessary for a model of behavior." [8] While sociologists can test their theories by comparing the computer's figures with statistics based upon actual human behavior, if the prediction is not good, only further research will tell whether the model, the way the computer forces them to simulate behavior, or the measure of behavior is at fault. Another aspect of this problem is the fact that, for some of the most interesting problems, data for a simulation does not yet exist in sufficient quantities. Computer models have a prodigious capacity for utilizing empirical data. In some areas, simulations may have to wait until sufficient data of the right type is available.

In spite of such problems, computers may well offer the first practical means for making the social sciences truly scientific and useful. Unfortunately, much of present-day sociology consists of studies of the relationships between two or more variables at a single point in time. Many sociologists have not yet learned to think in terms of "dynamics" although the study of variations in the relations between variables over time has now become practical. Computer techniques are so new that the full range of problems to which they can be applied is just beginning to be explored. A sociologist at Columbia University plans to apply the technique to the study of social mobility. Rates of social mobility[9] in Western industrial societies are known to be approximately the same but sociologists do not fully understand why. Computer simulation will permit the testing of hypotheses about the social processes that produce social mobility. The simulation currently being planned will study the processes that create social ties according to similarities between persons and that select individuals for promotion or demotion according to their abilities. The model will make it possible to study the movement over several generations of large samples of "individuals" whose characteristics will be determined by reference to known populations and will include genetic abilities, social ties, roles, age and sex.

An advertising executive recently stated that "it may soon be possible to give trial flights to promotional programs on electronic computers. They may make it possible to forecast with greater accuracy the behavior of consumers in response to marketing programs which are under consideration. I believe there are many indications that the decision-and-action process of consumers will soon be simulated, or at least reduced to a systematic set of mathematical functions which can be programmed onto an electronic computer." [10] To the extent that analysis of the process by which consumers select their purchases can illuminate human preferences in general, such research would be important to the sociologist.

Other sociological problems that could benefit from the application of simulation techniques include the study of urban sociology, mass communications and personnel turnover in organizations. Eventually it may even be possible to make the output of one simulation the input of another. Thus the findings from one model may become useful in developing the postulates of other models. If we can regard the real world as an assemblage of loosely linked systems, it should be possible to study experimentally by means of computer simulation the effects of one system upon another, for example, the effects of different policies upon the realization of certain goals. William McPhee has suggested that, as programs for certain basic processes such as learning and personal influence are developed, they may be used like building blocks and inserted in a wide variety of programs. Being able to reproduce, through computer simulation, much of the complexity of a whole society going through processes of change, and to do so rapidly, would greatly increase the opportunities for putting social science to work.

Other than simulation, computers can also serve less exciting but extremely useful purposes—in yielding the complete analysis of existing data. Because with machine procedures data processing has become so much simpler, it is now possible for the social researcher to explore all the questions, hunches and hypotheses that occur to him. He need no longer be restricted by his own time and energy. As a noted sociologist has explained:

> . . . the researcher is not forced to neglect questions that he would like to ask because he would have no feasible technique for examining the data. With computers at hand, he is encouraged, rather, to ask all relevant questions. Essentially, he is searching the the realm of the unknown. He is asking questions on the chance that if he locates some significant variation, it may give him a clue toward being able to explain the phenomenon that concerns him. At one time, this kind of procedure in social science would have been a luxury. Today it is a luxury, only as it poses problems of getting the data.[11]

The use of the computer to facilitate the task of empirical description has already been applied to the problem of characterizing the informal social structure of communities, student bodies and similar groups. The analysis of sociometric data which would have been nonobjective and time-consuming by older methods of data processing can now be accomplished by the computer in minutes. For example, programs have been developed that reveal cliques and subgroups among high school students from their sociometric choices.[12]

Critics of sociology may suggest that computer technology will lead to a totally planned society, that its consequences will be a social system in which machines turn human beings into automatons. This attitude, however, emphasizes the negative aspects of the new techniques. In a society as large and as complex as ours, planning is becoming more and more essential if we are to make the most efficient use of our resources and manpower. In future decades, computers may greatly improve the sociologist's ability to plan social action. Sociologists have long been aware that social planning even with the best intentions can produce unfortunate consequences. As Robert K. Merton has said: "Short-run rationality often produces long-run irrationality. Public health measures may go awry; financial incentives may lead to a decline rather than an increase in production; intensified punishment may aggravate rather than curb crime." [13] Only increased knowledge can prevent such mistakes. In the foreseeable future, the computer may provide the sociologist with the means to understand and, to some extent, control the immense complexity of variables affecting human relations.

FOOTNOTES

1. Thomas B. Morgan, "The People-Machine," *Harper's*, Vol. 222 (Jan. 1961), p. 54. See also Ithiel de Sola Pool and Robert Abelson, "The Simulmatics Project," *The Public Opinion Quarterly*, Vol. 25 (Summer, 1961).

2. For further information, see William N. McPhee, "Notes on a Campaign Simulator," *The Public Opinion Quarterly*, Vol. 25 (Summer, 1961), and William N. McPhee, "The Uses of a Computer Model of Voting," *The Public Opinion Quarterly*, Vol. 23 (Fall, 1959), 440-41.

3. Robert F. Bales, "Small Group Theory and Research," *Sociology Today*, ed. Robert K. Merton, L. Broom and L. S. Cottrell, Jr. (New York: Basic Books, 1959), p. 295.

4. A. P. Hare, "Computer Simulation of Interaction in Small Groups," *Behavioral Science* (July, 1961), 261-65.

5. For further information, see G. P. Clarkson and H. A. Simon, "Simulation of Individual and Group Behavior," *American Economic Review*, Vol. 50, (1960), 920-32.

6. See Guy H. Orcutt et al., *Microanalysis of Socioeconomic Systems: A Simulation Study* (New York: Harper and Brothers, 1961).

7. K. J. Cohen and R. M. Cyert, "Computer Models in Dynamic Economics," *The Quarterly Journal of Economics*, Vol. 75 (Feb., 1961), 122.

8. Nancy S. Anderson, "Comments on the Use of Computers in Psychological Research," *Behavioral Science*, Vol. 6 (July, 1961), 268.

9. Jack Ferguson, "Outline of a Computer Model of Social Mobility," paper delivered at the American Sociological Association Convention, New York City, 1960.

10. "Computer to Be Test Market of the Future: Clawson," *Advertising Age*, Vol. 30 (Jan. 5, 1959), 3.

11. E. F. Borgatta and J. Robbin, "Some Implications of High Speed Computers for the Methodology of Social Research," *Sociology and Social Research*, Vol. 43 (March, 1959), 262.

12. James Coleman and Duncan MacRae, Jr., "Electronic Processing of Sociometric Data for Groups up to 1,000 in Size," *American Sociological Review*, Vol. 25 (Oct., 1960), 722-27.

13. Robert K. Merton, "And Now the Case *for* Sociology," *New York Times Magazine* (July 9, 1961), 21.

ADDITIONAL BIBLIOGRAPHY ON COMPUTER SIMULATION

R. H. Adams and J. L. Jenkins, "Simulation of Air Operations with the Air Battle Model," *Operations Research*, Vol. 8 (Sept., 1960), 600-15.

Alex Bernstein, "Computer vs. Chess Player," *Scientific American* (June, 1958).

D. G. Malcolm, "Bibliography on the Use of Simulation in Management Analysis," *Operations Research* (March, 1960), 169-77.

W. H. Dennick and F. Olanie, "Bank Management Game," *Banker's Monthly*, Vol. 77 (Sept., 1960), 56-60.

R. F. Reiss, "The Digital Simulation of Neuro-Muscular Organisms," *Behavioral Science*, Vol. 5 (Oct., 1960), 343-58.

Walter R. Reitman, "Heuristic Programs, Computer Simulation and Higher Mental Processes," *Behavioral Science*, Vol. 4 (Oct., 1959), 330-35.

M. Shubik, "Bibliography on Simulation and Gaming," *American Statistical Association Journal*, Vol. 55 (Dec., 1960), 736-51.

L. Uhr, "Intelligence in Computers: The Psychology of Perception in People and Machines," *Behavioral Science,* Vol. 5 (Apr., 1960), 178-82. (Very good article)

S. G. Vandenberg, "Medical Diagnosis by Computer: Recent Attempts and Outlook for the Future," *Behavioral Science,* Vol. 5 (Apr., 1960), 170-74.

▪ *13* ▪

Voting Simulation:
The Manufacture of Consent

by Murray Mogel

A LAWYER IN NEW YORK CITY,
MR. MOGEL IS A GRADUATE OF THE
COLUMBIA UNIVERSITY LAW SCHOOL

"We gave everybody exactly what they wanted, what the largest percentage wanted, that is, and if this isn't Democracy I don't know what is." From *The Big Ball of Wax* by Shepherd Mead.

Computer simulation of the voting behavior of the United States electorate promises to answer the prayer of the political campaign manager. Through the artful combination of computer technology and social science theory, the blueprint necessary to win elections has become available. Laid bare is the complex pattern of social and psychological cross-pressures which determine voting choice and must be manipulated adroitly by the party strategists in order to win. Power is given to the campaign manager to create the protean candidate; the winning image with the faces of a majority, the surrogate of the voters' will. Into the voting booth on Election Day will step, not the undependable voter, but the instructed agent of the party.

One eminent social scientist has proclaimed the beginning of a new era in social science research as a result of the simulation of human behavior by computer technology. "This is the A-bomb of the social sciences. The breakthrough here is comparable to what happened at Stagg Field," Dr. Harold Lasswell has been quoted as saying.[1] Our enthusiasm for the breakthrough at Stagg Field has been diminished by our experience of its consequences. Perhaps some reflections upon the implications for a free society of the simulation of voting behavior are appropriate, for the power to simulate voting behavior has consequences, just as the A-Bomb has fallout. Let us examine the assumptions, process, uses and implications of voting simulations; and let us attempt to decide whether we ever again will answer the questions of political pollsters.

Somewhere along the continuum of coercive persuasion, at a point between the poles of buncombe and brainwashing, lies the optimum formula for producing consensus for a particular purpose. It is a formula which solves the practical problem common to businessmen and politicians: how can the greatest quantity of consent to the desirability of a product or political proposition be manufactured at the lowest cost per consumer or voter choice? It operates by coercing the consumer or voter. It is available through the good offices of the market researcher, an applied social scientist. Given the particular problem—sales or political campaign—he will assemble his staff, often from the social science faculties of universities, and his ideas, often from the reports of foundation sponsored research projects, and he will produce the formula. His services are costly, but time, money and man power will be saved by his clients: the commodity will be sold and the candidate elected.

A citizen's choices of a commodity or a political candidate are equivalent processes to the applied social science of market research. This premise is based upon a statement of leading social science empiricists and theorists that "the decisions that a modern Western man makes every few years in the political arena are similar to those he makes every day as a consumer of goods and services." [2] In short, the voter is a consumer, the candidate is a commodity, the political forum is a supermarket, and all are properly within the province of market research. And market research "is aimed predominantly at knowledge by means of which to forecast and control consumer behavior." [3]

"The political people-machine" is the nickname recently given to the process of computer simulation of voting behavior. [4] In view of the goals of market research, the nickname is appropriate for a synthetic electorate imprisoned within a computer program. The political people-machine merely calculates as it is instructed; the computer program is the guiding spirit of the synthetic electorate. One of its components is a mathematical representation, translated into computer language, of a sample of voters selected to represent the parameter of the United States electorate. Physically, the program is made of magnetic tape and punch cards. Analytically, the synthetic electorate consists of the coded political attitudes and correlated voting choices of each synthetic elector; they are the variables which are stimulated by the programmed political propositions. Operationally, it is a miniature political campaign and election conducted within a computer. A voting simulation estimates the effects of political propositions or images on the likely voting behavior of the synthetic electorate. That calculation is used as a contingent prediction of the vote of the United States electorate.

On its theoretical side, the political people-machine descends from the social science panel studies of voting behavior. The unique method of those studies was to interview the same groups of voters at different times during the course of a political campaign; its objective was to chart the development and change of political attitudes and voting choices. Its social scientific purpose was heuristic: to construct a model through which the decision-making process could be understood. Four propositions derived from those studies underlie the construction of the synthetic electorate: voter types and their correlated attitudes can be defined; voting preferences are learned and vary little throughout the life of the voter; voting preferences are the result of determinable socioeconomic and psychological cross-pressures; and as those cross-pressures are intensified or diminish voting preferences become more or less salient. For example, the effect on voting choice of the candidate's religion is shaped and determined by the cross-pressures of the voter's own religion and socioeconomic status. A voting simulation would calculate the precise incidence of voting choices elicited by the religious issue; and the social scientist-simulators would suggest how to manipulate those cross-pressures to coerce a designated voting choice.

The simulators can do their work in the furor of the campaign in a matter of hours, and guide the campaign strategists to the most effective political propositions and images. The objective of the campaign is to get votes for the candidate and the party. Until the advent of voting simulations, campaign strategy was determined primarily by the intuitive guesses of the party strategists. Today the most effective propositions and images can be winnowed by the voting simulation. Voting simulations test propositions and images on the synthetic electorate. In a sense, the voting simulation is an observation by the computer of a synthetic panel of voter types. Those types are derived from the "secondary analysis" of past political poll data—not election returns—in terms of political attitudes and correlated socioeconomic and religious indices; they are the synthetic electorate.

The synthetic electorate imprisoned in the political people-machine can be compelled to reveal the popularity of alternative political propositions presented to it through a computer program. The political proposition or image is mathematically represented and translated into computer language. The programmed proposition or image stimulates those variables in the synthetic electorate which determine voting choice; and the likely voting behavior which is elicited by that proposition or image is then calculated. That is a voting simulation. Since the political people-machine actually is a computer program in which a miniature campaign issue operates upon a miniature electorate, the likely voting behavior of the entire United States electorate under similar circumstances may be predicted contingently.

Only the popularity of a political proposition or image may be determined by a voting simulation. The synthetic electorate cannot determine whether a political proposition will be good for the political community or nation. The validity of a voting simulation is a statistical concept; it merely determines how accurately the popularity of a proposition or image was gauged by the voting simulation. In an actual simulation—to be described later—the correlation of the voting simulation and the actual vote was .82. Since the perfect and exceedingly rare correlation is 1.00, the validity of that simulation is statistically impressive. It is expected that future voting simulations will yield higher correlations as the synthetic electorate is improved by more refined political polling techniques and data. Poll data which might be used in voting simulations is constantly being gathered. It also must be noted that there is more than one technique and theory of voting simulation, but all have the same bases, objectives, applications and implications.

Voting simulation is an innovation of social science; but its context is an intricate idea and activity, one of strength and grace, the political community. No man, not even a social scientist, can consider it as a mere object to be studied dispassionately; for it is, as Walter Lippmann observed, "why young men die in battle for their country's sake and why old men plant trees they will never sit under." [5]

Voting simulation was invented by social scientists, but they have been reluctant to discuss its implications for the political community. The philosophy of science, they say, precludes their comment. They must remain morally autonomous to be scientists. Science seeks truth; discussions of utility are irrelevant. Taken at their word, they seem indeflectably loyal only to truth. Judged by their acts, they are the handmaidens of coercive persuasion. They drift along Madison Avenue, in and out of the consent factories, tightening a screw here and there, but never forgetting their fee. If asked, they will set up simulation shops. The consent factories, to their minds, are merely laboratories in which to sharpen methodology. Presumably the assumption that such applications have no implications, and "earn while you learn," are the saws which soothe the social scientific conscience into silence.

The thesis of this essay is that voting simulation, an instrument of market research in political behavior, cannot be accommodated within the structure of a free society. The objective of political market research is the control of political behavior. It is incompatible with the medium of debate as our constitutionally sanctioned method of government. It is in conflict with the functioning of elected officials as trustees charged with the duty of determining the good of the nation. And it can operate only through the invasion of privacy. Voting simulation necessarily supports coercive persuasion: the manufacture of consent.

SIMULATION, THE POLITICAL COMMUNITY, AND DEBATE

To understand the implications of voting simulations for the political community, we must review two basic concepts. What is the political community? And what is the medium of government in a free society?

The political community or nation includes all who are born into it and all who join it. It consists of all its members at a particular moment in its history and all who succeed them. The concept of continuity inheres in its nature, and its generations are united by the idea that it will be guided in a certain manner and by a certain spirit. The spirit of the political community is usually expressed in a constitution; it is the instrument which articulates and animates the political community.

Our nation consists of voters as well as nonvoters. The infant, the infirm, the incompetent, the ignorant and even the imprisoned—none are excluded from the political community because they do not or cannot vote. Executives and legislators are trustees for the nation, and they are charged with the duty of determining which political propositions are good for it. Their medium of government is determined by the Constitution.

Some political propositions which will further the good of the nation may not be popular with some members of the political community. The advocacy of those propositions may lose votes, but the interests of voters are not necessarily coextensive with those of the nation. Actually, approximately a third of the nation determines who shall be elected to the Presidency; less than that number determines the composition of the Congress.

Since the good political proposition is not necessarily the popular one, and the popular proposition is not necessarily the good one, how do members of the political community—voters and nonvoters, executives and legislators—distinguish the one which is good for the nation? The ingeniously intricate structure of government established by the Constitution reflects its underlying assumption that the process of debate is the only method whereby the good political proposition can be determined. The legislative, the executive and the judicial departments of government reciprocally check and balance each other for the single purpose of insuring the elucidating conflict of ideas which is debate. Implicit, also, is the assumption that what is popular may be a disguised evil for the nation.

Debate is a conflict of ideas within the forum of reason; its function is to assay ideas and to educate the debaters. It is the only medium of political education and action in a free society. Its precondition is that propositions of all qualities, good and evil, true and untrue, popular and unpopular, will be presented. Its participants are charged, like jurors, with the duty of analyzing and discriminating among the propositions presented. Only if all types of propositions are presented can debate proceed. Debate is the medium of the free society: it is exemplified by the Federalist papers, and its spirit permeates the Constitution.

Voting simulations and their attendant political polls threaten to destroy the elucidating litigation of political issues through debate. When our Constitution was being formulated and written, the suggestion that a science of human behavior someday might imperil political debate would have been dismissed as a "contemptible subtlety." Through the discoveries of such a science, it is today pos-

sible to merchandise the merely popular proposition as
the only good one. The coercive obliteration of debate is
the objective of the manufacture of consent. Ironically,
the site of the manufacture is Madison Avenue, an avenue
so named to perpetuate the memory of "the master
builder of the Constitution," James Madison. Let us examine the effect of manufactured consent, implemented
by political behavior simulation, upon our two political
forums—the political campaign and the government.

VOTING SIMULATIONS IN POLITICAL CAMPAIGNS

Political campaigns are debates among the candidates
and members of the political community whose purpose
is to assay the qualities and competence of the candidates.
The ultimate objective is to determine which candidate
is better equipped to represent the political community
in the more formal debate of government. The forum is
anywhere citizens and candidates gather. Ideally, anyone
can present issues for debate. Actually, only selected issues are presented for debate. The selectors are usually
the party strategists. Popularity—the power to win votes
—is the principle of selection. After all, the business of
the party is to get its candidate elected. Anything may
be said if it is popular. The candidates talk at us, a passive
mass media or mob audience, and only by their artful
words and images do we know them. The debate of issues
already has been seriously impaired.

Voting simulations threaten to destroy further the function of the political campaign as a debate of political issues.
Political propositions can now be pretested upon the synthetic electorate. Without the risk of alienating any voters,
the voting simulation can answer the question: How many
votes will the candidate win or lose if he advances proposition X? By pretesting the effect of a variety of alternative propositions and images through voting simulation,
the skeleton of the optimum coercive image of the candidate may be assembled. It will consist of a congery of
propositions and images whose lowest common denomi-
nator is popularity—that power to elicit votes for candidate and party. To the mass media manipulators—the

sociologically and psychologically oriented Ad-men and Flacks—will be entrusted the delicate task of molding the candidate's image according to the plan of the simulators. The image of the candidate which seduces the mind of the voter away from the critical and persistent alertness required by debate will be the winning image. It is the product of the optimum formula to manufacture consent for the goals of the party.

The described use of voting simulations in political campaigns is not an Orwellian fantasy; it is a product of 1960, not *1984*. During the last presidential campaign, a computer simulation of the likely voting behavior of the United States electorate was accomplished by a market research corporation for the political party which won the election. The party strategists were concerned with the effectiveness and popularity of the image of their candidate and the probable consequences of the religious issue upon voting choice. The most accurate description of the problem with which they were presented has been furnished by the social scientist-simulators in a learned quarterly. "The immediate goal of the project was to estimate rapidly, during the campaign, the probable impact upon the public, and upon small strategically important groups within the public, of different issues which might arise or might be used by the candidates." [6]

Clearly, the purpose of the simulators' project was to provide the party strategists with information and suggestions which could be used to guide campaign strategy. The simulators did supply reports, more than a hundred pages of them. Their entire content remains a secret. However, the efficacy of their own reports to the strategists has been evaluated modestly by the social scientist-simulators. "While campaign strategy, except on a few points, conformed rather closely to the advice in more than one hundred pages of the three reports, we know full well that this was by no means because of the reports. Others besides ourselves had similar ideas. Yet, if the reports strengthened right decisions on a few critical items, we would consider the investment justified." [7] It must be noted again that the correlation between the voting simulation of the effect of the religious issue and the *actual* vote was .82, a most impressive statistical index of validity.

As the synthetic electorate is improved through more refined polling techniques and data, we can expect that correlations will be even higher. We cannot expect that the full text of any secret reports to party strategists ever will be made public. But we may surmise that they would reveal the sly images and principles of *The Prince*, reshaped for modern politics by computer and social science technology.

POLITICAL SIMULATIONS AND GOVERNMENT

Using political simulations as a tool of government, as a means for discovering the consensus concerning the goals of our society, is a suggestion worthy of Machiavelli. It actually was suggested as a use for political behavior simulations.[8] In essence, the suggestion is that we inform our elected officials of the popularity of political propositions by running a simulation of the attitudes of the political community. Evaluated against the background of the Constitution and our discussion of it, the dangerous and hidden implications of this proposal emerge. For a full understanding of the proposal, let us explore its possible operation and effects.

The Constitution provides for three departments of governments—the executive, the legislative and the judicial—and a system of reciprocal checks and balances among them in order to insure debate and prevent the dominance of any department. A department called the "public opinion" was not articulated into the structure, nor a niche left for it. Ours is a democracy which operates through the medium of debate by elected representatives; public opinion is represented by them, but it does not dominate them. The reason for the omission of public opinion as a department is that the President and the Congress are trustees for the entire nation. The public weal, the good of the nation, not the limited but powerful groups of voters who can return them to office, determines their duty. Their function is to evaluate complex and detailed information related to political propositions, debate those propositions, and by that process determine which proposition will result in promoting the public weal, the good of the entire political community.

Can debate be expected of the executive and legislator whose chances of re-election are being appraised continuously by a political behavior simulation? Over the Capitol will hang the brooding omnipresence of the synthetic political community. Through the artful reports of the simulators, the elected executive and legislator will discover how much popular support he can expect to win or lose by his stand on a particular political proposition. Can debate really be expected under such circumstances? Instead of being guided by reason, refined by debate and reflection upon the public weal, the mind of the elected official will become enslaved by computer output and its subtle interpretation by the simulators. No practical politician can be expected to diminish knowingly his chances of re-election. Advocates of the unpopular and sometimes meritorious will retreat before the quantified whims of the synthetic community; debate will be supplanted as the medium of government if the proposal of government through political behavior simulation is adopted.

Assuming, for argument, that debate is possible before the simulated whims of the synthetic community, how can the following methodological obstacles be overcome? Who would conduct the simulations? The government? The political parties? How would impartiality of administration be assured? How would the content of the sample be determined? Only those eligible to vote? How could the issues be framed with the degree of particularity which would be understandable to all members of the political community? Would a simulated consensus overrule the contrary decision of other departments of government? How could lobbyists be prevented from skewing the sample? Our present method of debate by elected representatives of the political community is not subject to those difficulties; it is the only medium of government whereby a free society can be maintained. The Constitution provides for a government through reason and debate, not by simulated whims which may elicit votes, and the proposal of the simulators cannot be accommodated within it.

SIMULATION VERSUS DEBATE

Open forums for political debate can be maintained only by men whose access to all political propositions is unlimited. Simulations provide information about popular propositions which will win votes or insure re-election. To present and reinforce popular political propositions as the only good ones is the beginning of tyranny by special interests with limited ends. Simulations are undetectable instruments of coercive persuasion. As they become more accurate and precise through the refinement of polling techniques and data, they will become more effective and subtle blueprints for the manufacture of consent. To those who hire the simulators will accrue the power to manufacture consent for their purposes.

The simulators offer us counsel derived from the "political people-machine," an automaton bound to the past by its memory drum and punch cards. It can predict that the future will resemble the past, for it is programmed to analyze only the yesterdays of man. It cannot be programmed to simulate the spirit of liberty which animates and inheres in debate. The late Judge Learned Hand attempted to define it. "The spirit of liberty is the spirit which is not too sure that it is right; the spirit of liberty is the spirit which seeks to understand the minds of other men and women; the spirit of liberty is the spirit which weighs their interests alongside its own without bias. . . ." [9] This spirit is opposed to market research in political behavior, for the aim of that research is to control the constitutional right of every man to determine his own life and that of his nation.

Political party strategists should rethink the implications of possible decisions to use voting simulations. The impact of manufactured political consent upon the structure and spirit of the nation must be weighed against the transient and limited aims of the party and the candidate. All sane men want to win. But no sane man can justify coercive persuasion as a means. It degrades voters to consumers; it debases candidates to commodities; it deteriorates political forums to supermarkets. Its implement is the voting simulation, and its cost is the destruction of the spirit of liberty.

SIMULATION VERSUS PRIVACY: THE VOTER'S CHOICE

Whether voting simulations will succeed in destroying political debate as our medium of government depends finally upon the willingness of voters to permit intrusions into their privacy by the simulators and their allied pollsters. Let us explore the right and function of privacy in the analogous political and legal forums of our free society. Does the electorate have a right to privacy of deliberation analogous to the one enjoyed by a jury? If so, how can the voter protect his right of privacy?

Privacy is the implicit condition of freedom of discussion and the exercise of reason. It exists only if the forum of debate is free of subtle coercive influences, regardless of their efficacy. Whether the deliberations be those of the electorate or a jury, they must be conducted in an atmosphere free of any form or method of intrusion, regardless of its intent. Yet the right of privacy of deliberation is nowhere guaranteed in our Constitution. It seems to be an implicit condition of granted rights, such as trial by jury, which is protected by law only after it has been threatened by some intrusion.

Only after a social-science-oriented project invaded a jury room with its secret recording equipment and actually recorded the deliberations of four federal civil juries was the theretofore implicit right of a jury to privacy of deliberation protected by law.[10] The purpose of the jury-tapping was to determine how a jury arrives at its verdict; and the ultimate goal of the project was to increase the effectiveness of the jury system. Surely, no project could be more social scientific in its objective. But there is often a little more to such projects than is apparent immediately.

Let us suppose that the simulators had obtained the jury-tapping data. What would they have been able to do with it? They could have constructed a synthetic jury panel, imprisoned it in the computer and simulated the jury process. The effect of alternative techniques of jury persuasion could be determined by a jury simulation, and the optimum plan of coercive persuasion presented to the lawyer. Also, information on the type of juror to select for a particular type of case would become available. A litigant seeking a favorable verdict would look to market research instead of the law to determine his rights. Justice under law, tempered by the reason and mercy of the jury, would vanish. Fortunately, the simulators were never given the opportunity to ply their trade.

The Congress viewed the intrusion into the privacy of the jury as a threat to a fundamental institution. It enacted a Federal penal statute which makes the recording of jury deliberations a crime punishable by fine and imprisonment.[11] A United States Attorney lucidly formulated the issue raised by jury-tapping. "Is there any objective, any circumstance, which justifies an invasion of the traditional privacy and confidence of jury deliberation by permitting surreptitious eavesdropping by means of hidden microphones and recording devices? Is the confidence of the jury part of the system [of justice] itself?" [12]

Analogously, may it not be asked: Is the confidence of the electorate part of the system of a free society itself? Is there any objective which justifies the invasion of the deliberations of the voter through electorate-tapping by voting simulations and their attendant political polls? Is our Constitution to be construed according to the questionable canons of social science?

The individual voter has the power to prevent his imprisonment in and by the synthetic electorate. His responses to the questions of political pollsters are the raw material of which voting simulations are made. To simulators and pollsters the voter is just another cipher to be fed into a computer. The voter must debate with the men who really count—his neighbor, his elected official, the candidate and himself—about the value of political propositions for the good of the nation.

Without the responses of voters to the questions of political pollsters, the simulation of voting behavior would become impossible. I do not suggest that every voter clamor for the enactment of a Federal statute to prohibit voting simulations and their attendant political polls. But I do suggest that every voter consider the uses to which his answer will be put before he decides whether or not to reply to the questions of a political pollster. The Constitution has determined that the only proper place for the voter's definitive expression of political choice is the voting booth on Election Day. Whether that right shall remain inviolate is the voter's choice.

FOOTNOTES

1. Thomas B. Morgan, "The People-Machine," *Harper's Magazine*, Vol. 222 (Jan., 1961), 53-57.
2. Seymour M. Lipset, Paul F. Lazarsfeld, Allen H. Barton and Juan Linz, "The Psychology of Voting: An Analysis of Political Behavior," in *Handbook of Social Psychology*, ed. by Gardner Lindzey (Cambridge, Mass.: Addison-Wesley, 1954), Vol. II, 1124.
3. Arthur Kornhauser and Paul F. Lazarsfeld, "The Analysis of Consumer Actions," in the *Language of Social Research*, ed. by Paul F. Lazarsfeld and Morris Rosenberg (Glencoe, Ill.: The Free Press, 1955), p. 393.
4. Morgan, *op. cit.*
5. Walter Lippmann, "The Public Philosophy" (New York: Mentor Books, 1956), p. 35.
6. Ithiel de Sola Pool and Robert Abelson, "The Simulmatics Project," *The Public Opinion Quarterly*, Vol. 25 (Summer, 1961), 167.
7. *Ibid.*, 173-74.
8. Morgan, *op. cit.*, 57.
9. Learned Hand, *The Spirit of Liberty* (New York: Alfred A. Knopf, 1952), p. 190.
10. *New York Times* (Oct. 6, 1955), 15:3.
11. *New York Times* (Aug. 6, 1956), 12:4. Cf. 18 U.S.C.A. §1508.
12. *New York Times* (Oct. 14, 1955), 26:5.

· 14 ·

Computer Models
in Dynamic Economics*†

by Kalman J. Cohen and Richard M. Cyert

CARNEGIE INSTITUTE OF TECHNOLOGY

The development of the electronic digital computer has been an extremely significant technological innovation for science, probably ranking on a par with the inventions of the telescope and the microscope. As the first such com-

* Reprinted from *The Quarterly Journal of Economics*, February, 1961, Copyright ©, by the President and Fellows of Harvard College, by permission of the Authors and Harvard University Press.
† This paper is based on research supported by grants made by the Graduate School of Industrial Administration, Carnegie Institute of Technology from the School's Research Funds and from funds provided by the Ford Foundation for the study of organizational behavior. The authors owe a considerable debt to their colleague, James G. March, for citicisms of an early draft and for many fruitful discussions of the contents of the article.

puter, the ENIAC, was completed less than fifteen years ago, our experience with electronic computers is still too limited for anyone to predict the ultimate significance which these machines will have in both the natural and the social sciences. However, our knowledge has increased so rapidly from the years immediately after World War II, when computers were viewed only as larger and faster desk calculators, that it seems worth-while to examine some of the implications which electronic digital computers have for research methodology in the social sciences.

It is undeniable that electronic computers, when used as routine calculating devices for performing statistical analyses and clerical data-processing operations, can be extremely useful in social science research. The purpose of this article is not to consider the importance of such routine uses of computers in the social sciences, but, rather, to explore the possibilities of using computers to stimulate the behavior of complex social systems. The specific illustrations used are all drawn from the field of economics, but the concepts seem equally relevant to other fields of social science. We shall use the term "computer model" to refer to a formal model designed for digital computer simulation. In this article, we propose to examine the characteristics of computer models and to survey some of the economic computer models that have been formulated. In addition, we shall attempt to evaluate the future achievements which might reasonably be expected from further work with computer models.

THEORY CONSTRUCTION (MODEL BUILDING)

The professional in any science works within a framework of definitions and concepts that becomes second nature to him. As a result, basic methodological points are frequently taken for granted. In appraising a methodological innovation, however, it is useful to re-examine such points. The explanation and evaluation of computer models can be simplified by examining the nature of theory construction (model building) itself.

A theory consists of three elements—definitions, as-

sumptions and conclusions. The following is a simple and
familiar example of a theory: [1]

Assumptions: (1) Firms attempt to maximize profits.
             (2) The marginal revenue curves intersect
                 the marginal cost curves from above.
             (3) The marginal curves are continuous.
Conclusion: A firm will produce that output corres-
                 ponding to the point of intersection of
                 its marginal revenue and marginal cost
                 curves.

It is obvious that this theory depends also on a set of subject matter (extralogical) definitions—profits, marginal
cost and marginal revenue.

There are a number of relevant points that can be noted
from this example. The conclusion is a logical implication
of the assumptions. The language in which the conclusion is derived from the assumptions is a matter of the theoretician's choice. In general, there are three languages
that have been commonly used by economists for drawing
a conclusion from a set of assumptions—ordinary prose,
pictorial geometry and formal mathematics. In the particular theory under discussion, it is obvious that the conclusion can be derived using any of the three languages. It
would also, of course, be possible to state the assumptions
and the conclusions in any of the three languages. Generally it is most convenient to state assumptions and conclusions in prose alone or a combination of prose and mathematics. The question of which language to use is answered quite nicely in the following quotation:

If mathematics is no more than a form of logical
reasoning, the question may be asked: why use
mathematics, which few understand, instead of logic
which is intelligible to all? It is only a matter of efficiency, as when a contractor decides to use mechanical earth-moving equipment rather than picks and
shovels. It is often simpler to use pick and shovel,
and always conceivable that they will do any job;

but equally the steam shovel is often the economic proposition. Mathematics is the steam shovel of logical argument; it may or may not be profitable to use it.[2]

Another point to note is that the conclusion is true only in the sense of logically following from the assumptions. The theory must be tested empirically before it can be said that the theory "proves" anything about the world. As has been said a number of times, it is not possible to prove by an a priori argument that a particular proposition is true of the real world. With most economic theories, unfortunately, testing is difficult, as it is with any nonlaboratory science.[3] One important reason for this difficulty in economics is that for the most part we are dealing with static theories, whereas the world in which we must test the theory is dynamic. As a result, it is usually difficult to find satisfactory data for testing purposes. Therefore economists frequently use artifacts of one kind or another to establish a "subjective" probability of the validity of a theory. One frequently used artifact is the determination of whether or not the assumptions correspond with the facts. This procedure has provoked a sharp attack by one economist which has resulted in an interesting controversy.[4] We do not intend to be sidetracked by this controversy, other than to comment on the fact that the practice is the result of difficulties in testing directly the conclusions of most theories. We mention the issue because, as will be argued below, we feel that computer models can reduce the difficulties of developing models that can be directly tested, although some new statistical problems may arise.

An additional point should be recognized about the nature of most economic theories which is relevant to the problem of testing. The point has been effectively made by Professor Samuelson:

The general method [of economic theory] involved may be very simply stated. *In cases where the equilibrium values of our variables can be regarded as the solutions of an extremum (maximum)*

*or minimum) problem, it is often possible, regardless
of the number of variables involved to determine un-
ambiguously the qualitative behavior of our solution
values in respect to changes of parameters.*[5]

This means that the testing procedure consists in making
numerical measurements to determine whether or not
the direction of change of certain parameters is the predicted direction. In general, economic theory seems more
successful in yielding propositions about directions of
change than propositions about numerical magnitudes of
particular variables.

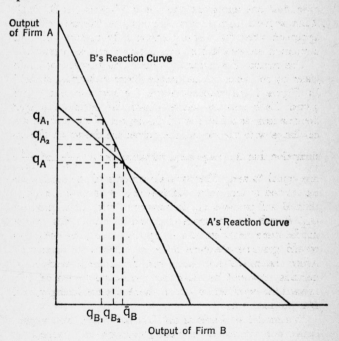

Output of Firm B

GENERAL CHARACTERISTICS OF COMPUTER MODELS

A computer model is a model in which the implications
of the assumptions, that is, the conclusions, are derived
by allowing an electronic digital computer to simulate the

processes embodied in the assumptions. Computer programs can thus be considered to be a fourth language in which the assumptions of a theory can be expressed and its conclusions derived. Actually, computer models might be viewed as special cases of mathematical models. We shall not pause to debate taxonomic subtleties, however, for it is more important to examine some of the features which characterize computer models.

We have stated above that there are a number of languages that *could* be used in model building. There are also a number of criteria that might be used to determine which language *should* be used. It seems obvious, however, that one important criterion is efficiency, as R. G. D. Allen argued. Computer models may be the most efficient approach when the model portrays a dynamic process and numerical answers in the form of time series are desired.

The notion of a dynamic process can perhaps be made clear by reference to the simple Cournot duopoly model.[6] In Figure I the reaction curves for rivals A and B are given. Each reaction curve shows the optimum output for one firm as a function of the output of its rival. In accordance with the model, the curves are drawn on the assumption that the conjectural variation terms $\left(\dfrac{q_A}{\partial q_B} \text{ and } \dfrac{\partial q_B}{\partial q_A} \right)$ are equal to zero. The dynamic process of the model can be started at any point. Assume that A is producing q_{A_1}; then B will produce q_{B_1}. In answer to this, A will produce q_{A_2}. B will then produce q_{B_2}, and so on. If this simple model were analyzed as a computer model, the computer would generate the time series of outputs for each firm. After the model had been run for a large number of periods, it would be clear that the outputs were tending toward the equilibrium values where A is producing q_A and B is producing q_B.

In a model as simple as the Cournot model, we are generally not interested in tracing through the process by which equilibrium is reached, but only in deriving the equilibrium values. These values are easy to find by simple mathematical analysis. However, the addition of a few assumptions about the behavior of the two firms can complicate the model sufficiently so that a computer simulation will be the most efficient method for determining the implications of the model. The volume of conclusions derived from a model is within the control of the model builder. However, in complicated computer models there are, generally, a large number of potential implications generated, many of these being time series of particular numerical values.

The fact that conclusions drawn from computer models may consist of a series of numerical values has in itself a number of interesting consequences. Numerical solutions should be contrasted with the analytic solutions usually derived from mathematical models. In terms of our earlier discussion on theory construction, we could say that the conclusions sought from a mathematical model are usually in the form of relations among the variables and parameters (including, frequently, derivatives or differences of the variables or parameters), while in computer models the conclusions obtained typically are in the form of time series of specific numerical values. This suggests that computer models are less general than mathematical models. The reason for this is that the amounts of input for computer models are greater than for the usual mathematical models. The increased input places greater restrictions on the relationships among the variables and parameters and, therefore, produces a less general but more specific model. One advantage to economists of computer models is that their conclusions are presented in immediately testable form.

It should be emphasized that the above characterization does not imply that computer models are necessarily less general or mathematical models necessarily less specific. Our considerations are related primarily to questions of convenience and efficiency. It is possible to use a computer model, for example, to gain insight into the effects of rates of change of particular parameters on the results of the model. This end is accomplished by varying the parameters of the model from one simulation run to another, and comparing the output time paths which are generated. If the model can be solved analytically, however, such a result could be more easily achieved by mathematical analysis.

COMPARISON OF COMPUTER MODELS WITH OPERATIONS RESEARCH SIMULATIONS AND ECONOMETRIC MODELS

In order better to understand the nature of computer models and the problems of using them, it is desirable to examine the use of simulation in the burgeoning field of operations research.[7] Additional clarification can be gained by comparing computer and econometric models.

There are two basically different approaches which can be followed in using computer simulation to study a complex system. The actual approach taken, of course, depends on the questions to be answered and the kind of information known at the time of the investigation. The approach generally taken in operations research or management science might be entitled synthesis. This approach aims at understanding the operating characteristics of a total system when the behavior of the component units is known with a high degree of accuracy. The basic questions answered by this approach relate to the behavior of the overall system. In principle, the entire system response is known once the characteristics of the structural relations are specified. If the system is complex, however, it may be difficult or impossible to determine the system behavior by current mathematical techniques. In this situation, simulation by an electronic computer can be utilized to determine the time paths traced by the system.

In social science, generally, the situation is quite the reverse. The behavior of the total system can be observed. The problem is to derive a set of component relations which will lead to a total system exhibiting the observed characteristics of behavior. The usual procedure is to construct a model which specifies the behavior of the components, and then to analyze the model to determine whether or not the behavior of the model corresponds with the observed behavior of the total system. When this model is sufficiently complex, either because of the nature of the underlying functions or the number of variables contained in it or both, computer simulation may be the most convenient technique for manipulating the model. It is logical to call this approach to simulation analysis. The actual output of the model is a set of time paths for the endogenous variables being studied by the model.

Traditional econometric models are essentially one-period-change models. Any lagged values of the endogenous variables are, in effect, treated as exogenous variables. They are assumed to be predetermined by outside forces rather than by earlier applications of the mechanisms specified in the model. Hence the output of econometric models is the determination of the values of the endogenous variables for a given time period. To determine these values for the next period, new values would have to be assigned to the lagged endogenous variables. For this reason, most econometric models should be regarded as determining the changes which take place in the world from one period to another. They should be contrasted with process or evolutionary models which attempt to exhibit the unfolding of dynamic processes over time.

The mechanisms of a computer process model, together with the observed time paths of the exogenous variables, are treated as a closed dynamic system. In such a model, the values of the lagged endogenous variables are the values previously generated by the system. Computer models may thus be forced to operate with errors in the values of the endogenous variables made in previous periods, there being no correction at the end of each period to assure correct initial conditions for the next period as in econometric models.

The contrasts between econometric and computer models have not been offered as invidious comparisons. It is clear that economics has benefited, and will continue in the future to benefit, from work in econometrics. Rather, our analysis is aimed at showing the nature and peculiar attributes of an important new research technique for social science.

METHODOLOGICAL PROBLEMS OF COMPUTER MODELS

As with any new research technique, there are methodological difficulties connected with the efficient utilization of computer simulation. There are three basic classes of problems which arise in using computer models. These problems are the specification of functional forms, the estimation of parameters and the validation of the models.

The problem of specifying functional forms is literally an example of the "embarrassment of riches." Most mathematical models have been formulated in terms of linear equations in order to facilitate the attainment of analytic solutions. Since this restriction is unnecessary for computer models, the way is opened for nonlinear functions having a wide variety of forms. The solution to this problem will probably come from two sources. First, as our empirical information (the collection of which will be stimulated and guided by attempts to formulate computer models) increases, some clues as to the proper forms to use to explain and predict behavior will be available. Second, technical statistical criteria will be developed to select efficiently the proper forms of the equations, presumably on the basis of predictive power.

The problems of parameter estimation have, of course, been much discussed in statistical and econometric literature. A major advance has been the proof that unbiased and efficient estimates can be obtained only by acknowledging the simultaneity of the equations of a model.[8] If this result carries over to computer process models, obtaining maximum likelihood estimates of all the parameters in such models will be a forbidding task.

A more feasible approach to the parameter estimation problem may be to restrict attention to the joint determination of only the current endogenous variables within a single period and to consider that the values of the lagged endogenous variables are subject to errors. The parameter estimation problem must then be considered within the framework of an "errors in the variables" model rather than an "errors in the equations" model. A few econometricians have investigated this kind of estimation problem, and their results may prove applicable to computer models.[9]

The likelihood of a process model incorrectly describing the world is high, because it makes some strong assertions about the nature of the world. There are various degrees by which any model can fail to describe the world, however, so it is meaningful to say that some models are more adequate descriptions of reality than others. Some criteria must be devised to indicate when the time paths generated by a process model agree sufficiently with the observed time paths so that the agreement cannot be attributed to mere coincidence. Tests must be devised for the "goodness of fit" of process models with the real world. The problem of model validation becomes even more difficult if available data about the "actual" behavior of the world is itself subject to error.

Although the formal details have not yet been adequately developed, there appear to be at least three possible ways in which the validation problem for process models can be approached.[10] First, distribution-free statistical methods can be used to test whether the actual and the generated time series display similar timing and amplitude characteristics. Second, simple regressions of the generated series as functions of the actual series can be computed, and then we can test whether the resulting regression equations have intercepts which are not significantly different from zero and slopes which are not significantly different from unity. Third, we could perform a factor analysis on the set of generated time paths and a second factor analysis on the set of observed time paths, and we can test whether the two groups of factor loadings are significantly different from each other.

REVIEW OF THE LITERATURE

Although the notion of utilizing the computer as a tool in model building is still relatively new, there are several ongoing research projects and several segments of research in economics that have been completed which have followed this approach. A review of some of this work will give some specific indications of the versatility of computer models; our review is intended to be illustrative, rather than exhaustive, of the applications of computer models in economics which have been reported in the literature.

Simulation of households: A large-scale simulation which has as its ultimate goal the simulation of the total economy of the United States has been underway for several years under the direction of Professor Orcutt.[11] Currently the project is concentrating on the analysis of households. The ultimate goal is to develop a general model consisting of the ten flow-of-funds sectors used in national income accounting.

The first step in Orcutt's approach is to develop a stratified sample of households classified along the dimensions of some twenty-three variables. These variables, such as race, age, sex, education, income, debt, stocks of assets and the like, are the inputs to the decision units in the model. The outputs of the household model include relevant data for forecasting population, purchases of durables, nondurables, services and housing, net change in debt and net change in assets for the household sector.

The individual decision units of the model must be endowed with values of the various input variables in accordance with the actual system being simulated. The unit is viewed as having alternative types of behavior available. With each alternative there is associated a probability, empirically determined. Random numbers are generated to select specific actions for each unit in a manner consistent with the assigned probabilities. In this way outputs are determined for each unit. The outputs are then used to modify the inputs for the next series of decisions.

The above description is, of course, only the skeleton of the model. Orcutt discusses many other problems connected with the model such as parameter estimation, discrepancies between generated series and the actual, and so on. Orcutt sees his model as providing an instrument for "consolidating past, present, and future research efforts of many individuals in varied areas of economics and sociology into one effective and meaningful model; an instrument for combining survey and theoretical results obtained on the micro-level into an all-embracing system useful for prediction, control, experimentation, and analysis on the aggregate level."[12]

Firm models: In another early work, Hoggatt has developed a simulation of a perfectly competitive industry.[13] His objective was to study the stability of a model in which entry and exit conditions, as well as the formation of price expectations, are specified. The model consists of the following:

(1) A market demand function dependent on two parameters.

(2) A long-run average cost curve dependent on two parameters.

(3) A total cost curve for each firm dependent on the same parameters as (2).

The assumption is made that entering firms will expect the then current price to prevail in the future, and they therefore select that plant size which will maximize profits given the current price. The usual neoclassical decision rules for determining output of the firms prevail. The model is ready to operate when the four parameters in (1) and (2), the initial number of firms and the size of plant for each firm are specified.

Hoggatt begins by choosing values which give an equilibrium position for the industry. He assumes all firms to be of equal size. The output of the model is the price in the market and the production and profits for each firm. (There are also a number of other outputs which are used for analyzing the system.) The demand curve is then shifted to the right by changing one of the parameters, and the results studied. One interesting conclusion the model brings forth is the "possibility that the market variables (price and industry supply) may be nearly stationary even though there is considerable entry and exit activity on the part of firms in the industry."[14] The model is particularly interesting as an example of the type of complex questions that can be asked of an old model with the technique of simulation.

Industrial dynamics: Another use of computer models has been made by J. W. Forrester.[15] He utilizes time lags within a system to demonstrate the types of fluctuations that can develop within a company as a result of a shock to the system, for example, an increase in demand. The model utilized consists of five component parts. These are factory, factory warehouse, distributors, retailers and customers. The customers' order rate is as an exogenous variable. There are given time lags through the whole system in terms of the delivery of goods from retailer to customer, distributor to retailer, and so on, back to the factory lead time for production. There are also a series of time lags in the information system. The lags are in the timing of orders for goods, transmitted from component to component. The last aspect of the model is a description of the policy followed in placing orders at each level and the rules for maintaining inventory.

Once the parameters (time lags and policies) are fixed, the system is set in motion and can be analyzed for any given customer order rate. The model is nonlinear and would be difficult to analyze by any method other than computer simulation.

Forrester also analyzes a further model in which advertising is introduced with a similar set of time lags. It is clear that a number of additional variables can be introduced, and their effects on fluctuations in production, employment and investment analyzed for the firm. Forrester's main aim is to utilize such analysis for the improvement of business management.

Industry analysis: Perhaps the most detailed published attempt at using computer models in economics is the study of the shoe, leather and hide industries by K. J. Cohen.[16] This work was designed to explore the usefulness of computers in economic analysis. The models in the study are based on the empirical research of Mrs. Ruth P. Mack.[17] Several different models are constructed in Cohen's study, but only the outline of the general approach will be discussed here.

The industry can be divided vertically into five segments—consumers, shoe retailers, shoe manufacturers, cattlehide leather tanners and hide dealers. The major variables on which attention is focused are the selling prices of each sector (other than consumers), the purchases of each sector (other than hide dealers) and the production of retailers, manufacturers and tanners. The models are an attempt to explain the monthly values of each of these variables from 1930 to 1940. The major exogenous variables used are disposable personal income, the Bureau of Labor Statistics consumers' price index, and hide stocks in the hands of hide dealers. As can be seen from the above descriptions, the models are formulated in terms of two major classes of variables, prices and physical flows.

The dollar expenditure on shoes by consumers is determined by disposable personal income and a seasonal factor, both exogenous variables. The physical volume of retailers' sales is simply the consumers' expenditures divided by the retail price of shoes. The retailers' receipts of shoes are determined basically by demand considerations accompanied by some price speculation on inventories: retailers always try to have available for sale at least enough shoes to meet their anticipated demand; the extent to which they try to push their inventory levels beyond this point depends upon their changing evaluations of future market prospects. The manufacturers plan their shoe production in response to retailers' orders for shoes, spreading these orders evenly over the available lead time to obtain some smoothing of production. The leather purchases by manufacturers are designed at least to provide for their current production requirements, but the manufacturers frequently build up their leather inventories beyond current needs in response to price speculation motives. The production of finished leather by tanners depends upon the relation between their leather shipments and their leather stocks, but, because tanners attempt to smooth production rates, finished leather production is also tied to the previous months' production and hide wettings. Tanners' hide wettings depend upon the turnover rate of tanners' finished leather stocks, but again efforts are made to prevent rapid changes from occurring in the rate of production. Tanners' purchases of hides are determined by a reduced form relation which reflects both their current needs (the higher the rate of wettings, the more hides the tanners will order) and their view of the supply situation (the lower the price of hides last month, the more hides tanners will buy).

The retail price of shoes is determined in the models by a rigid markup on factory shoe prices. In setting the factory shoe price, manufacturers consider both the strength of consumer demand and the costs of production, as reflected in recent leather prices. Current leather price depends upon lagged leather price and current and lagged hide prices. Current hide price is determined in the models by a reduced form relation which reflects interactions between supply and demand considerations. The supply aspects are summarized in the final reduced form equation in terms of the ratio of leather and hide stocks in the hands of buyers to the leather and hide stocks in the hands of sellers; the higher this ratio, the lower the relative size of sellers' inventories, and the higher the price the sellers require to induce them to sell hides. The demand side is reflected in the reduced form equation by actual uses of hides by tanners, i.e., by hide wettings and finished leather production, and by factory shoe price, which serves as a proxy for underlying forces causing shifts in the demand schedule for hides.

There are several important interactions between prices and physical flows in the models. The physical volume of retail shoe sales is directly affected by retail shoe price. Retailers' purchases of shoes, manufacturers' purchases of leather and tanners' purchases of hides are affected, largely through price speculation on inventories, by prices which are endogenously determined. The most important converse effect in the models is the dependence of hide price upon the purchases of leather by manufacturers and the finished leather production, hide wettings and hide purchases by tanners.

Both one-period-change and process models were formulated. Mathematically, the forms of the models are nonlinear systems of lagged simultaneous difference equations. Simulation techniques were used to trace the time paths generated by the models for all endogenous variables. These generated series were then compared with the observed values of these variables between 1930 and 1940. While these comparisons do not result in complete agreement between the hypothetical and the actual time series for the endogenous variables, they do indicate that the models may incorporate some of the mechanisms which in fact determined behavior in the shoe, leather and hide industries.

Oligopoly theory: In recent years there has been an increased emphasis on studying the decision-making processes of firms. One of the difficulties has been to find a convenient language in which a model encompassing the complex of relevant variables could be constructed. An attempt at using computer models to describe firms in a duopoly market which goes into the internal decision-making mechanisms of the firms has been described by Cyert, Feigenbaum and March.[18] It is a homogeneous duopoly, and the major decision that each firm makes is an output decision. No discrepancy between production and sales is assumed, and thus no inventory problem exists in the model. The duopoly is composed of an ex-monopolist and a firm developed by former members of the established firm.

The decision-making process postulated by the theory begins with a forecasting phase. In this phase, competitor's reaction, the market demand curve, and the firm's average unit cost curve are estimated. Concurrently, a profit goal is established (goal specification phase). An evaluation phase follows, in which an effort is made to find the best alternative, given the forecasts. If this best alternative is inconsistent with the profit goal, a re-examination phase ensues, in which an effort is made to revise cost and demand estimates. If re-examination fails to yield a new best alternative consistent with the profit goal, the immediate profit goal is abandoned in favor of "doing the best possible under the circumstances."

Specific values were assigned to the parameters and a demand curve which varied over time was assumed. The model was allowed to run for forty-five periods. To demonstrate that the model as a whole has some reasonable empirical basis, comparisons were made with the can industry, an industry having some of the structural characteristics of the model. Specifically, the ratio of the two duopolists' profits and market shares generated by the model and the corresponding actual ratios for American Can Company and Continental Can Company were compared for forty-five periods. The predictions were viewed by the authors as satisfactorily approximating the observed data.

FUTURE OF COMPUTER MODELS

We have examined the nature of computer models, the associated methodological problems, and some of the current literature utilizing computer models. It is now appropriate to evaluate the role of computer models in social science research. We clearly maintain that computer models are an important new tool for the social sciences. Computer models should be viewed as a supplement to available procedures rather than as a replacement for all existing techniques.

The basic advantage of computer models is that they provide a language within which complex dynamic models can be constructed. In addition, and because of the richness of the language, such models can incorporate the relevant empirical variables. This does not imply that economists should no longer be interested in general models, but it does mean that economists are no longer forced to deal *only* with general models.

Computer models provide a bridge between empirical and theoretical work. The requirements of a computer model can provide a theoretical framework for an empirical investigation, and, in return, the empirical information is utilized in developing a flow diagram for the model. Through this process of working back and forth, it is possible to know when enough empirical information has been gathered and whether it is of the proper quality. Once the model is simulated, a more rigorous test of the validity of the model can be made, as indicated earlier, by comparing the time series generated by the model against the actual observed behavior of the system.

Because computer models have such a large capacity for utilizing empirical data, a burden may be placed on the actual collection of empirical information. We know of no obviously optimal procedure for gathering information that exists inside firms or inside consumers' heads. Nevertheless, this is the kind of information which economists desire and which computer models can readily handle.

Once the reduction of a system to its individual decision-making units has been accomplished, there is great hope for a solution of the aggregation problem. Thus, through computer models, we see the possibility of developing working models of the economy that will have a solid empirical basis.[19]

FOOTNOTES

1. George J. Stigler, *The Theory of Price* (New York: Macmillan, 1946), pp. 4-6.
2. R. G. D. Allen, *Mathematical Economics* (London: Macmillan, 1957), p. xvi.
3. For a lucid and penetrating analysis of the problems of testing economic propositions see Emile Grunberg, "Notes on the Verifiability of Economic Laws," *Philosophy of Science*, Vol. 24 (Oct. 1957), 337-48.
4. Milton Friedman, *Essays in Positive Economics* (Chicago: University of Chicago Press, 1953), pp. 3-43. For criticism of some of Friedman's arguments see the following: Tjalling C. Koopmans, *The State of Economic Science* (New York: McGraw-Hill, 1957), pp. 137-42; Eugene Rotwein, "On 'The Methodology of Positive Economics,'" *The Quarterly Journal of Economics*, LXXIII (Nov. 1959), 554-75; Emile Grunberg, *op. cit.*, p. 343 (fn. 26).
5. Paul A. Samuelson, *Foundations of Economic Analysis* (Cambridge: Harvard University Press, 1947), p. 21.
6. A. Cournot, *Researches into the Mathematical Principles of the Theory of Wealth*, trans. Nathaniel T. Bacon (New York: Macmillan, 1897), Chap. 7.
7. A broad survey of the scope of operations research simulations can be found in the *Report of the Systems Simulation Symposium*, ed. D. G. Malcolm (American Institute of Industrial Engineers, 1958). The number of operations research simulation studies which have been discussed in professional meetings or journals is too numerous to permit us to undertake here any further discussion of them (e.g., at the Sixteenth National Meeting of the Operations Research Society of America in Pasadena, California, November, 1959, there were

approximately twenty papers presented dealing with computer simulation).

8. See, e.g., Lawrence R. Klein, *A Textbook of Econometrics* (Evanston, Ill.: Row, Peterson and Co., 1953), Chap. III.

9. Recent surveys of the state of econometric methodology regarding errors in the variables models can be found in J. D. Sargan, "The Estimation of Economic Relationships Using Instrumental Variables," *Econometrica*, Vol. 26 (July 1958), 393-415, and in Albert Madansky, "The Fitting of Straight Lines When Both Variables Are Subject to Error," *Journal of the American Statistical Association*, Vol. 54 (Mar. 1959), 173-205.

10. These have all been suggested by Professor Jack Johnston, of the University of Manchester, in private conversations with the authors.

11. Guy H. Orcutt, Martin Greenberger and Alice M. Rivlin, *Decision-Unit Models and Simulation of the United States Economy* (Lithograph draft, Harvard University, 1958).

12. *Ibid.*, p. 36.

13. Austin C. Hoggatt, *Simulation of the Firm*, I.B.M. Research Paper, RC-16 (Aug. 15, 1957).

14. *Ibid.*, p. 62.

15. Jay W. Forrester, "Industrial Dynamics—A Major Breakthrough for Decision Makers," *Harvard Business Review*, Vol. 36 (July-Aug. 1958), 37-66.

16. Kalman J. Cohen, *Computer Models of the Shoe, Leather, Hide Sequence* (Englewood Cliffs, N. J.: Prentice-Hall, 1960).

17. Ruth P. Mack, *Consumption and Business Fluctuation: A Case Study of the Shoe, Leather, Hide Sequence* (New York: National Bureau of Economic Research, 1956).

18. R. M. Cyert, E. A. Feigenbaum and J. G. March, "Models in a Behavioral Theory of the Firm," *Behavioral Science*, Vol. 4 (Apr. 1959), 81-95.

19. A more detailed discussion of the problems of and of the potential for combining individual microlevel models into an aggregate level computer model is contained in Kalman J. Cohen, "Simulation of the Firm," *American Economic Review, Papers and Proceedings*, L (May, 1960), 534-40.

Part Six

IMPLICATIONS
FOR
GOVERNMENT

■ *15* ■

*Government by Computers?**

by David Bergamini
ASSISTANT EDITOR, *Life* MAGAZINE

Instead of moving pins on a map, today's generals and admirals are able to feed the immensely complicated strategies and logistics of an entire modern war into a machine and, within a matter of minutes, be told who won. The process is still somewhat crude, but those who make and use electronic computers claim that the predictions are becoming increasingly accurate.

What is more, the computers' findings are beginning to affect important government defense decisions. It is not easy to demonstrate these effects, for most of the computerized calculation that goes into such decisions—like its old-fashioned human equivalent—is highly classified. But last December, largely as a result of a bitter conflict between Pentagon planners over competing nuclear strategies, the public was treated to a brief glimpse of just what the computers are up to.

* Reprinted from *The Reporter* Magazine, August 17, 1961, Copyright 1961 by David Bergamini, by permission of Harold Matson Company.

The Air Force was pushing hard for a costly "counter-force strategy" predicated on graduated and highly se-lective retaliation against enemy military targets. The Navy and Army argued that the best and cheapest deter-rence was the threat to destroy the enemy's population centers. During this argument, according to a series of articles in the Washington *Star,* Air Force planners put the strategic alternatives to their computers. All-out nuclear war was fought mathematically again and again on the machines—in terms of population distributions, bomb sizes and defenses—each time with a different set of assump-tions. And each time, no matter who struck first, with how much, against whatever possible preparations, the calcu-lations showed that as long as cities were the targets, 55 to 90 per cent of Americans would die as against only 20 to 35 per cent of Russians.

If they do nothing else, these appalling statistics un-derscore the evidence on every hand that whether we like it or not, the business of government at every level is be-coming more and more the business of computers. It is not that computers are on their way to staging a *coup d'état*—they definitely are not—but rather that big government has found in them a means of growing bigger more quickly and inexpensively than ever before. The growth is not in personnel or pay roll, or even in power as yet, but in the fundamental prerequisite of all control and real power: the ability to gather and use information.

What makes this possible is the ability of computers to look up, store and analyze copious facts, to present them in fresh combinations that can illuminate fresh contexts, and to manipulate numbers and simple logical propositions with superhuman speed and accuracy. Two processes are involved: sorting data and solving equations. Whenever the two can be put together and the data understood well enough to be handled logically and mathematically, the machines can be used to predict the results of actions and to help human beings make decisions.

During the eight years of the Eisenhower administra-tion, the amount of information processing done by the government increased several hundredfold. Within a few years it will have increased so much that the entire population of the country working full time would not be able to handle manually the paper work involved in its own government. But on magnetic tapes a great many of the unused facts that pile up in a bureaucracy are suddenly becoming usable and accessible.

Much of the information involved has to do with property, with tanks and thumbtacks, rockets and light sockets. But information about people is also increasing in availability. By consulting the data-processing machines of the various state and Federal agencies, it has become theoretically possible to assemble an amazingly quick and complete file on any citizen, including, for instance, his age, birthplace, Social Security number, employer, dependents, investments, dividends, liabilities, insurance coverage, license number, veteran's status, security clearance rating —even such intimate items as hobbies, organizational affiliations, physical blemishes, medical history or ability to speak French. As Representative James C. Oliver (R., Maine) is reported to have put it, after hearings last year on computers by the House Subcommittee on Census and Government Statistics: "It's my impression that these machines may know too damn much."

The potential of the machines for big-brother prying is certainly great. But in the long run, defending the rights of real individuals should be less difficult than defining the rights of that imaginary individual, the collective or average man, who has hitherto been studied chiefly by polltakers and insurance-company actuaries. Through computers, it appears possible to know all about John Doe and, by knowing him, to regulate him and his society in a great many exact statistical ways. According to a Congressional report on government data processing, "the prospects for future development may make the recent past seem like mere prologue. Not only the Federal Government but the entire national economy is involved."

Whether the computers' latent ability to run a nation with a tight, efficient hand is ever used in the United States depends on political decisions still to be made. But whether or not it is used here, it will certainly be used in the Soviet Union. Much of the most basic theoretical work on the application of computers to efficient national management has been done by Soviet mathematicians; and although the United States is ahead in computer technology, the Soviet state planning agency, Gosplan, is spending freely for computer hardware in Western Europe and making every effort to bring Soviet practice up to Soviet theory.

The reason Russia does have to catch up in the technology is that modern computing, for all its overtones of state planning, is a highly American product. Since the first of the old punch-card machines, which was invented in 1890 for the Bureau of the Census, machine techniques have generally been originated for government agencies and adapted later for use in business. Techniques of the Social Security Administration have become insurance-company techniques. The theory of automatic gun sights and fire control has evolved into the theory of automatic oil refineries, and so on.

But the true flowering of machines in government, and of computing in general, came after the Second World War, with the advent of fast, accurate electronic computers to replace slow, inaccurate punch-card machines.

When the first electronic system was installed at the Census Bureau in 1951, it would have been difficult to foresee what lay ahead. The number of Federal employees running electronic computers was to grow to 4,000 by 1958 and to 9,000 by 1961. If present projections are accurate, it will grow to 13,000 by 1963 and some 30,000 by 1966. In the last official count, made a year ago, the Federal Government had 524 electronic computers doing nonclassified work and another hundred or two, mostly of the big sophisticated sort, under wraps. State governments used 101, counties 17, and cities 13.

At state, county and municipal levels, data-processing machines are beginning to do efficiently many of the dull, time-consuming clerical jobs that used to be done expensively, carelessly, churlishly or not at all. In Ohio, they study possible rights of way, tot up the estimated property values involved in purchasing them, and pick out those which best combine cheapness with directness and construction ease. Then they work out most of the engineering problems for the new highways to be built over them.

In California, by keeping track of the physical characteristics and operating methods of criminals, they have frequently enabled police to know a hoodlum by his job almost as soon as it is done. In New Orleans, they print
due notices for parking tickets and keep dunning until the
culprits pay. At many state universities they process ad-
missions, grade examinations, keep watch on scholastic
standings, schedule classes and assign students to sections,
so that conflicts and problems of overcrowded classrooms
and overburdened professors can be held to a minimum.
Almost everywhere and at every level of government they
make up pay rolls and keep the personnel records. In
New York, plans are well under way to machine-audit
state income-tax returns.

The most fully automated county government is Los
Angeles, where computers do all the accounting, will soon
do all the vote tallying and have been used to determine
the most economical routes for 258 garbage trucks. Researchers in California are even trying to develop diagnos-
tic machines that will compute illness from symptoms
reported by a patient or measured by the machine itself.
In early experiments the machines have made few wrong
diagnoses and have shown an honest tendency in a lot
of cases to say "I don't know."

Surprising as the chores are that machines do for state
and local government, they are errands for boys compared
to the work of the Federal computers. Computers write
the government's checks, issue its bills, credit its sums received to individual accounts, break down the national
census, manage the purchasing, stockpiling, and flow of
good for the armed services, help look up fingerprints for
the FBI and patents for the Patent Office, register the
transactions of participants in the Social Security, veterans'
benefit and income-tax programs.

A great deal of this bookkeeping is simply a matter of
knowing where things are. For instance, the Air Force has
a hundred thousand airplane engines representing an investment of some six billion dollars. When they are not
on the move, they are in overhaul, using up tools and lu-
bricants and spare parts. Determining where the engines

need what is the job of an electronic engine-management system whose main computer is in Oklahoma City. By means of some seven thousand reports a day from nine hundred Air Force installations around the world, the computer keeps tabs on existing engines and parts, and issues orders for the procurement and shipment of new ones. It does this with so little red tape that in most instances the only requisition needed is a punch card. As a result the number of engines needed in storage or repair to backstop every four engines in the air has decreased from five to one.

Knowing where engines are is a round-the-clock operation, but there are many items in the inventories of a technological society whose whereabouts need to be known only when they are not working correctly. For instance, assume that Atlantis Flight 107, en route from New York to Paris, is forced to ditch in mid ocean. The pilot reports that his passengers are disembarking onto life rafts. Navy, Coast Guard and Air Force turn to their computers. In the machine memories are the latest reports on speeds, locations and destinations. From these they start plotting the position of every ship and plane in the ocean. This would once have taken hours, but now within seconds the Coast Guard's RAMAC machine in New York City Customs House comes up with a Panamanian tramp that should be within a few miles of the life rafts. The tramp steamer is radioed and soon her crew is hauling the last of the survivors from the water.

The Coast Guard computer's lifesaving bookkeeping illustrates an important trait of machines. A machine will continue to do its job, to keep track, say, of all ships and planes in the North Atlantic, even when it has no incentive except a program of instructions and an electric current. Under the same circumstances, and in the absence of any crisis, a human being will probably fail at his job out of sheer boredom.

The road to good government bookkeeping and to optimum management of government property is being traveled fast, but it is longer and more full of pitfalls than most government planners care to admit. Air Force engine management, for instance, is still not nearly as good as it could be. The central computer in Oklahoma City is fast and accurate, but the flow of information to it is slow and faulty. Clerks at bases sometimes punch carelessly when they order what they want on punch cards. The cards are sometimes mutilated or go astray in shipment to Oklahoma. Even when they arrive safely, they must still be sorted and their information put on magnetic tape for use by the computer. Eventually these steps will be eliminated, and each clerk at each base will have a simple keyboard through which he can send in daily or weekly orders of new parts over communication lines that put him in direct touch with the computer.

In other areas of armed forces procurement, the awkward transition from a clerk system to a machine system has not always been thought out ahead of time. At the Newport, Rhode Island, destroyer base, the procedures for feeding information to a computer are so confused and the computer itself is so ill chosen for its job that destroyer men report waits of up to eight days from the time they make port until they can get requisitions filled—even requisitions for fresh food. A similar blunder at Norfolk, Virginia, led the Navy to abandon a million-dollar investment in data-processing machines and scrap the operation entirely.

Keeping or losing track of people and things by electronic bookkeeping has all sorts of legal implications. The quick mechanical flow of events can make it difficult to assign responsibility for a mistake. It is easy, for instance, to imagine horrors taking place in a well-automated financial community: a millionaire ruined by a single credit-impugning smudge on a magnetic tape, corporations accidentally sold at bargain-basement prices, entire pay rolls made up of million-dollar checks. Unscrambling such messes by present legal means might take decades.

There is also the possibility of devious financial fraud perpetrated by computer. At least one Wall Streeter has already tried it. He adopted the simple expedient of manufacturing punch-card credits to his own account and punch-card debits to a company interest account—all to the tune of $170,000. Less crude approaches are sure to

be devised; and though designers of financial systems may
make fraud increasingly difficult, the net result may simply be fewer crimes but bigger ones.

The literal-minded machines have a way of showing up
the gap in society between written laws and regulations
and their observance. For instance, the data that led to
last spring's revelations about expense-account living
and about outright tax evasion were turned up for the
Treasury Department by Internal Revenue computers.
Fittingly enough, the added appropriations the revelations
were intended to justify were for more machines.

The Bureau of Internal Revenue is engaged in installing
a vast new machine system for processing and auditing
returns and catching chiselers. The new system was not
supposed to become fully operative until 1969, but the
department's computer men say they are far ahead of
schedule and could finish up by 1965 if they continue to
receive enough funds.

According to the law, Internal Revenue has broad rights
of access to personal information when it wants to check
on income-tax returns. The new system can take advantage of these rights routinely. Magnetic tapes from the
machines of large corporations declaring dividends or paying numerous employees are borrowed and copied by the
District Director's office. Then the names of stockholders
and employees are automatically matched with names on
returns from people in the district and the amounts of
income declared are all verified.

By next year, one of nine satellite computers at district
offices will be in operation and its complete tapes will be
transshipped to a master computer in Martinsburg, West
Virginia, and compared with the returns of people in the
entire country. With the help of the computers, not just a
sample of returns but eventually all returns will be audited.
When the system is completed, some hundred million returns will be compared with 450 million documents per-
taining to personal finances. As automated finance continues to expand, there is no reason why Internal Revenue
should not scrutinize charge and credit-card accounts,
the records of charities, hospitals, and hotels, and ulti-

mately even the deposits and withdrawals in an urbanite's machine-handled checking account.

If the present laws remain unchanged and the present level of computer technology is fully utilized, it is difficult to imagine any kind of paper noncash transaction that will not before very long be scrutinized routinely by government computers and called to the attention of inspectors whenever anything is irregular. A great deal of petty thieving that has seeped into reputable American business during the decades of increased taxes may be automated out of existence.

The Utopian possibilities have evoked a good deal of silence from industrial and government computer men. They are encouraged in their silence by what one of them calls "the official eggs-in-the-mouth and eggs-underfoot public-relations policy of computer manufacturers" and by what another terms "the quick hysteria and deep ignorance about all things automatic" that is exhibited by "liberally educated journalists, politicians, and labor leaders." Whoever is at fault, the subject certainly needs airing. Computer men are quick to agree, off the record, that the main obstacle for improved computerized law enforcement is political rather than technological or financial.

The Federal uses for computers discussed so far have mainly involved the machines' ability to store and shuffle the information on papers. Add to this their prodigious capacity for doing arithmetic and solving problems, and one can see a whole new range of applications.

Consider STRETCH, an extremely large and expensive IBM machine at Los Alamos that conducts mock weapons tests for the Atomic Energy Commission and simulates H-bomb explosions. What it really does, of course, is to calculate the probabilities of innumerable nuclear events that take place in microtime and microspace and follow them down a laborious chain of cause and effect to radiation and blast results that take place in macrotime and macrospace. This is a stupendous performance, involving up to 250 billion computations for each explosion. But throughout the latter part of the test suspension it has enabled the United States to carry out nuclear tests without actually detonating any bombs and to develop new weapons like the compact one-megaton warhead for Minuteman or the one-man nuclear rocket Davy Crockett without actually firing them. Unless the Russians have been testing in secret, STRETCH has enabled the United States to maintain its position in the development of nuclear armaments without cheating during the voluntary suspension of nuclear testing.

This sort of simulation—of bombs, of next month's weather, of the economic effects of a projected bond issue —is one of the newest and potentially greatest uses of computers in government. How great is difficult to tell. To be of value, simulations must apply to complicated real events, events in which individual actions are imponderable but in which collective results may be predicted as probabilities. Most real events, of course, are not well enough understood, at this point anyway, to be reduced to mathematics. And it may be that many can never be predicted because their possible outcomes are all equally improbable until real, unpredictable people make choices to tip the scales. Even so, simulations of some fairly complicated events are already being made and used to help in the formulation of national policy.

All the armed services, as well as the RAND Corporation, employ computers in war games to simulate specific battle situations and to try out tactics and strategies. Pentagon brass have sometimes even used the results of such studies and the great prestige of the machines without proper explanation, to publicize and gain support for their own views and interests in Washington. In 1960, after the Air Force simulation of nuclear wars already described, there is said to have been a veritable battle of computers, with Air Force and Navy men tossing studies at each other in a rapid exchange of attack and counterattack.

There are certain obvious dangers in the use of these machines. It is, of course, always possible to ask them loaded questions or to misrepresent their answers to honest questions or to ask them no questions at all and make up answers out of whole cloth. Some executives and officials simply like to have computers around as status symbols or magic talismans. As a result, many of the calculating machines in industry are often out of work, and one company, Computer Usage, even does a profitable business in buying their idle hours to sublet to firms without full-time machines of their own. After politics, computer men say, vanity is the greatest obstacle in the way of getting the most out of machines.

If computers that simulate and predict the future seem impressive, they become far more so when their performance is geared into the present and used for split-second decisions in a fast-breaking situation. Monitoring and anticipating events as they happen is known in computer jargon as a "real-time operation." A real-time use of a computer is to follow the flight of a rocket from its pad, compare what is happening to a flight plan simulated beforehand, and then warn the range safety officer to blow it up immediately if it begins to deviate.

This sort of computer, operating in real time and warning of tendencies that need to be corrected, is the nerve center of automatic factories and oil refineries. But when it is connected to automatic control devices so that it runs a whole system without human intervention, it takes on yet another characteristic of sophisticated machines: it becomes not only "real-time" but also "on-line." Because of what it does, an on-line computer can be conveniently thought of as one that has expanded out of the normal roomful of circuit-crammed black boxes and has sprawled out across a building, a city, a nation or a continent. In sprawling, it has acquired communication lines to act as its nerves and, at the end of communications lines, satellite black boxes to act as its senses. The communication links may be telephone or telegraph lines or sound waves, heat, light, radio or microwaves. The senses may be simple keyboards where clerks record deposits and withdrawals or elaborate electronic eyes in orbiting earth satellites.

The most formidable on-line system now operating is SAGE, the radar network that automatically gives early warning against bomber attack. Through its many radar antennae it senses all aircraft entering United States airspace. The sightings are automatically relayed over its telephone and microwave links to its central computers, which then decide whether the encroaching planes are accounted for by flight plans on file or whether they constitute a possible attack. If they do, it warns its human attendants, or can, under certain conditions, release Bomarc interceptor rockets automatically.

SAGE has been widely criticized as an expensive white elephant. It gives no warning against ballistic missiles although it was being created at a time when ballistic missiles were already coming into use. It has caused many false alarms—and one scramble complete with H-bombs—because it cannot always tell a flight of bombers from a flock of birds or a cloud full of lightning. Yet for all its failings it has provided invaluable experience for the building of other sophisticated military computer systems.

At present count, the Air Force has at least a dozen big security-shrouded systems in development and the Army and Navy almost as many. Some of the best publicized—by leaks—are the Air Force L-systems, of which SAGE or 416L is the first. Others include the NORAD Joint Service Command and Control System, which will also guard against bomber attacks; the Strategic Air Command's intelligence system; SAC's command and control center in Omaha; and B-MEWS, the Ballistic Missile Early Warning System.

Most of the L-systems are not truly operational and some are not scheduled to be until early in the 1970's. But some are already at work. One necessarily fictionalized example will illustrate the state of the military-systems art that has been or will soon be reached.

It is a dark 3:00 A.M. in Karachi. An agent listening in on Russian code transmissions frowns, writes rapidly in a notebook, and with the help of a code book transcribes what he has written in the form of a long number strewn with punctuation marks. Then he turns on his transmitter and begins to chant, "Omega, calling Omega."

Nine thousand miles away in the light of a late afternoon somewhere in the United States, another man hears and answers.

"I think I need a new flight pattern," says the man in

Karachi, and he proceeds to dictate the long number from his notebook.

"O.K., got it," says Omega. "I'll let you know if it fits."

The second man types out the long number at the console of a computer. The machine responds at once by decoding the number back into the form heard by the agent in Karachi. Then, following a pattern of instructions from a tape in one of its storage sections, it gets to work, and after a few minutes it confirms the agent's suspicion that the Russian code is a new one. After a few hours—or sometimes months—with occasional helpful interruptions from its operators, and after it has tested several million possibilities and done several centuries of clerical work, it breaks the code and types out the intercepted Russian radio message on its teleprinter.

Translated into English, the message tells of troop and aerial movements involved in a Russian training exercise north of the Pakistan border. Though fairly routine, this information is relayed at once to a United States command center. Again keyboards are punched and again computers respond. With help from their human operators, they look up enemy objectives and calculate what United States counterforces could best be spared elsewhere and could most cheaply be flown in to support the Pakistanis if necessary. Then one of the computers issues a list of standby orders that ought to be ready in case of trouble and of logistic preparations that ought to be made. Its recommendations amount to an up-to-date battle plan. No one expects this to be used, but in order to have a plan ready, just in case, it is phoned and wired to the United States bases that would be involved.

The computer systems already operational are impressive enough, but they do not compare with the sophisticated systems that are under study and on order for delivery in the early 1970's. In some of them the on-line concept is carried so far that if a reconnaissance satellite should send in a report of Russian rocket launchings, it would automatically generate a retaliatory battle plan from one computer that would automatically be put into action by other computers, aiming and firing Atlases, Titans and Polarises on and under land and sea. The only interruption in the sequence, except for the system's own safety checks and repeats, would be a token one of a few minutes for the President of the United States to exercise freedom of will and say "fire."

What to do about this choiceless choice, how to extend the time for decision and make the machines as accurate as possible, is the subject of serious concern and study by several groups of computer men who address themselves exclusively to command and control problems. Actually, the ultimate on-line system coveted by advanced military planners may be ten years, twenty years or a pipe dream away. Some computer men doubt that it would be trustworthy even if it could be designed and built. The most reliable components, they point out, sometimes fail. Other computer men insist that such machines can be made as reliable as necessary. Insurance against component failure can be bought at the expense of "redundancy"—by having two tubes or transistors for every job. In the same way, insurance against mistake-producing static or "noise" in communication lines can also be bought by redundancy —by making every message sent in the system wordy and repetitive so that its meaning cannot—repeat, cannot —be misunderstood.

What is probably more important than the prerogatives of the President in some hypothetical emergency is the mere fact that computers can and do make decisions in a number of less dramatic but extremely important situations. In a recent speech D. B. Paquin, president of the National Machine Accountants Association, made the statement that 80 to 90 per cent of the executive decisions in United States industry would soon be made by machines. It is tempting to think that such decisions would not be the ones that really count, not "creative" ones, but studies by such eminent computer theorists as John Von Neumann and A. M. Turing indicate that there is probably nothing in any human decision, no matter how creative, that cannot be reduced eventually to the sort of logic, probability calculations and random choices machines can handle.

In the long run the civilian machines will do far more to change man's society and way of life than secret L-systems that simply watch at the ramparts. In developing them, engineers have first to develop civilian "senses" comparable to the radar antennae of a SAGE. Devices for reading typewritten symbols are already on the market. Devices for deciphering handwriting and spoken words are being developed by several laboratories, notably Bell Telephone. They work astonishingly well, but by scientific standards they are still relatively crude and inaccurate.

Language is also a barrier between the machines themselves. Each make has its own programming language for giving the machines instruction or information. After a tremendous effort by government officials who wanted the machines of their various agencies to be compatible, the computing industry finally developed a common machine language called COBOL on which most manufacturers would agree. But a lot of adaptation still needs to be done before machines of one make can use the magnetic tapes of other makes, much less communicate with each other directly on an on-line basis. A better approach may grow out of basic research by a team of computer engineers under Professor Anthony Oettinger at Harvard. This group has developed a technique of mathematical analysis that will enable machines to translate any human or machine language into any other. At the moment the technique has no economic importance because only a large, sophisticated computer can handle it. But in a vast civilian on-line system, communicating directly with all sorts of computers in private industry and in various branches of government, a single large computer to do all the translating might become financially feasible.

The question at once arises as to what such a monstrous system would be doing. And the only logical answer is: monitoring and analyzing the trends of the national economy and keeping endless, boring watch over the national welfare. It is not at all inconceivable that some day every inventory computer in industry, every government agency computer, every bank and corporation computer, and indirectly every flow meter, every electric cash register, adding machine and typewriter could be put on-line with

a huge analyzer in Washington. The analyzer would automatically receive news of every transaction in the country
and of every product produced, of every horsepower
generated and every watt burned, of every acre planted,
carload shipped, hopper emptied, bucket mined, barrel
pumped, bushel picked or dollar spent. It could then be
used to give warning of every unhealthy economic turn.
There are conservative mathematicians at conservative institutions like IBM who believe that such a fantastic computer can and will be built.

Before then, there will be many lesser developments of
the same revolutionary social stripe. Some of them were
described recently in a speech at UCLA by Dr. Simon
Ramo, executive vice-president of the Ramo-Wooldridge
Company.

"Two or three decades from now," he said, "every prac-
ticing attorney might have in his office a means for convenient electronic connection to a huge national central
repository of all the laws, rulings, regulations, procedures,
and commentaries upon them that he needs. He or his assistant will be able to query the central repository by
operating an electronic input device looking a little like a
typewriter. Almost immediately, there will be displayed
to him on a special viewing screen any information that is
available on his question, and this display will cover not
just the few possibilities that an unaided, though trained,
human brain might have produced in a few days of research in a law library. Instead, the intellectronics system
will scan, select, and present in a few seconds the equivalent results of dozens of trained searchers covering many
decades of records over the entire nation. . . .

"The physician . . . will also routinely introduce
his data on a patient into a network of 'consultative wis-
dom.' . . . The system will quickly react to give the doctor key portions of the equivalent of many consultations
with other physicians. . . . It will give statistical probabilities . . . of relative effectiveness of various treat-
ments. . . .

"Some day currency and coins will be for the rural areas.
Even checks and most other forms of today's original rec-

ords may become extinct. If you buy a necktie or a house, your thumb before an electronic scanner will identify you and the network will debit your account and credit the seller. . . ."

If there is any validity to the predictions of Dr. Ramo or the less outspoken but equally revolutionary predictions that almost any computer man will make in private, great social changes lie in store for which almost no one is preparing, at least not in public.

One problem already inhibiting a more effective use of the machines is the severe shortage of properly trained computer men: of systems engineers to build the right machines and of programmers to feed them safe, well-conceived sets of instructions. Sloppy systems engineering has already resulted in several computer misfits like the one the Navy had to clear out and throw away at Norfolk, Virginia. It has also resulted in some mistakes that would be sad if they were not funny—for instance, the computer that overestimated the city of Seattle's tax revenue by $1.8 million and started city officials on a glorious spending spree before the mistake was detected. Equally careless programming or design of the military L-systems might not be funny at all. But mistakes just as bad will inevitably be made unless the present silence is broken and more well-trained students are encouraged to seek careers in computing.

In spite of the hazards, computers offer the first practical means for making the social sciences truly scientific and useful. Princeton's celebrated economist Oskar Morgenstern says: "The computer is to economics what the telescope was to astronomy. But we do not know yet how to make anything like full use of it." Eventually simulation, perhaps of the entire national economy, may become the major task of computers in government. The possibility at least is there, and one might assume that social scientists, and especially economists, would have shown an active interest in computers and publicized their possibilities. But the few who have seem content to play with mathematical curves and graphs representing generalities and

broad, ill-understood trends. A well-known atomic physicist who has used computers to handle scientific problems
more precisely says:

"The economists should not be worrying about matching derived curves with factual graphs. The important
job is to get data. Here are all these machines in Washington filling themselves up with data all the time, but no
one asks—no one of these economists asks—if it is the correct data. Ten years from now they will find that the wrong
questions have been asked on all those forms we fill out and
the wrong answers copied on to all the magnetic tapes.
Someone should be worrying whether ABC agency and
XYZ agency are collecting information that is compatible
and scientific. If they are not, we lose ten years, because I
would say about almost any complicated social problem,
that you need at least ten years of good information before
you can begin to make an analysis."

If the social scientists are not yet with it, at least one
would assume that the computer companies themselves
must be. IBM, American Telephone and Telegraph,
General Electric, RCA, Honeywell—some of America's
greatest and most progressive corporations are involved.
Surely some of them are trying to overcome the educational barriers and face up to the future. But instead, they
find themselves in an anomalous position: they are both
merchants of the tools of information and control and at
the same time businessmen dedicated by tradition to secrecy, hunch and *laisser-faire*, to whom government
planning is anathema. As a result, none of them are doing
much about educating the public and none of them—as
corporations rather than collections of smart private individuals—have done all they should to educate themselves. Even IBM, the one company that has made a major
educational effort, has never been able to go beyond a
timid fumbling with the issues involved. In the sumptuous
old Guggenheim mansion at Sands Point, Long Island,
where IBM conducts a regular school for its promising
young executives, engineers are taught classical economics and economists are given a smattering of computer
knowledge years behind work in IBM's own laboratories.

The Soviet Union, not surprisingly, has no such inhibitions about the social and political implications of computers. The stern Soviet way is conveyed by the following quotation from Academician A. I. Berg, of the Soviet Union's state planning agency:

Under Socialism economic development is determined and guided by the state plan which embodies the policy of the Communist Party in the sphere of economic development. Therefore, the chief area for application [of computer technology] . . . is that of national economic planning. The preparation of the plan must be based on timely information which is adequate in total volume and in detail, information which is precise. The preparation of such information is the chief task of accounting and statistics, which together with planning are the most important areas of application.

A breezy American version of the computer dream is to run the country by a sort of automated New England town meeting. It is explained by Dr. Ramo at the end of the speech already referred to:

Let us imagine a somewhat extreme situation, doubtlessly beyond either practicality or desirability, in which it is the custom for the registered voters several times a day to identify themselves to the home voting machines—with their scanned thumbprints —and to put in a "yes" or a "no." . . . The highly technological society of the future can be one in which communications are so widespread and efficient that frequent voting is easy, participating is virtually guaranteed, interest is heightened, and apathy and ignorance are virtually eliminated.

The real point in all this is not that thinking machines are going to become the masters of men, but rather that men must think out quite carefully—and quite soon— what they want the machines to do and how the machines are to be fitted into the social fabric without painful rents and tears.

Part Seven

IMPLICATIONS
FOR
EDUCATION

▪ *16* ▪

*Programmed Instruction and Its Place in Education**

by P. Kenneth Komoski

DIRECTOR, COLLEGIATE SCHOOL
AUTOMATED TEACHING PROJECT

Two thousand years ago the world's first public school administrator, a gentleman by the name of Quintillian, wrote what might be called a handbook for teachers. In it he has one bit of advice which will serve as an excellent starting point for a discussion of programmed instruction and its potential uses. Quintillian's advice is this: "Do not neglect the individual student. He should be questioned and praised . . . he should strive for victory, yes, but it must be arranged that he gains it. In this way let us draw forth his powers with both praise and rewards."

* Reprinted from the Report of the Twenty-fifth Educational Conference, *Measurement and Research in Today's Schools,* Copyright © 1960, by permission of the Author and the American Council on Education.

Quintillian's advice has dutifully been given lip service for some nineteen centuries, but in reality we know that during those centuries educators have not taken very seriously the idea that they must arrange victories for students and that, in so doing, they might help students to discover their individual powers. We are well aware that historically education has used the threat of failure rather than the arranging of success as a way of inducing students to learn. However it is interesting to note that Quintillian's advice, though unheeded for centuries, agrees precisely with the findings of present-day research in human learning—which point out that a student learns best when conditions have been so arranged that he can answer questions successfully; when he is praised and rewarded for answering successfully; and when he is instructed individually.

Of course, the idea of individual instruction has always been the goal of every teacher worthy of the name, and all good teachers are constantly striving to reach each individual child, to encourage him and explain things to him as clearly as possible. However, because of TV or film instruction, but to gear the day-to-day progress of any student to anything but his own individual capacity to learn is to condone both inefficient learning and wasted human resources.

Nevertheless, I fear we have begun to convince ourselves that such mass instruction is actually a *good* thing. We seem pleased to hear reports that it is improving instruction in some of our schools. Actually, we should be shocked by such conclusive proof of how *bad* some of our more conventional methods are. The fact that we can lock-step thousands of students together with TV education and then find improvements should mean only one thing: that we must radically re-examine the goals which we in education have been content to set for ourselves. The goal of education in this country should be to give each individual the opportunity of developing himself to the fullest potential. And in order to achieve such a goal we in this country should not be content until we have developed a practical method of making it possible for each child to learn as much as he possibly can at his own individual pace. With our traditional approach to teaching, the demand for such a method seems like the most starry-eyed, if not "Dewey-eyed," idealism. But if we in education are willing to look beyond these traditional approaches and to study the significant progress which has already been made in laying the foundations of such a method, we might begin to see how we can use these foundations as the basis for developing a practical, economical and broadly applicable method of individual instruction for our schools.

What is the nature of this so-called significant progress? Who has laid these foundations, and what has been accomplished? First of all, this progress has been made largely by experimental psychologists who have studied the problem of identifying and arranging the conditions under which human beings best learn. But, lest we jump to the conclusion that this is all a theoretical and untried product of the ivory tower, it is important to note that these conditions have also been identified and incorporated into a teaching method by a man who has undertaken one of the greatest educational tasks of modern times, the task of teaching the world's one billion illiterates to read.

The story of Frank Laubach, the man who devoted himself to this enormous educational problem, is a valuable object lesson for us educators. Using a method developed over thirty years ago and only recently substantiated by experimental findings, Frank Laubach has opened up a new world for millions of illiterates. And yet never has the educational community in general been less aware of a significant educational advance. I suppose that it is somewhat understandable that educators as a group have not been aware of the work of the experimental psychologists. After all, until a few years ago when some of them began to interpret psychological research, educators had a difficult time seeing the practical educational implications of many of the experiments which these psychologists had conducted. But thirty years ago when Frank Laubach, who has been called "a one-man Point IV program," described his method of teaching in words which any educator could clearly understand, no one listened either.

The point is that both these situations offer dramatic illustrations of the fact that organized education has not
committed itself to any sort of radical examination of how
learning can be both analyzed and substantially improved.
Education has not committed itself to a policy of research,
yet without such a commitment our various methods of
teaching can never be objectively labeled as good, bad,
better or best, but only fashionable or unfashionable.

Instead of developing a firm foundation of research to
build on, education has been content to act as the dead
weight at the end of a pendulum, oscillating between the
modern and the out-of-date. Therefore, educators should
listen to Laubach and the experimental psychologists,
not because they have done a good job or have a "modern"
method, but because they have developed a method which
has been shown to be more effective than the techniques
which education has traditionally employed. With this in
mind, let us then listen to these techniques as Mr. Laubach has set them down in his autobiography, *Thirty
Years with the Silent Billion*:

> We must prove to the student that he can learn
> easily, quickly, and delightfully, no matter how old he
> is. Every step must be so short that any ordinary man
> can take it easily. Our charts must provide for this
> . . . for there must be no embarrassing pauses, never
> a question the student cannot answer, and no examina-
> tion to find out what he knows. . . . We must keep
> out of the student's way—neither pushing him nor re-
> tarding him. For [a student] is happy only when he
> feels free to take his own natural gait. . . . The or-
> dinary textbooks used in the schools of America re-
> quire constant talking on the part of the teacher, but
> our . . . texts are as nearly self-teaching as we can
> make them. They require little talking by the teacher
> and a maximum of participation by the student.

These words of course could be a direct quote from any
of the many articles which have recently appeared on the
subject of teaching machines. Yet they come from a man
who, when he wrote them, was not only completely un-

aware of the existence of these devices but who probably could not afford to use them even if they were as educationally valuable as some people would have us believe. The real value of these machines is that they represent an attempt to introduce into education the techniques which both Laubach and the experimental psychologists agree are necessary if effective learning is to take place. The *techniques* are what are important! The machines may or may not be a helpful way of making use of them. The psychologists, of course, base these techniques on principles which they state precisely and in great detail. But when they describe how these principles can be applied in a practical teaching situation we find that they speak Laubach's language almost exactly.

These psychologists tell us that if we want students to learn better, we must arrange subject matter in such small steps that any student can advance from the first to the last without hesitation or confusion. We are told also that the student should proceed at his own pace and that we must guarantee his active participation by getting him to emit a response at each step along the way. One thing merely implied by Laubach is, however, greatly emphasized by the psychologists. This is the idea that the student should know whether or not he is correct immediately after he makes each required response. It has been demonstrated that this practice of constantly feeding back to the student reports on how he is doing greatly reinforces the learning which has taken place. A teaching machine then, in a sense, may be thought of as a feedback mechanism or a reinforcement device which may also be used to present the step-by-step arrangement of subject matter called a program. However, it has also been demonstrated that machines are not the only way to keep the student informed of his progress. In fact, a *good* program can give feedback much more simply but just as effectively as a machine. Programs, it would seem, are without question the really important element of this type of instruction.

With this in mind then, let us recognize the fact that the words teaching machine are inappropriate as a name for such instruction. For of course, machines, while helpful, are by no means essential to the method. If proof of this be required, we need only point out that Laubach has used so-called teaching machine instruction for years without making use of any mechanical devices. Furthermore, we may note that today most trials of so-called "teaching machines" are currently being carried on without making use of any sort of mechanical devices. This fact may come as a surprise; however, it is true. It is also true that present evidence indicates that programs without machines may continue to demonstrate their effectiveness even when mechanical devices become more reliable and less expensive. But whether we call this method of instruction "learn-o-mat" (a name that has been seriously suggested), "auto-instruction" or "teaching machine instruction," we still don't have a name which adequately describes the kind of instruction we are talking about. What is needed is a name which constantly reminds us not of machines but of the much more significant development of a scientific method of instruction which, mechanized or not, can have an enormous positive effect on education. We have already identified the program, or the step-by-step arrangement of subject matter, as the really essential element of this method. Therefore, I would suggest the adoption of the only name which adequately reflects this essential element. "Programmed instruction," I think, does this. The word program has long been accepted by those in the field as a descriptive term for the process of creating the carefully constructed step-by-step learning sequences which are the very heart of this method. It is self-evident that teaching machines without the essential program are useless. But, as many people have conclusively shown, programs printed in books and presented without these machines are an extremely effective way of individualizing instruction, no matter how many students need to be taught. For when each student has his own copy of a program, a group of three, thirty or three hundred students can become three, thirty or three hundred completely independent learning situations, in which the student, the programmer and the subject matter which has been programmed are in constant interaction. No matter how large the group, the instruction is completely individualized.

As I mentioned a moment ago, most programs in use today are being presented without machines, that is to say, in book form. In connection with this, it is interesting to note that recent research findings indicate that students learn with equal effectiveness by means of either programmed texts or programs presented by the machines that are currently available. Therefore, until we have the results of further research on this question, it would seem wisest for schools interested in using programmed instruction to use programs printed in the type of books which, as I just mentioned, are known as programmed texts. I say this not only because the value of the machines currently available has not yet been ascertained, but also on the grounds of simple economy. For instance, should an interested educator buy a number of rather sophisticated, multiple-choice machines at $5000 apiece, or a number of the programmed text simulators of these machines which cost $2 to $3 apiece? By the same token, should educators purchase a group of what are called write-in teaching machines? These machines, which cost from $20 to $160 apiece, all do essentially the same thing; that is, turn the printed pages of a program mechanically and prevent the student from cheating. However, if one is willing to give up this cheatproof feature and have students turn pages by themselves in the usual way, it then becomes possible to present programs far more economically. Moreover, the programmed text offers a highly desirable flexibility in that with such a text a student can work anywhere, anytime; he does not have to wait for a machine to become available. This flexibility may well be an absolute necessity if programmed instruction is to become a practical and broadly applied method of learning. Many teachers have already begun to assign materials in programmed texts as homework. It has been found that this is an excellent way of having a student prepare for class without using a machine and without pre-empting any class time. Classes held after the completion of this type of homework are able to cover facets of the subject matter which never would have been covered under the more customary conditions.

Another point which needs to be made clear regarding

programmed instruction is that programs are *not* tests.
There is often confusion on this point because at each step
in a program a student is required to respond to what for
the want of a better name we will refer to as a question.
However, it must be understood that these questions are
not questions in the usual sense at all, but a carefully constructed information-laden question which often contains
its own answer. For instance, here is an example of one of
these so-called questions taken from a program designed
to teach a layman something about programmed instruction:

> One of the characteristics of programed instruction
> is the student's being reinforced by obtaining con-
> firmation of a correct response. If you answer this item
> correctly, you will be *reinforced* by obtaining con-
> firmation of your correct ————. (In this step, the
> student is asked to supply the missing word, which,
> of course, is the word response.)

Obviously anyone could answer this question but in it
there is also information which is going to form the answer
to future questions of this type. Thus, by beginning with
something as self-evident as this example, a programmer
is able to take a student step by step on to more and more
difficult material until he, the student, has achieved a
rather complex and sophisticated knowledge of the subject which he has learned. Questions, then, are asked in
order not to test but to guarantee that the student becomes
actively involved in using the knowledge which he has
just acquired. Therefore, when the correct answer to each
question is immediately supplied to a student, it is not with
the idea of forcing him to grade himself, but simply to
supply him with feedback so that a constant interaction
will be maintained between the student and the subject he
is learning. With these things in mind, perhaps it would
be more to the point if, instead of asking whether we need
cheatproof teaching machines, we ask ourselves whether
we as teachers are capable of convincing students that
programs are opportunities to learn and not tests on which
they are to be graded. If we find we are not capable of

convincing students of this fact, then I suggest that we need machines and need them badly!

But not only must we convince a student that he is not going to be tested until he has learned something. We must also, of course, convince him that once a program has been put into his hands he has a job to do, namely, to respond to each step in the program. If he does this conscientiously, we must be able to guarantee that he will learn. If, however, he doesn't learn from a particular program it must be assumed that there is something wrong with *it*—not him! If students are willing to meet a programmer halfway by answering all his questions, then the programmer must fulfill his half of the bargain by asking them all the right questions.

Clearly, then, "the program's the thing." Of course, for teaching certain things the right kind of machine can be a help, but, in order to have the right kind of machine, the needs of the program must dictate its design. For instance, if a language program containing sound and pictures seems desirable, then by all means let's have a machine which can supply these. But let's not make the mistake of using a machine which may end up programming us. That is to say, let's not find ourselves having to teach by multiple choice simply because we have bought multiple-choice machines. Or let's not be forced into using a map, two by two inches, simply because that is the size window our device happens to have. As educators, however, we must recognize that these and similar restrictions are not restrictions imposed on us by the techniques of programmed instruction as such. They are merely the shortcomings of currently available teaching machines. The point is that educators must begin to become well-informed about the nature of programmed instruction in order to be able to make important decisions on which the future of this method will depend. I don't mean simply that educators will have to decide whether or not programmed instruction will be used in schools. Anyone familiar with the tenor of education today knows that it will be used. The question which educators must answer is how will it be used.

We have all heard that supposedly teaching machines

can be used to solve the teacher shortage. Or that they can teach everything which is taught in school, thereby replacing all teachers except those who can pass the qualifying exam as machine repair men. We are also warned that, as the entire curriculum is to be taught by machine, our schools will soon be producing responsive little robots who recite rather than stimulated students who can think.

Such glib statements indicate a totally unrealistic picture. First of all, people who make such statements are either reacting to the machines as if they were bogeymen or are overly impressed by them. But, as we have seen, programmed instruction is not dependent on machines. Second, rather than replace teachers or solve any teacher shortage, programmed instruction will demand better, more thoroughly trained teachers than ever before. Lastly, programmed instruction cannot teach the entire curriculum for the simple reason that it cannot educate a person. The word "instruction" in the phrase "programmed instruction" is used advisedly. We can instruct a pupil to spell, to punctuate, to use words properly—we can even instruct him how to apply agreed-upon criteria of criticizing his own or other people's writing. Hence, all these things can and are being programmed. They all represent cumulative skills or knowledge in which one step leads to another and, as such, they are ideally suited to the discipline of programming. However, no method of instruction can teach a person how to write or think creatively, for such things depend on far more subtle processes than accumulation and practice. Skill and knowledge are often the bases of such things—but there has to be something else. I think (and as I am a teacher I suppose I am being presumptuous) that a teacher can often engender this important something else. Programmed instruction is instruction, but teachers are educators—which, as Quintillian would tell us, means growers. Recent research has shown that programmed instruction is able to implant knowledge with great efficiency and thoroughness. But if teachers are not able to cultivate in students the ability to interrelate this knowledge and use it creatively, these students will end up as well instructed but uneducated persons. Programmed instruction can teach a person mathematics; it can teach him economics; but it cannot guarantee that he will *not* cheat on his income tax. The people who talk about replacing teachers with machines talk nonsense.

Thus we see that programmed instruction has a clearly delineated place in education, but that *it is not* education. Given this proper place, then, what are the potential uses of programmed instruction? And how can educators help to see that these potential uses are realized? First of all, as has been indicated, programmed instruction is a practical method of individual instruction. With programmed instruction the presentation of subject matter is geared to the speed and capabilities of each individual student. Today we make much of two-, three-, or four-track systems of teaching. With programmed instruction a class of thirty students can operate on a thirty-track system. This is not simply because each of the thirty students is proceeding through the same material at his own pace, but because it is also possible to accelerate the very bright student even more by allowing him to follow a special track through a program which doesn't require him to cover as much review as his less talented classmates. The really slow student can, however, be guided with as much care as is needed through minutely stepped sections of the program which are especially designed to meet his needs. Furthermore, in order further to individualize instruction, some programs currently being constructed are making tutorial sessions with the teacher an integral part of their structure. For instance, at the end of a given unit of work each student is directed to "go and see the teacher." As a result of the fact that each student reaches the end of this unit at a different time, the teacher is able to tutor each student in the art of interrelating and of applying what he has learned to new and challenging non-programmable situations. If a discussion group or class seems desirable, then it is a simple matter to take all students who have recently finished an appropriate unit and meet with them for a session devoted to the exchange of ideas, comments and questions.

Of course such practices, if broadly applied, will necessitate radical changes in the design, administration and orientation of school life. But we exist in a world of change, and, since the procedures suggested here are as old as Quintillian, I think it is time education took them seriously.

But, as was previously mentioned, education should not adopt programmed instruction simply because this venerable Roman endorsed its methods, or because it is a new and exciting method or because it will solve a teacher shortage. Nor should it be adopted simply because we are ready for a change. That is, ready for another swing of the educational pendulum. All these reasons do not supply a sound basis for such adoption. They are simply invitations to continue the kind of oscillating pattern of methodology with which education has lived far too long. The only sound basis for the adoption of programmed instruction is the fact that its effectiveness can be clearly demonstrated in precise, objective terms. In other words, in programmed instruction education has a method by which different approaches and attitudes toward various subjects can be subjected to detailed scientific scrutiny. For example, the relative worth of two, three or five different programs in physics can be objectively evaluated, not only as to content and student achievement but also as to the different approaches which each one takes to the subject. Most important of all, however, is the fact that weak spots in any of these programs can be immediately identified by referring to the data supplied by carefully conducted field tests. Thus we see that one of the most important uses of programmed instruction may be its suitability as a tool for experimental educational research— research which will tell us what is wrong with what we are doing and not the type of research so often indulged in for the sole purpose of convincing ourselves that what we are doing is right.

There is yet another aspect of programmed instruction, one which has only recently received attention—namely, the fact that the creation of programs is a remarkably effective teacher-training tool. During the past year I have attempted to help many experienced teachers learn how to program. Almost without exception these teachers agreed that the experience of programming even one lesson had taught them more about their own teaching, and instruction in general, than any other teacher training they had had. There are many reasons for this, such as new and detailed analysis of familiar material, analysis of methods and approaches, practical experience of seeing students try to learn from the programs and others too detailed to be summarized briefly. All these constitute a rigorous training ground in sound pedagogy. It is for this reason that I believe that teachers colleges might investigate the possibilities of programming as an effective means of teacher training.

We have covered quite a large area in a rather short time, and of course it is impossible to remember all the details. What, then, should we remember? It seems to me that the substance of what I have said today can be contained under three general headings: foresight, research and responsibility. We ought to have the foresight to recognize what we have, to learn about it in detail and to work our way forward with informed caution. We ought to realize that research is primarily responsible for our progress to date in programmed instruction, but it has not brought us to an apogee. We must continue with research and utilize the feedback thereby made available in order to train our future teachers and refine our techniques and goals. Last, we ought to accept the responsibility that programmed instruction places upon us. It is education that has a vested interest in this method of instruction, an interest to investigate, evaluate and improve itself. Other more commercially oriented organizations are eager to have a vested interest here too. If we miss our opportunity by default and allow such organizations to dictate to us, we shall have denied our responsibility to education.

If we can take away these three ideas—foresight, research, responsibility—we shall have begun an intelligent approach to programmed instruction.

in the facetious thought that any man who has the courage to stand up and claim that the replacement of man's brains will not have a very important effect on society takes the risk of having his brains among the first to be replaced.)

By hindsight, what is happening would appear to have been entirely predictable centuries ago. We might consider all of man's history until now arbitrarily broken up into two periods, the second of which is now in transition to the new and third one.

In the first period, which might be called the "pre-science" era, man was not consciously employing science to alter his society. Of course, he was aware of the world about him, and he sought to adapt himself to nature's laws. But when he objectively began to develop organized ways of thought and experimentation to further his knowledge of nature, then he entered the era of the discovery of science and its utilization. One step in this second period is the so-called Industrial Revolution.

In this second era, now coming to an end, man learned to communicate and navigate, to create and harness sources of power well beyond his own muscles, all with the natural result of increased production and fast transportation. In such an era man would be expected to learn gradually more and more about matter and energy, so as to make possible the release of larger and larger amounts, to the eventual point where he could quickly destroy civilization. He would be expected to so increase and speed up production, transportation and communications as to tie the entire globe together in an enormous network of automatic machinery, cables and moving vehicles. In time he would have such potentialities in the control and generation of energy and in communications and transportation as to make possible intercontinental ballistic missiles, space satellites and rockets to the moon. So, finally, he would spread out from the surface of the earth to all the space surrounding it.

And the transition is happening just this way to the new technical age. What makes the present period singular is that now, for the first time, a sharp coincidence between the needs and the state of the art exists. The requirements for the new society, the pressure and the strength of resources to bring it about now match a sufficiently deep understanding of the laws of nature to make these big steps practical.

CONSIDERING THE NEEDS

Consider first the needs. As one example, note that we are already at the point in air transportation where we badly need a major entry of automatic techniques in the overall system for air-line navigation and traffic control. Today we are alarmed about occasional accidents. But it will hardly take very much increase in the number of cities originating plane flights, or in the amount of air freight to be handled, or in the spectrum of speeds from the very low-speed helicopters to the high-speed jets, or in the demand for reliable operations in all-weather conditions before we approach near chaos at the airports and intolerable dangers in the air lanes.

Similarly, the military situation demands the extension, and often the replacement, of man's brains and senses by automatic gadgetry. The guided missile is taking over in many areas from manned airplanes. Getting up into the skies swiftly in response to detection of enemy bombardment vehicles, finding the location and the expected future path of such enemy vehicles, making the decisions as to what path should be chosen to effect an interception —these functions, to be accomplished with tremendous rapidity for fast vehicles in all weather, and involving a great deal of mathematical complexity in the decisions, are well beyond the pilot's eyes, ears and brain.

Business and industry—whether it be department stores, insurance companies, banks, railroads or ordinary factories —have become so large and complex that the sound containment of their operations from an organization standpoint becomes more and more impossible without the use of automatic techniques.

Now the status of science is such that, without a single new discovery—without even one more new law's being discovered by an Einstein concerning the nature of the universe or the secrets of the nucleus—we can set out to design mechanical and electronic systems that will take over, and do better, many of the things we now do with our brains and senses.

This rapid and potentially dislocating scientific advance can be expected to heighten . . . the coming crisis in education. Already, the increasingly technical world uses more scientists and engineers, yet the very industrial development that is part of the growing technical society takes the engineers and scientists away from the university and high school facilities, and the fast world in which we live makes the long study of science seem unattractive to the youngsters. The technical society is complex, rapid and uncreasingly dangerous. We can blow up the whole world, yet such a premium is put on the use of our human and physical resources for everything but education that it seems that the new technical society is going to be accompanied by a weakened ability to keep pace educationwise.

Now, if the world were in transition to something different on a very, very slow scale, we could argue that these factors would take care of themselves. Supply and demand would then presumably set to work to make the teaching profession pay off better. Further, the new technical society would be expected to cease to develop rapidly if there were not enough engineers and scientists to make possible that development. So the pace would have to adjust itself to one that would allow all the factors to settle into their respective permanent relative magnitudes.

But we are moving much too rapidly for that, and our technical growth is paralleled by social maladjustments still left over from previous eras. The adjustments, instead of being slow and stabilizing, could be chaotic. Obviously, something new is needed. Education should be at the head of the list for priority attention. Our hope for attaining any kind of stability in the highly technical world ahead must rest on the ability to look ahead, to understand the world and to adjust to it. We must reject such solutions as that we do indeed blow ourselves up; and we cannot accept something approaching a robot-controlled world that consists largely of ignorant and uneducated masses who are slaves to a few individuals who push all the buttons on the machines.

A NEW TECHNIQUE OF EDUCATION

I should like to propose that these very technological advances about which we normally speak when we talk about the new technical society must include advances in the field of education, and it is part of the obligation of those of us who are engaged in the engineering side of modern science somehow to apply ourselves to help the process of education. What is needed is a technique of education which is in keeping with the world ahead.

Picture this new technical society—in which the entire air-line system, from reservations to blind landing and take-off, is done almost automatically, with the pilot going along only for the ride; in which money is used only in the country communities, and when we buy something in a store we simply put our thumbs up against a little window, our fingerprints are automatically scanned against our balance, and the proper change is made in the respective accounts of the customer and the store—and ask: What will a high school look like at that time?

We have a choice here of two ways to discuss this. We could take it in very gradual steps, starting with the popular suggestion of greater use of television as a teaching aid, or we can allow our imaginations to open up. Let us accept the risk of poor accuracy in prediction and even the risk of exaggeration in order to make a point. We shall describe a technically feasible, even though in some other ways perhaps unacceptable, "modern" high school of the future. But in doing this, please remember that I am neither predicting nor recommending the school I am about to describe, but only using it as a vehicle for making some points later.

First of all, we will get the student registered. I won't burden you with the details here; when the registration is complete and the course of study suitable for that individual has been determined, the student receives a specially stamped small plate about the size of a "charga-plate," which identifies both him and his program. (If this proves too burdensome for the student, who will be required to have the plate with him most of the time, then we may spend a little more money on the installation and go directly to the fingerprint system.)

When this plate is introduced at any time into an appropriate large data and analysis machine near the principal's office, and if the right levers are pulled by its operator, the entire record and progress of this student will immediately be made available. As a matter of fact, after completing his registration, the student introduces his plate into one machine on the way out, which quickly prints out some tailored information so that he knows where he should go at various times of the day and anything else that is expected of him.

A typical school day will consist of a number of sessions, some of which are spent, as now, in rooms with other students and a teacher and some of which are spent with a machine. Sometimes a human operator is present with the machine, and sometimes not.

One thing needs to be said at the outset. Any attempt to extend the teaching staff with any kind of mechanical aids would appear to have at least one very fundamental limitation. It would seem that, unless a highly intelligent, trained and authoritative teacher is available, there is no equivalent way of adapting the material to be presented to the individual student's need, or to judge the understanding and reception of the material and adjust it to the student during the presentation, to discover his questions, weaknesses and misunderstandings, nip them in the bud, and otherwise provide the feedback and interaction between teacher and student that are so essential in transferring knowledge from one person to another.

It is for this apparent reason that, although we can use motion pictures and television to replace a lecturer and can, in theory at least, be more efficient in the use of one skilled teacher's time, enabling him to reach a larger audience, we can only use such techniques for a limited fraction of the total school day. However, you will see in the systems that I propose that, in principle at least, modern technology can go a long way toward removing this apparently fundamental limitation. The whole objective of everything that I will describe is to raise the teacher to a higher level in his contribution to the teaching process and to remove from his duties that kind of effort which does not use the teacher's skill to the fullest.

Let us follow a student who is including in his schedule a course in trigonometry. He will spend a few hours a week on this study in automated classrooms. In the case of trigonometry, only a small part of his time need be spent with a human teacher. Some of his classroom exercises will involve presentation of basic concepts in trigonometry in the company of other students in short lectures, delivered by a special sound motion picture, which uses some human actors who enunciate or narrate the principles to the accompaniment of various and sundry fixed and animated geometrical diagrams.

However, this classroom has some special equipment. Each chair includes a special set of push buttons and, of course, that constant slot into which the student places his identification plate. The plate automatically records his presence at that class, and it connects his push buttons with the master records machine.

If the class is large, our student is much less likely to sleep or look out of the window than in a normal lecture by a human teacher, because throughout the motion picture that presents some phase of the fundamentals of trigonometry he is called upon to respond by pushing various keys. He is asked questions about the material just presented, usually in the form of alternatives. Sometimes he is told that the concept will be repeated and the questions reasked, this time for the record. He may even be asked whether, in his opinion, he understood what was being presented.

In other words, he is in constant touch with the "teacher"; but something else equally important needs now to be added. His progress and score are used by the electronic master scheduling device to prepare for the special handling of that student in the other portions of the trigonometry course.

At certain other periods during the week, this student continues his trigonometry instruction in a different kind of environment. This time he is seated in front of a special machine, again with a special animated film and a keyboard, but he is now alone and he knows that *this* machine is much more interested in his individual requirements. It is already set up in consideration of his special needs. It is ready to go fast if he is fast, slow if he is slow. It will considerably repeat what he has missed before and will gloss over what he has proven he knows well. This machine continues the presentation of some principles and asks for answers to determine understandings. Based upon the student's immediate answer, it may repeat or go on to the next principle.

With some hints and assistance by the lecturer in the movie, and with appropriate pauses (not accompanied by a commercial), the student is allowed a period for undisturbed contemplative thought before registering his answer.

This machine is prepared to take a single principle and go over it time after time if necessary, altering the presentation perhaps with additional detail, perhaps trying another and still another way of looking at it, hoping to succeed in obtaining from the student answers that will indicate that the principle is reasonably well understood before it goes on to the next one.

Before the student receives the material from this machine, it will have rapidly selected from its file the appropriate films for presentation. These films are already set up with a number of alternatives at each step, and with such inner workings that the machine is prepared to repeat, advance or substitute material determined by the student's performance.

You will see from this one example that we are placing the machine and the subject matter in contact with the student and vice versa, in a feedback relationship. Of course, we do not cover all possibilities; we do not even cover every possibility that a human teacher dealing with that one pupil could observe. But we handle a great many of the more common ones; we will strive for a very efficient and dynamically interesting presentation of a large amount of the material; we will do a very efficient job of examination of some of the student's understanding.

A brilliant student could romp through trigonometry in a very small fraction of the course time. A dull student would have to spend more time with the machines. The machines can be so set up that if a student fails to make progress at the required rate, he can be automatically dropped from the course. Of course, before that happens or before the brilliant student is allowed to complete the course, a special session with that student by a skilled teacher is indicated. But the teacher will be aided by having before him the complete records of what could be weeks of intensive machine operations.

This will make easier a personal study of that student's understanding and his way of thinking about the subject. The teacher will even be able to judge in what way the operation is inadequate and needs to be supplemented, both to take care of that particular student and to improve the automatic techniques. Some students will learn better than others with these machines. Ultimately, with the proper cooperation among experts in education, expert teachers, experts in trigonometry and experts in engineering these automatic systems, we can evolve that high level of match between the human teacher and the machine that we seek in that improved high school.

We can further illustrate these concepts by other special cases. Let us take the memorizing machine, for example. It is important in many studies to do a certain amount of memorizing of facts and data. As a scientist, I know that a facility in study of an advanced subject oftentimes requires that background information be instantly available to the mind. But what a drudgery it is to memorize the weights of all of the chemical elements! In fact, about the best way to do this kind of memorizing is to get help from another individual who sits with the facts spread out before him and before whom the memorizer attempts to recite.

The memorizing machine could remove much of this drudgery and make it interesting and efficient. For instance, for the series of chemical elements the machine could go through the list while the student punches out the corresponding atomic weights on a cash-register type of keyboard. When he misses one, not only does the red light go on (and the sign say "TILT!"), but the machine remembers that he has missed it. As it continues to chase through the list, it will throw in some of those questions that the student has already answered correctly, just to be sure and to give him the repetitive exercise, but it will more often come back to those where he had trouble previously.

A few minutes a day spent with memorizing machines, each of which is equipped with thousands of records to cover the important information to be memorized about various subjects, will probably accomplish more for the student than much more time spent in other ways.

Of course, it should be clear that this type of dynamic teaching and studying requires such a concentrated effort that it could not be used as the exclusive and total diet of the student, even if it had no limitations whatsoever. However, before we discuss these limitations, and before we try to make certain that we understand the fundamental difference that this kind of technical development could make in educational processes, let us take one or two other examples.

It is clear that the use of machines in which the student and the presentation are in responsive communication should be helpful in the presentation of theoretical concepts in science and mathematics, in the learning of basic principles and the acquisition of information in most other fields as well. But what about such things as chemistry laboratory, English composition and the teaching of languages?

Let us take the chemistry laboratory first—and remember that we are speaking here not of the principles of chemistry in the theoretical sense, which would be handled much as in the case of trigonometry, but rather of the physical handling of matter in the laboratory and the acquisition of appreciation of the scientific method of observation and deliberation. I think much can be done here.

Picture, first, the student seated again before a special viewing screen and certain apparatus. The chemistry professor in the movie has the equivalent apparatus in front of him. He turns some valves and allows some fluid to go into a container. He adds to this another different fluid. He observes the characteristics of the combination, he refers to the theory, he describes what is happening and why it

happens. He then asks the student to turn the valves in
front of him to let so much red fluid into the glass below
and so much blue fluid into the same glass. He tells the
student that, if he has indeed poured the right amount in
and observed every other requirement as described, he
can expect certain results.

To show the possibilities, imagine that the instructor
suggests that the liquid should be pink and asks the student to push Button A if he has obtained this result, and
Button B if he has not. Now let us suppose that the student pushes Button A. The moment he does this, the film
immediately switches to one in which the professor points
an admonishing finger at the student and says, "Oh, oh,
oh—now look at that liquid! That isn't pink. You were
simply led by suggestion to expect the result. You didn't
use your own powers of observation. Clearly, if you look
honestly at that liquid, it is, if anything, slightly on the
yellow side. You must learn the first principle of science.
That is to be honest—not to expect a result, but to seek
to observe what result you do indeed have and report it
accurately."

On the other hand, if the student refuses to push Button A and pushes Button B instead, a different film will
congratulate him on being objective and having the necessary characteristics for the scientific approach. It is quite
possible for experts in chemistry and education, I believe,
to create a large number of laboratory setups that can
easily be kept full and ready by operators, so that the
student can conduct his laboratory experiments without
detailed supervision and with great efficiency and good
records.

Teaching English and composition is difficult, as is in-
stilling into one an appreciation of good literature. But
even here we certainly can add to the exposure of the
student to good literature and, by probing the student's
understanding and response, we can alter the speed and
nature of the presentation. We can improve his knowledge of the tools of good expression so that we leave only
the more creative aspects (which must rest at least partially, presumably, on these tools and on the knowledge

of the characteristics of good literature) to his personal contacts with the skilled teacher.

Similarly, in the teaching of languages, vocabulary improvement, grammar and understanding the spoken language could be advanced by these feedback machines. Even the ability of the student to speak the language could be enhanced by machine. He could respond orally to the animated film in front of him, repeat the foreign words spoken to him by an expert into the microphone, play back the results immediately, and repeat the whole process. This, you see, goes a substantial step beyond the use of records, which I understand is quite common in the courses now available commercially for learning foreign languages the "easy way."

Let us see what physical and human resources this high school would have. To begin with, the physical plant would include a large amount of apparatus that does not now exist but that can be designed and constructed with today's art.

There would be administrators and clerks who would handle all of the administrative processes but who would not be at all concerned with, and not be trained in, education. There would be a group of highly skilled teachers. The more conventional type of teaching would still be a substantial part of the total operation. For the new, automated material, these teachers would work closely with the experts on the subjects, and with the education engineers who design all of the electronic equipment that is basic to the process.

A NEW INDUSTRY

To back this up, of course, one would have a very substantial new industry in the United States concerned with the creating of these educational machines and the motion pictures and memory data used by the machines. In general, the industrial organizations concerned with the creation of machines that make possible the teaching of mathematics would have to employ experts in education, experts in mathematics and experts in engineering. And this industrial team would have to be in good contact with the skilled teachers who make up the high school staff in order that they might be able to improve their machines, create the proper material and learn the shortcomings of all of their designs—either of the machine or of the material.

In addition, the high school teaching staff would include education analysts, probably specializing in the various subjects. These individuals would go through the records of the individual students. They would be constantly seeking to discover the special problems that need special attention by the direct contact of teacher and pupil.

We notice a number of very significant points here. The high school becomes partially transformed into a center run by administrators and clerks, with a minimum of the routine assigned to the teaching staff. The teaching staff is elevated to a role that uses the highest intelligence and skills. A smaller number of teachers makes possible the education of a larger number of pupils. The creation of educational material moves partially out into industry, which goes into the education business in partnership with educators.

There is probably a new profession known as "teaching engineer," that kind of engineering which is concerned with the educational process and with the design of the machines, as well as the design of the material.

One might imagine, for example, that a course in solid geometry, with its three-dimensional patterns, would be based around 3-D animated communicative-response systems and that some of the experts on the teaching of solid geometry should better be employed in industry than in the school. Those teachers who would be employed in the schools themselves would be individuals able to handle the more difficult problems that are left for the human teacher and the analysis of the processes that involve the use of the machine.

From the standpoint of the student, I do not know that his life need be changed in any fundamental way. It may be, of course, that the evenings and week ends would cease to be times for doing homework. The equivalent of homework, as well as the basic presentation periods, would be done perhaps during the normal working day, five days a week, with the evenings and the week ends used for the broader cultural, social and athletic events. That is, the evening would be a time for a more relaxed participation in the learning and broadening programs.

I think it is true that, with this kind of an educational system, the student need not feel that he is dealing with cold machines in place of warm human teachers any more than he feels that way today when he reads a book by himself instead of listening to an oral presentation by a human teacher.

It is interesting now to look for a moment at the economics of such an educational system. In principle, it obviously has application to the lower grades and certainly to the university as well. But, wherever it is applied, it is quite easy to show that it is an enormously expensive operation.

Use that course in trigonometry, for example. As a motion picture, it would involve not one hour or two hours but, say, one hundred hours of expensive teaching material. Unlike a motion picture, it would not be viewed by tens of millions of people all over the world. The audiences, for the most part, would be small, and unless we could unite all trigonometry students for a number of years in the common use of this same material, it is apparent that the cost would be rather large. If we pay something like fifty cents an hour to see an ordinary motion picture, then a trigonometry course would cost thousands of dollars per student, and the complete high school year would cost tens of thousands.

If we reflect for a moment on this matter of economics, we are reminded again that something is very wrong in the balance between that part of the national economy we devote to education and the part we are willing to devote to other things. To bring this point out, let us use the analogy of the Egyptians building the pyramids by the use of thousands of slaves pulling huge rocks—that is, by the most laborious and inefficient way possible in terms of the use of human beings. We imagine that we could have walked up to the Pharaoh and said, "This is not the way to build your huge monument. For this you should use bulldozers and cranes and steamshovels; why, a handful of men and a handful of machines would replace your thousands of human operators." But then the Pharaoh would have said, "Ah—but will it save me any money?" So we would figure it all out and discover that it would cost him much more if he changed to the machines because he paid his slaves so little.

In this system that I have described, we seek to elevate the teacher to the exclusive use of the higher abilities and qualities he possesses. It is a system that makes possible more education for more people with fewer skilled teachers being wasted in the more routine tasks that a machine should do for them. And we come up against this economic question. Today the teachers are doing all of these things—the routines and the handling of those levels of teaching requiring the highest of intelligence and training—and they are doing them for less than the cost of the machines, which could only hope to replace the lower level of the teaching art and skill!

The examples I have presented here illustrate what I think is the most important point that can perhaps be contributed to a discussion of the relationship of the technological revolution and the educational process. While being defensive about these specific ideas, I won't go so far as to say that there is nothing in them. My work has accustomed me to the idea of being willing to allow imagination to roam freely, and my associates in science attribute a quotation to me which goes something like this: "Don't be ashamed to propose a ridiculous idea. Though worthless today, in ten years it may be of no value whatsoever."

Part Eight

IMPLICATIONS
FOR
LEISURE

· 18 ·

*Leisure and Work**

by Paul Goodman
AUTHOR OF *Growing Up Absurd*

The Greeks had a word for leisure, σχολή, meaning serious activity without the pressure of necessity; and another
word, διατριβή, which meant playful amusement to pass
the time. Both were excellent things. Serious leisure was
the chief way that a free man grew in character, and that
the city made the culture that we still look to today, as I
am looking to it here. Pastime was the recuperation from
serious pursuits, including leisure. Theater, athletics, art
and even conversation were serious leisure. The tragedies
made you howl and groan and cleaned you out; the com-
edies were mordant political satires and strenuous aphro-
disiacs; the athletics were close to war exercises, though
more honorable because they had style and were religious;
artistic interest produced civic monuments; and social
conversation in the public square was often heatedly aimed

* Reprinted from *Esquire* Magazine, "The Mass Leisure Class,"
July, 1959, Copyright © 1959 by Paul Goodman. Reprinted
by permission of the Author and *Esquire*.

toward decisions in the mass juries and political assemblies
in which all free men often participated. After such hard-
working leisure, a man needed to relax playing knuckle-
bones and to have a drink (of wine mixed in varying degrees with water).

Now, in our country, with a steadily shorter work week
and longer vacations, the Americans have more and more
time off. It has even been darkly hinted that, with electronic robots, a lot of people will be productively surplus
and can stay home altogether. "The problem of what two
hundred millions of us will do with our increasing leisure
time," Harvey Swados has said, "is so awesome in its magnitude as to be terrifying." Isn't that a peculiar thought,
that leisure is a terrifying problem?

To old-fashioned philosophers, like Bellamy or William
Morris or Bertrand Russell, the prospect of our modern
leisure was bright and promising; it roused the hope that
modern man could turn again to a high leisure-culture
like the Athenians of antiquity, and make our great technological adventure pay off historically, the automatic
machines being our slaves. But this hope was naïve to the
point of absurdity, it was too sensible. (Indeed, it is
remarkable how far common sense can get shrewd thinkers out of touch with the facts of social life.) These philosophers forgot that the Athenians worked at their leisure
with deadly earnestness; that, quite apart from their slaves
and their empire, they earned their leisure by being content with a fantastically low standard of private life for all
classes, and got their deep satisfactions from patriotic service and civic culture. American life is not frugal; it is less
and less political or patriotic; and our notion of community
is restricted to philanthropic contributions. Finally, as I
intend to show, the peculiar style of our economic life
makes it impossible for us to work earnestly at our leisure.
Thus, far from offering a hope of culture in the Greek
style, or of the art of living in the old Japanese style, our
mass leisure threatens us with a "terrifying problem,"
namely, that people will goof off and get into trouble.

Millions of people with long hours and days heavy on
their hands! When the sociologists discuss mass leisure, we
find that this is what they are concerned about. They are

not talking about serious activity at all. They are not talking about culture and relaxation as the poles of leisure, but simply how to save people from fooling around or from being drowned in canned entertainment and dying of spectatoritis; how to provide them something which *is* an activity and does not disintegrate personality. To quote a succinct remark of Russell Lynes, "In the simplest terms, the primary problem of leisure is how to avoid boredom." His own solution for this problem is to encourage people to become Connoisseurs of the Arts and so maintain Civilized Standards. And since the sale of records and hi-fi equipment and of Japanese prints and new-process reproductions is indeed tremendous, he is optimistic.

Eric Larrabee, another well-known sociological journalist and the editor of an anthology in this field called *Mass Leisure,* sets great store on do-it-yourself activities as planned and purposive alternatives to passivity and boredom; and the sale of beautiful hand tools and remarkable power tools has also indeed been tremendous (six billion dollars in 1954). If all those fine tools were being used with love, skill and invention, there would be a revolution in our notions of craftsmanship, utility and beauty; but when I look out the window at the new housing and at the new cars going by, I fail to see this revolution taking place.

Just think of it! these categories of the sociologist, of fooling around versus planned purposive activity, were precisely those that a philosopher, John Dewey, used to stress as important for the pedagogy of *children.* One is struck with dismay to see grown-up sociologists satisfied to apply them to grown-up human beings.

In brief, the ancient view of leisure was activity free from the pressure of necessity, and vitally important to the individual and the city that it be done well; glory or shame, liberty or slavery, culture or barbarism depended on it. The American view of leisure is an activity free from the pressure of necessity, but one that must by no means be vitally important to the individual or the nation. We may (indeed, must) spend money on consumption goods, but we must not interfere with the serious Business as Usual of Society. Is not this powerfully reminiscent of a dilemma of the WPA in the days of the Great Depression? If the unemployed were given useless jobs, called boondoggling, it was considered morally bad for them; but if they were given useful work, like the excellent WPA Theater, then they were in competition with private enterprise and that was disapproved. What in the devil were they supposed to work at?*

We cannot understand the problem of our leisure in isolation from the work that it is leisure from. We must remember that when people had less leisure, they had different jobs that gave them a different attitude toward what leisure they did have. Many worked for themselves and set their own standards; there were many more farmers; the pace was slower; often the routine was less. Plants were smaller; the methods and rules of work were by and large controlled by the workmen. A man's job was

---

* Let me point out just in a footnote—for otherwise it would take us too far—that there is a dilemma in *any* High Standard of Living in a profit economy. I am referring to the embarrassing truth that the best things in life are free. For most people, I think, a candid self-examination will show that their most absorbing, long, and satisfactory hours are spent in things like friendly competitive sports, friendly gambling, love-making and sex, earnest or argumentative conversation, dedicated political activity, solitary study and reading, contemplation of nature and Cosmos, art-working, music, religion. Now, none of these requires the use of many commodities; indeed, elaborate arrangements and equipment take the life out of them. Friends use one another as resources; and God, nature, and creativity are free. Health, luck, and a simple heart are the only requirements for good sex. Good food requires taking pains more than money. On the other hand, it is a necessity of a profitable economy, with high employment and expanding by reinvestment, to *increase* the number of commodities consumed, and therefore to prevent, curtail, or debauch the profound satisfactions of life; that is, to see to it that a "high standard of living" is a bad, wasteful, and unsatisfactory but titillating standard of living. In our present political and economic dispensation, an advanced technology *cannot* be humane. The moral is to change the dispensation.

likely to have family, friend and neighborhood connections.

At present nearly all the sociologists—seldom does one read such a consensus—speak of the disaster of the Calvinist Ethic. They argue as follows: since the Americans were brought up to believe that only hard work is righteous and that play time must be earned and designed to make them fit for more work, now, in easier times, they find it difficult to enjoy themselves. I don't think that there is much in this; for our problem is not that the Americans don't enjoy his leisure, but that there's little *in* it to enjoy. A good time is not, and cannot be, a goal; it is always the blessed accompaniment of some successful vital activity. Furthermore, the Calvinist Ethic is essentially true. If a man doesn't give himself without timidity to a real effort that satisfies his best standards of honor, integrity and utility, he *is* not in a state of grace. How many men have such jobs? Few.

In this respect women are still much better off. The housewives of a Westchester suburb play cards for two hours every weekday on the average. (Unemployed men of the same community play less than half as much, employed men not at all.) But go behind the statistics: the ladies have fed their families, gotten them off to school and work, cleaned up and bought supper and taken care of the baby; all this is honorable endeavor, unquestionably useful, and justified. They are entitled to their social game; it is like a coffee-break and made real by gossip about the children.

Like the women, the plain working stiff who just has a job without prestige is better off than the more pretentious employee, for when he is at leisure his mind is free of the job. But if we now inquire into the underlying work attitude of this same man, we begin to see clearly what it is that makes serious leisure impossible in America. Let me report here a little study of industrial workers by Robert Dubin that takes us to the heart of our subject.

Dubin set himself to study the attitudes and choices of the workers at a plant, in order to find means to cement the loyalty of the men to the organization. Using psychological questionnaires to test their evaluations on three issues, he found: (1) for a thumping majority, as an important life interest the job left them cold: "They found their preferred human associations and preferred areas of behavior outside of employment." (Therefore, Dubin concluded, the employer might as well give up trying to make the work as such more attractive, for the men would not buy it.) *But* (2) even though they didn't care about the job, a good majority *did* find in the job their notions of how to behave correctly in life, how to be accepted, how to succeed, how to give orders and obey. These normative standards of behavior did *not* come from individual judgment, family, friends or community, but were learned from the rational impersonal organization and its staff. And (3) in their choices with regard to technique, efficiency, quality of material and equipment, cleanliness, accuracy, carefulness—all the things that we would consider as part of a man's craftsmanlike and esthetic capacity—again a good majority proved to be oriented, not to sports, not to home economics and do-it-yourself, not to arts and crafts, but to the job at the plant.

Reflect on what these findings mean, unsurprising as they are, and you will understand the problem of our leisure. What the men are apparently interested in is the time off the job; they are just waiting for the whistle to blow so they can get to their "important" interests; but strangely, these important life interests are *not* directive, controlling, rewarding; they are *not* the areas of learning how to belong and how to avoid being excluded. Such things are rather learned on the job, in which, however, they are not interested! Also, the men do not respect the style or technique that they might spontaneously develop in their off-time interests; that's all bungling. The arts are for sissies or kids; sports are sham fights. The dance of life, they believe, is correctly and seriously performed only on the job, in which they are not interested. But, then, what on earth can be the quality of home or leisure activities where there is no belief in their righteousness or their style? The leisure activities *must* lack daring, confidence and invention; they must be inhibited and conformist, herding together for security and trying to have a good time without asserting oneself. In fact, they are American mass leisure.

And with whom will one have the good time? The possibilities seem to be people one meets on the job, or in the community, or old friends, or one's family. Dubin's findings rule out comrades from the job. Other studies demonstrate the obvious proposition that no one has a good time with members of his family. In America we have no community relations to speak of. (This was, by the way, the great advantage of the Greeks; it was their city that gave them confidence in their rightness and style.) This leaves us only friends, friends with whom one has no vocation in common, no sexual or paternal relation, no political or community enterprise, no deep respect for one another's skill or authority. It is not much to go on. As we know, the most exciting use of such buddies is to get into trouble with them; but for fathers of families this is excluded. The permissible residual possibilities are things like mild drinking or bowling.

My own hunch is that for very many the most rewarding leisure moments are those spent alone, especially if one has the excuse of seeming to be occupied, and therefore not masturbating. Driving in the car alone, sitting in the bar with a glass of beer, or pretending to be busy with a magazine or hobby or do-it-yourself, but really passing in and out of fantasy. It is a pathetic picture but not lacking in warmth. And you can see workingmen on sunny holidays spending a vast amount of time "fixing the car." This is obviously useful and money-saving, and not uninteresting in itself; and it is a connection with the machine that gives freedom to go. His car is a workingman's assertiveness. But he does not much know *where* to go, so he goes to the movies, parking the car outside.

If we now skip up a class or two in prestige, the work-leisure pattern is psychologically more desperate. The industrial worker is not trapped in the job and he has the comfort and protection of the union. But the white-collar worker, the salesman, the technician, the junior-executive are committed Organization men. Their work is demanding and actively engages the mind, and their position is esteemed as important. So their orientation toward the job is not only strong but it overflows into off time. The Organization dictates the right clothes, the right conversation pieces and often the right wife; and a man goes to sleep with his work problems. Salient, of course, is the need to compete and the fear of being displaced from eminence, with no recourse to a union. All this is familiar.

White-collar leisure has the same complex tone as the job (unlike working-class leisure which is simple and disorderly). Though basically conforming to the approved class activity, nevertheless a man's performance must be individualized and expert, and, if possible, competitively One Up. His sports clothes and equipment are not bought from army surplus as good enough and durable; they must be bought for the fashion and the label. If he plays bridge, he uses conventions appropriate for champions although they are less effective for an amateur than his own good card sense. He buys beautiful standard equipment to Do It Himself and he must end up with a product that looks standard. (In this respect Do It Yourself is different from Arts and Crafts which did not develop as a leisure pursuit but as part of a rather shaggy theory of Organic Life, and therefore emphasized personal expression growing from the process and the materials.)

Whether at golf or the expensive lunch on the firm or the barbecue in the patio, business and leisure are inextricably entangled. The tone must be having-a-grand-time-glad-you-are-here, but the undertone is often an ulcer-producing fear.

But a man is sensitive, and in this prestige group he is likely to be of more than average intelligence and education; he even reads books about himself by Spectorsky and Whyte; he suffers all the more the feeling of being trapped. The status and salary are esteemed but, on the inside, the job itself is not esteemed, and the conditions are very hard. It is rarely that a man can apply to his Organization his highest standards of honor, integrity and utility, or say his best say, or use his best powers; a man is lucky if, in a thoughtful moment, he does not have a twinge of conscience or a sense of self-betrayal. One consequence of this is the common fantasy of a Flight to the Woods, which is a leisure activity pretty sharply restricted to this prestige group. "Wilderness travel," concludes a typical survey, "is an exclusive recreation. Education data confirm the high status of canoeists. More than half had either completed college or received graduate degrees. Only one respondent (out of 45) had not completed high school." In the Woods a man is again independent, pure, manly, simple and accompanied by uncompetitive buddies or an understanding and sexy wife. But alas! the equipment for the camping trip was bought at Abercrombie and Fitch, and the wife complains that she was roped in.

An even more touching leisure object of this class is the kind of fiction published in the *New Yorker*, which is a sensitive nostalgic memory of a live and rebellious episode of childhood leading to resignation. (I suppose the best author is Salinger.) One would be at a loss why this particular formula is saleable if one did not understand these readers. I once sent a story to the *New Yorker*, retelling a true incident, almost as it occurred, of an architect who refused a commission because it involved demolishing a fine building. The editors rejected it, saying it was absurd, for no professional would behave that way; no grownup *can* be serious; that belongs to ingenuous children.

Another more global response to the situation is to shrink from the job altogether, and set up as commuters in a garden city or the near countryside and devote oneself to bringing up the new generation. Shall we call this a leisure activity or a kind of schizophrenia? There is no doubt that the New Fatherhood is an attempt by the man to horn in on his wife's occupation that contains some satisfactory reality. The bother with it is that when both parents devote themselves just to bringing up the children, the children do not have much world to grow up toward.

Possibly the chief serious and worth-while leisure that these persons do engage in is nonmedical psychoanalysis or other psychotherapy, which, in its peculiar way, is not very different from the ancient Socratic conversation whose

aim was to Know Thyself. We would phrase it, Find Yourself. This vital pursuit has, in fact, immense mass attrac-
tiveness in America, but it is unfortunately not mass available because understaffed. In one small Middle Western
city the pastor of the largest and richest church organized
a series of group therapies for his flock, led by psychologists
flown from New York, in order to revive enough community spirit to make possible his Christian ministry at all.
This roused enthusiasm, broke up a couple of bad mar-
riages and got him into equally hot water with the town
orthodox and the near-by psychiatric hospital.

It's a strange world. I know one psychologist, an honest
fellow, who works a good deal with the vocational troubles of the younger men of the middle-class group we are
discussing. In some cases he has had marked success,
resulting in their suddenly quitting their prestigious jobs
and getting other jobs that made more sense and paid
much less money, so that he had to reduce the fees.

Jump a few more rungs up the ladder of prestige, and
we come to the respected company of retired or semi-
retired businessmen and professionals who have made
their mark and a lot of money. What do these distinguished oldsters, who used to work very hard, do with
their now free time?

Along with the mothers of grown children, their chief
activity is likely to be community service, especially
philanthropies; and they provide us with a jolly illustration of the work-leisure pattern in America. The actual
case work in our community services, whether in nurseries,
with the needy, in hospitals, or in the prevention of delinquency or prejudice, is of course severely restricted
to experts; for both better and worse, an amateur do-
gooder is kept out of contact with the raw facts of people.
But our retired men of distinction are put to use in finance
and administration, in fund-raising, in distributing the
community chest, on building committees. Naturally this
suits them perfectly, with their prestige, their skill in
public relations, and their business acumen, it is just what
they are expert at; it is what they have always done. The
jolly part is the conviviality and spirit with which they

throw themselves into it; some of them blossom and feel complacent for the first time in their careers. One could cite instances (I shall not) of fund-raising by sharp practice, like blackmailing and threats of slander against the stingy, which previously our businessman would not have ventured for fear of landing in jail, but now he can give his best because it's in a good cause.

So let us go back to the dark hint we began with, that a lot of people are productively surplus altogether. In a surplus technology, many are retired before they have even gone to work. What then becomes of the pattern of work and leisure?

As I pointed out in *Growing Up Absurd*, we have here a major explanation of the phenomenon of the so-called Beat Generation. They illustrate the pattern of work and leisure when one of the terms has vanished; they are only at leisure. Critics, who are incensed that the Beats have low cultural values (and yet people pay attention to them), have failed to ask themselves where the cultural and work-manlike standards of the productively surplus could possibly come from. Perhaps the valuable contribution of these youngsters is that they forthrightly demonstrate the extreme of our problem of mass leisure. There is nothing *needing* to be done, and so they take no part in the social work at all, and try to withdraw from the market. They refuse to be tricked into behaving as though they were economically or culturally necessary, when they are patently not necessary. They refuse to make the effort to get the conventional leisure satisfactions. They are On Strike with blank sandwich boards.

Naturally, since it does not participate, Beat has no positive cultural forms, and therefore picks up from other marginal groups, like Puerto Ricans, Negroes, juvenile delinquents, far off Trobrianders and dead Japanese. But the Beat psychology is the very opposite of delinquent. They are not juvenilely rebellious but often went through college and may now be in their late twenties and thirties. They grew up in families, on whom indeed they still sponge, maintaining embarrassed relations. Their desires, manners and show-down behavior are rather blander

than the average solid citizens'. This is being cool; it is their
way of not suffering. For they are displaced persons, born
on the wrong planet. So they are at leisure. It is that in-
wardly they *cannot* identify with the values of father and
his society, for they are too hip; yet on the other hand
they cannot rebel against them, disregard them, or trans-
form them or take them over, for they aren't hip enough.
After a while the present group we see will make some
conventional adjustment. Madison Avenue has some of
them and will soon be chockful. But they will be replaced
by others, for their name is Legion.

To me they seem, as they stand there goofing off with
mask faces, cool, and tapping a foot to progressive
jazz, to be rich and poignant with history. For they cel-
ebrate the unfulfilled promise of the American Revolution,
the failure of the French Revolution and the Revolution of
1848, the betrayal of the Russian Revolution and the
fizzling out of our Sit-Downs. It is not with impunity that
mankind misses its opportunities to make a brave new
world, for after a while people no longer remember what
it is to be serious in either work or leisure. Especially young
people are disillusioned when they learn that society's way
of life is not authentic; and ceasing to believe, some refuse
to take part. For most men there is no man's work and
also therefore no man's play.

▪ *17* ▪

*A New Technique of Education**

by Simon Ramo

EXECUTIVE VICE PRESIDENT,
THOMPSON RAMO WOODRIDGE, LOS ANGELES, CALIFORNIA

We are in rapid transition today to a new world which threatens to be dominated by technological advance. In that new world, (1) man will have learned so much about nature's store of energy and its release that he will have the ability to virtually destroy civilization; (2) production, communications and transportation will all be automatic —these operations of man's material world will have become so vast and complex that they will have to proceed with a minimum of participation by man, his muscles, brains and senses; and (3) man will conquer space.

There seems little question that these three factors will have dominant effects in the coming decades. The effects are already being felt. (There is even a serious note

* Reprinted from *Engineering and Science Monthly*, a publication of the California Institute of Technology, October, 1957, Vol. 21, by permission of the Author and Mr. Edward Hutchings, Jr., Editor, *Engineering and Science Monthly*.